A-Level

Mathematics

for Edexcel Core 3

The Complete Course for Edexcel C3

Contents

About this book

In this book you'll find...

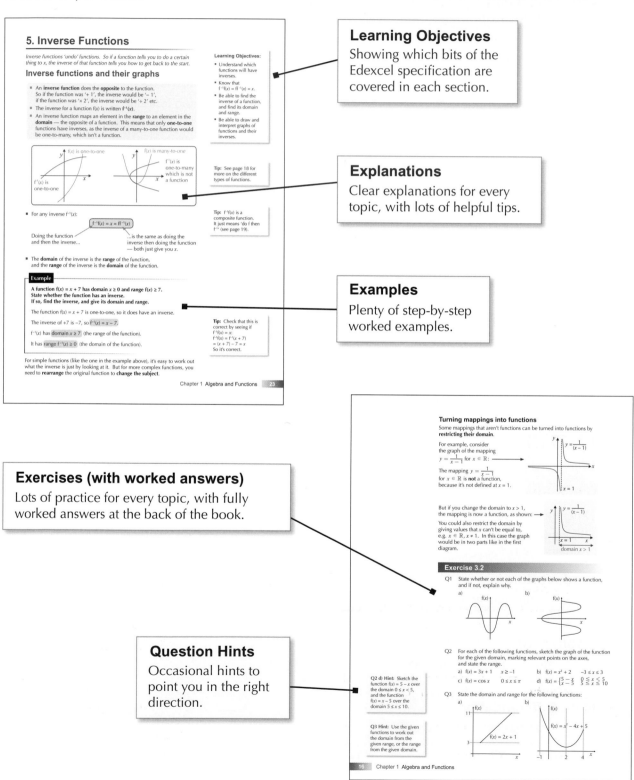

Learning Objectives
Showing which bits of the Edexcel specification are covered in each section.

Explanations
Clear explanations for every topic, with lots of helpful tips.

Examples
Plenty of step-by-step worked examples.

Exercises (with worked answers)
Lots of practice for every topic, with fully worked answers at the back of the book.

Question Hints
Occasional hints to point you in the right direction.

Review Exercise — Chapter 1

Q1 Simplify the following:
a) $\frac{4x^2 - 25}{6x - 15}$ b) $\frac{2x + 3}{x - 2} \times \frac{4x - 8}{2x^2 - 3x - 9}$ c) $\frac{x^2 - 3x}{x + 1} \div \frac{x}{2}$

Q2 Write the following as a single fraction:
a) $\frac{x}{2x + 1} + \frac{3}{x^2} + \frac{1}{x}$ b) $\frac{2}{x^2 - 1} - \frac{3x}{x - 1} + \frac{x}{x + 1}$

Q3 Use algebraic long division to divide $x^3 + 2x^2 - x + 19$ by $x + 4$.

Q4 Write $2x^3 + 8x^2 + 7x + 8$ in the form $(Ax^2 + Bx + C)(x + 3) + D$.
Using your answer, state the result when $2x^3 + 8x^2 + 7x + 8$ is divided by $(x + 3)$.

Q5 For the following mappings, state the range and say whether or not the mapping is a function.
If not, explain why, and if so, say whether the function is one-to-one or many-to-one.
a) $f(x) = x^2 - 16$, $x \geq 0$
b) $f : x \rightarrow x^3 - 7x + 10$, $x \in \mathbb{R}$
c) $f(x) = \sqrt{x}$, $x \in \mathbb{R}$
d) $f : x \rightarrow \frac{1}{x - 2}$, $x \in \mathbb{R}$

Q6 $f(x) = \frac{5}{2x + 1}$ defines a map.
a) Evaluate f(0) and f($\frac{1}{2}$).
b) Draw the mapping diagram for the domain
$\{x \in \mathbb{N}, x < 6\}$ and list the range.
c) Is the map a function for the domain $x \in \mathbb{Z}$?
If not, explain why not.
d) Is the map a function for the domain $x \in \mathbb{R}$?
If not, explain why not.

> **Q6 Hint:** $\mathbb{Z}$ is the set
> of integers (positive and
> negative), and $\mathbb{N}$ is the set
> of natural numbers (positive
> integers, not including 0).

Q7 a) Sketch the graph of the function
$f(x) = \begin{cases} x^3 - 2 & -2 < x < 2 \\ 2 & \text{otherwise} \end{cases}$.
b) State the range of the function.

Q8 For each pair of functions f and g, find fg(2), gf(1) and fg(x).
a) $f(x) = \frac{3}{x}$, $x > 0$ and $g(x) = 2x + 3$, $x \in \mathbb{R}$
b) $f(x) = 3x^2$, $x \geq 0$ and $g(x) = x + 4$, $x \in \mathbb{R}$

Q9 $f(x) = \log_{10} x$ and $g(x) = 10^{x+1}$.
a) Find the values of fg(1), gf(10) and $g^2(-1)$.
b) Explain why $f^2(1)$ is undefined.

Q10 $f(x) = 3x$ and $g(x) = x + 7$, both with domain $x \in \mathbb{R}$.
Find the composite functions fg(x), gf(x) and $g^2(x)$.

Chapter 1 Algebra and Functions 41

Review Exercises

Mixed questions covering the whole chapter, with fully worked answers.

Exam-Style Questions — Chapter 1

1 Write $\frac{2x^2 - 9x - 35}{x^2 - 49}$ as a fraction in its simplest form.
(3 marks)

2 Simplify the following:
a) $\frac{x^2 - x - 20}{7x + 4} \div \frac{x^2 - 16}{x + 2}$
(3 marks)

b) $\frac{x^2 - x - 20}{2x + 4} - \frac{x^2 - 16}{x + 2}$
(3 marks)

3 In words, describe what happens to the curve $y = x^3$ to transform it into the curve
$y = 2(x - 1)^3 + 4$.
(3 marks)

4 The functions f and g are given by: $f(x) = x^2 - 3$, $x \in \mathbb{R}$ and $g(x) = \frac{1}{x}$, $x \in \mathbb{R}$, $x \neq 0$
a) Find an expression for gf(x).
(2 marks)

b) Solve $gf(x) = \frac{1}{6}$.
(3 marks)

c) The function $f^{-1}(x)$ does not exist.
(i) Explain why
(1 mark)

(ii) Suggest a restricted domain for f(x) so that the function $f^{-1}(x)$ exists.
(1 mark)

5 Write $x^3 + 15x^2 + 43x - 30$ in the form $(Ax^2 + Bx + C)(x + 6) + D$,
where A, B, C and D are constants to be found.
(3 marks)

6 For the functions f and g, where
$f(x) = 2^x$, $x \in \mathbb{R}$ and $g(x) = \sqrt{3x - 2}$, $x \geq \frac{2}{3}$,
find:
a) fg(6)
(2 marks)

b) gf(2)
(2 marks)

c) (i) $g^{-1}(x)$
(2 marks)

(ii) $fg^{-1}(x)$
(2 marks)

Chapter 1 Algebra and Functions 43

Exam-Style Questions

Questions in the same style as the ones you'll get in the exam, with worked solutions and mark schemes.

Formula Sheet

Contains all the formulas you'll be given in the C3 exam.

Glossary

All the definitions you need to know for the exam, plus other useful words.

Practice Exam Papers (on CD-ROM)

Two printable exam papers, with fully worked answers and mark schemes.

II

Published by CGP

Editors:
Mary Falkner, Paul Jordin, Simon Little, Matteo Orsini Jones, Caley Simpson, Charlotte Whiteley, Dawn Wright.

Contributors:
Katharine Brown, Jane Chow, Margaret Darlington, Dave Harding, Frances Knight, James Nicholson, Charlotte O'Brien, Andy Pierson, Manpreet Sambhi.

ISBN: 978 1 84762 813 8

With thanks to Alastair Duncombe for the proofreading.

Groovy website: www.cgpbooks.co.uk

Printed by Elanders Ltd, Newcastle upon Tyne.
Jolly bits of clipart from CorelDRAW®

1. Simplifying Expressions

Simplifying expressions in C3 involves a lot of algebraic fractions. You'll have to factorise, cancel, multiply, divide, add and subtract them. You'll find that this will come in handy in other parts of maths, so it's a pretty important skill.

Simplifying algebraic fractions

Algebraic fractions are a lot like normal fractions — and you can treat them in the same way, whether you're adding, subtracting, multiplying or dividing them. All fractions are much easier to deal with when they're in their **simplest form**, so the first thing to do with algebraic fractions is to simplify them as much as possible.

- Look for **common factors** in the numerator and denominator — **factorise** top and bottom and see if there's anything you can **cancel**.

- If there's a **fraction** in the numerator or denominator (e.g. $\frac{1}{x}$), **multiply** the whole thing (i.e. top and bottom) by the same factor to get rid of it (for $\frac{1}{x}$, you'd multiply through by x).

Learning Objectives:

- Be able to simplify rational expressions (i.e. algebraic fractions with linear or quadratic denominators) by factorising and cancelling.

- Be able to simplify rational expressions by adding and subtracting algebraic fractions.

- Be able to simplify rational expressions by multiplying and dividing algebraic fractions.

Examples

Simplify the following:

a) $\dfrac{x-1}{x^2+3x-4}$ ← Try factorising the denominator first.

$= \dfrac{x-1}{(x-1)(x+4)}$ ← There's an $(x-1)$ on the top and bottom which will cancel.

$= \dfrac{1}{x+4}$

b) $\dfrac{3x+6}{x^2-4}$ ← Here, both the numerator and the denominator will factorise.

$= \dfrac{3(x+2)}{(x+2)(x-2)} = \dfrac{3}{x-2}$

Tip: Watch out for the difference of two squares — see C1.

c) $\dfrac{x^3-1}{2x^2+5x-7}$ ← Factorise top and bottom again.

$= \dfrac{(x-1)(x^2+x+1)}{(2x+7)(x-1)}$ ← This quadratic won't factorise any further.

$= \dfrac{x^2+x+1}{2x+7}$

Tip: You should have come across methods for factorising cubics in C2.

Tip: Take your time with messy expressions and work things out in separate steps.

d) $\dfrac{2 + \frac{1}{2x}}{4x^2 + x}$ ⟵ Factorise the denominator.

$= \dfrac{2 + \frac{1}{2x}}{x(4x + 1)}$ ⟵ Get rid of this fraction by multiplying the top and bottom by $2x$.

$= \dfrac{\left(2 + \frac{1}{2x}\right) \times 2x}{x(4x + 1) \times 2x} = \dfrac{4x + 1}{2x^2(4x + 1)} = \boxed{\dfrac{1}{2x^2}}$

Exercise 1.1

Simplify the following:

Q1 $\dfrac{4}{2x + 10}$

Q2 $\dfrac{5x}{x^2 + 2x}$

Q3 $\dfrac{6x^2 - 3x}{3x^2}$

Q4 $\dfrac{4x^3}{x^3 + 3x^2}$

Q5 $\dfrac{3x + 6}{x^2 + 3x + 2}$

Q6 $\dfrac{x^2 + 3x}{x^2 + x - 6}$

Q7 $\dfrac{2x - 6}{x^2 - 9}$

Q8 $\dfrac{5x^2 - 20x}{2x^2 - 5x - 12}$

Q9 $\dfrac{3x^2 - 7x - 6}{2x^2 - x - 15}$

Q10 $\dfrac{x^3 - 4x^2 - 19x - 14}{x^2 - 6x - 7}$

Q11 $\dfrac{x^3 - 2x^2}{x^3 - 4x}$

Q12 $\dfrac{1 + \frac{1}{x}}{x + 1}$

Q14 Hint: You need to multiply the top and bottom by the same term to get rid of the fractions. Don't just multiply the top by $2x$ and the bottom by x.

Q13 $\dfrac{3 + \frac{1}{x}}{2 + \frac{1}{x}}$

Q14 $\dfrac{1 + \frac{1}{2x}}{2 + \frac{1}{x}}$

Q15 $\dfrac{\frac{1}{3x} - 1}{3x^2 - x}$

Q16 $\dfrac{2 + \frac{1}{x}}{6x^2 + 3x}$

Q17 Hint: Once you've multiplied through by $x + 2$ this is not as bad as it looks.

Q17 $\dfrac{\frac{3x}{x + 2}}{\frac{x}{x + 2} + \frac{1}{x + 2}}$

Q18 $\dfrac{2 + \frac{1}{x + 1}}{3 + \frac{1}{x + 1}}$

Q19 $\dfrac{1 - \frac{2}{x + 3}}{x + 2}$

Q20 Hint: Multiplying each term by x^2 will get rid of all the fractions.

Q20 $\dfrac{4 - \frac{1}{x^2}}{2 - \frac{1}{x} - \frac{1}{x^2}}$

Adding and subtracting algebraic fractions

You'll have come across adding and subtracting fractions before in C1, so here's a little reminder of how to do it:

1. Find the common denominator

- Take all the individual 'bits' from the bottom lines and **multiply** them together.
- Only use each bit **once** unless something on the bottom line is raised to a **power**.

> **Tip:** The common denominator should be the lowest common multiple (LCM) of all the denominators.

2. Put each fraction over the common denominator

- Multiply both top and bottom of each fraction by the same term — whatever term will turn the denominator into the **common denominator**.

3. Combine into one fraction

- Once everything's over the common denominator you can just **add** (or **subtract**) the **numerators**.

Examples

a) **Simplify:** $\dfrac{2}{x-1} - \dfrac{3}{3x+2}$

- Multiply the denominators to get the **common denominator**:
$$(x-1)(3x+2)$$

- Multiply the top and bottom lines of each fraction by whatever term changes the denominator into the common denominator:
$$\frac{2 \times (3x+2)}{(x-1) \times (3x+2)} - \frac{3 \times (x-1)}{(3x+2) \times (x-1)}$$

> **Tip:** Always check if there's any more factorising and cancelling that can be done at the end. Your final answer needs to be fully simplified to get all the marks in an exam question.

- All the denominators are the same — so you can just subtract the numerators:
$$\frac{2(3x+2) - 3(x-1)}{(3x+2)(x-1)} = \frac{6x+4-3x+3}{(3x+2)(x-1)} = \boxed{\frac{3x+7}{(3x+2)(x-1)}}$$

b) **Simplify:** $\dfrac{2y}{x(x+3)} + \dfrac{1}{y^2(x+3)} - \dfrac{x}{y}$

The individual 'bits' here are x, $(x+3)$ and y, but you need to use y^2 because there's a y^2 in the second fraction's denominator.

- The common denominator is: $xy^2(x+3)$

- Multiply the top and bottom lines of each fraction by whatever term changes the denominator into the common denominator:
$$\frac{2y \times y^2}{x(x+3) \times y^2} + \frac{1 \times x}{y^2(x+3) \times x} - \frac{x \times xy(x+3)}{y \times xy(x+3)}$$

> **Tip:** In theory there's nothing wrong here with having a common denominator of all the denominators multiplied together (i.e. $xy^3(x+3)^2$). You'd still get the same final answer by cancelling down. Being a bit clever about it saves you a lot of effort though, so always try to use the simplest common denominator possible (the LCM).

- All the denominators are the same — so you can just add the numerators:
$$= \frac{2y^3 + x - x^2y(x+3)}{xy^2(x+3)} = \boxed{\frac{2y^3 + x - x^3y - 3x^2y}{xy^2(x+3)}}$$

Simplify the following:

Q2 Hint: Both denominators are a multiple of x. So the common denominator will just be another multiple of x.

Q1 $\dfrac{2x}{3} + \dfrac{x}{5}$

Q2 $\dfrac{2}{3x} - \dfrac{1}{5x}$

Q3 $\dfrac{3}{x^2} + \dfrac{2}{x}$

Q4 $\dfrac{x+1}{3} + \dfrac{x+2}{4}$

Q5 $\dfrac{2x}{3} + \dfrac{x-1}{7x}$

Q6 $\dfrac{3x}{4} - \dfrac{2x-1}{5x}$

Q7 $\dfrac{2}{x-1} + \dfrac{3}{x}$

Q8 $\dfrac{3}{x+1} + \dfrac{2}{x+2}$

Q9 $\dfrac{4}{x-3} - \dfrac{1}{x+4}$

Q10 $\dfrac{6}{x+2} + \dfrac{6}{x-2}$

Q11 $\dfrac{3}{x-2} - \dfrac{5}{2x+3}$

Q12 $\dfrac{3}{x+2} + \dfrac{x}{x+1}$

Q13 $\dfrac{5x}{(x+1)^2} - \dfrac{3}{x+1}$

Q14 $\dfrac{5}{x(x+3)} + \dfrac{3}{x+2}$

Q15 Hint: Factorise the first denominator before you do anything else.

Q15 $\dfrac{x}{x^2-4} - \dfrac{1}{x+2}$

Q16 $\dfrac{3}{x+1} + \dfrac{6}{2x^2+x-1}$

Q17 $\dfrac{2}{x} + \dfrac{3}{x+1} + \dfrac{4}{x+2}$

Q18 $\dfrac{3}{x+4} - \dfrac{2}{x+1} + \dfrac{1}{x-2}$

Q19 Hint: To turn the 2 into a fraction just use '1' as the denominator.

Q19 $2 - \dfrac{3}{x+1} + \dfrac{4}{(x+1)^2}$

Q20 $\dfrac{2x^2-x-3}{x^2-1} + \dfrac{1}{x(x-1)}$

Multiplying and dividing algebraic fractions

Multiplying algebraic fractions

You **multiply** algebraic fractions in exactly the same way that you multiply normal fractions — multiply the numerators together, then multiply the denominators. Try to **cancel** any **common factors** before multiplying.

Examples

Simplify the following:

a) $\dfrac{x^3}{2y} \times \dfrac{8y^2}{3}$

$\dfrac{x^3}{1\,\cancel{2y}} \times \dfrac{\cancel{8y^2}^{\,4y}}{3}$ ⟵ Cancel all common factors.

$= \dfrac{x^3 \times 4y}{1 \times 3} = \dfrac{4x^3 y}{3}$ ⟵ Then multiply top by top and bottom by bottom.

b) $\dfrac{x^2 - 2x - 15}{2x + 8} \times \dfrac{x^2 - 16}{x^2 + 3x}$

$= \dfrac{\cancel{(x+3)}(x-5)}{2\cancel{(x+4)}} \times \dfrac{\cancel{(x+4)}(x-4)}{x\cancel{(x+3)}}$ ⟵ Factorise the expressions in both fractions and cancel.

$= \dfrac{(x-5)(x-4)}{2x} \left(= \dfrac{x^2 - 9x + 20}{2x}\right)$ ⟵ Then just multiply as before.

> **Tip:** Check whether you can cancel down any further at the end, just in case you missed something before.

> **Tip:** In cases like these, it's a lot easier to do all the factorising and cancelling before you multiply.

Dividing algebraic fractions

To **divide** by an algebraic fraction, you just **multiply** by its reciprocal. The reciprocal is $1 \div$ the original thing — for fractions you just turn the fraction upside down.

Examples

Simplify the following:

a) $\dfrac{8}{5x} \div \dfrac{12}{x^3}$ ⟵ Turn the second fraction upside down.

$= \dfrac{8}{5x} \times \dfrac{x^3}{12} = \dfrac{\cancel{8}^{\,2}}{5x} \times \dfrac{\cancel{x^3}^{\,x^2}}{\cancel{12}_{\,3}}$ ⟵ Cancel all common factors.

$= \dfrac{2 \times x^2}{5 \times 3} = \dfrac{2x^2}{15}$ ⟵ Now multiply.

b) $\dfrac{3x}{5} \div \dfrac{3x^2 - 9x}{20}$

$= \dfrac{\cancel{3x}}{\cancel{5}} \times \dfrac{\cancel{20}^{\,4}}{\cancel{3x}(x-3)}$ ⟵ Turn the second fraction upside down, and then cancel. Note that the $3x^2 - 9x$ has been factorised first.

$= \dfrac{4}{x-3}$

Simplify the following:

Q1 Hint: Remember — cancelling **before** you multiply will make things a whole lot simpler.

Q1   a) $\dfrac{2x}{3} \times \dfrac{5x}{4}$ b) $\dfrac{6x^3}{7} \times \dfrac{2}{x^2}$

c) $\dfrac{8x^2}{3y^2} \times \dfrac{x^3}{4y}$ d) $\dfrac{8x^4}{3y} \times \dfrac{6y^2}{5x}$

Q2   a) $\dfrac{x}{3} \div \dfrac{3}{x}$ b) $\dfrac{4x^3}{3} \div \dfrac{x}{2}$

c) $\dfrac{3}{2x} \div \dfrac{6}{x^3}$ d) $\dfrac{2x^3}{3y} \div \dfrac{4x}{y^2}$

Q3 $\dfrac{x+2}{4} \times \dfrac{x}{3x+6}$

Q4 $\dfrac{4x}{5} \div \dfrac{4x^2+8x}{15}$

Q5 Hint: Always be on the look out for hidden 'difference of two squares' expressions.

Q5 $\dfrac{2x^2-2}{x} \times \dfrac{5x}{3x-3}$

Q6 $\dfrac{2x^2+8x}{x^2-2x} \times \dfrac{x-1}{x+4}$

Q7 $\dfrac{x^2-4}{9} \div \dfrac{x-2}{3}$

Q8 $\dfrac{2}{x^2+4x} \div \dfrac{1}{x+4}$

Q9 $\dfrac{x^2+4x+3}{x^2+5x+6} \times \dfrac{x^2+2x}{x+1}$

Q10 $\dfrac{x^2+5x+6}{x^2-2x-3} \times \dfrac{3x+3}{x^2+2x}$

Q11 $\dfrac{x^2-4}{6x-3} \times \dfrac{2x^2+5x-3}{x^2+2x}$

Q12 $\dfrac{x^2+7x+6}{4x-4} \div \dfrac{x^2+8x+12}{x^2-x}$

Q13 $\dfrac{x^2+4x+4}{x^2-4x+3} \times \dfrac{x^2-2x-3}{2x^2-2x} \times \dfrac{4x-4}{x^2+2x}$

Q14 Hint: Turn the fraction you're dividing by upside down and multiply.

Q14 $\dfrac{x}{6x+12} \div \dfrac{x^2-x}{x+2} \times \dfrac{3x-3}{x+1}$

Q15 $\dfrac{x^2+5x}{2x^2+7x+3} \times \dfrac{2x+1}{x^3-x^2} \div \dfrac{x+5}{x^2+x-6}$

2. Algebraic Division

Algebraic division (dividing one expression by another) is just another way of simplifying an algebraic fraction.

Algebraic division

Important terms

There are a few words that come up a lot in algebraic division, so make sure you know what they all mean.

- **Degree** — the highest power of x in the polynomial.
  For example, the degree of $4x^5 + 6x^2 - 3x - 1$ is 5.
- **Divisor** — this is the thing you're dividing by.
  For example, if you divide $x^2 + 4x - 3$ by $x + 2$, the divisor is $x + 2$.
- **Quotient** — the bit that you get when you divide by the divisor (not including the **remainder** — see below).

Method 1 — using the formula

There's a handy **formula** you can use to do algebraic division:

> A polynomial f(x) can be written in the form:
>
> $$f(x) = q(x)d(x) + r(x)$$
>
> where: q(x) is the quotient,
> d(x) is the divisor,
> and r(x) is the remainder.

This comes from the **Remainder Theorem** that you met in C2. You'll be given f(x) and d(x) in the question, and it's down to you to work out q(x) and r(x).

Example

Divide $4x^5 - 7x^2 + 3x - 9$ by $x^2 - 5x + 8$.

This bit is f(x).
It has a degree of 5.

This bit is d(x), the divisor.
It has a degree of 2.

Here's a step-by-step guide to using the formula:

- First, you have to work out the **degrees** of the **quotient** and **remainder**, which depend on the degrees of the polynomial and the divisor.
  The degree of the quotient is **deg f(x) – deg d(x)**, and the degree of the remainder has to be **less** than the degree of the divisor.
- Write out the division using the formula, but replace q(x) and r(x) with **general polynomials**. A general polynomial of degree 2 is Ax^2 + Bx + C, and a general polynomial of degree 1 is Ax + B, where A, B, C, etc. are constants to be found.
- The next step is to work out the values of the **constants** (A, B, etc.). You do this by substituting in values for x to make bits disappear, and by **equating coefficients**.
- It's best to start with the **constant term** and work **backwards** from there.
- Finally, write out the division again, replacing A, B, C, etc. with the values you've found.

Learning Objectives:

- Be able to simplify algebraic fractions with linear or quadratic denominators by using algebraic division.

Tip: A **polynomial** is an algebraic expression made up of the sum of constant terms and variables raised to positive integer powers. For example $x^3 - 2x + \frac{1}{2}$ is a polynomial, but $x^{-3} - 2x^{\frac{3}{2}}$ is not as it has a negative power and a fractional power of x.

Tip: The ≡ symbol means it's an identity.

Tip: The degree of the divisor will always be less than or equal to the degree of the polynomial.

Tip: Equating coefficients means comparing the coefficients of each power of x on the left hand side and the right hand side of the identity.

When you're using this method, you might have to use **simultaneous equations** to work out some of the coefficients. (Have a look back at your C1 notes for a reminder of how to do this if you need to.) The method looks a bit intense, but follow through these examples to see how it works.

Example 1

Divide $x^4 - 3x^3 - 3x^2 + 10x + 5$ by $x^2 - 5x + 6$.

- First, work out the **degrees** of the **quotient** and **remainder**:
  f(x) has degree 4 and d(x) has degree 2, which means that the quotient q(x) has degree $4 - 2 = 2$. The remainder r(x) has degree 1 or 0 (it must be less than the degree of d(x)) — so assume it's 1.

- Write out the division in the form **f(x) $\equiv$ q(x)d(x) + r(x)**, replacing q(x) and r(x) with general polynomials of degree 2 and 1:
  $x^4 - 3x^3 - 3x^2 + 10x + 5 \equiv (Ax^2 + Bx + C)(x^2 - 5x + 6) + Dx + E$

- d(x) factorises to give $(x - 2)(x - 3)$:
  $x^4 - 3x^3 - 3x^2 + 10x + 5 \equiv (Ax^2 + Bx + C)(x - 2)(x - 3) + Dx + E$

- Substitute $x = 2$ and $x = 3$ into the identity to make the q(x)d(x) bit disappear. This gives the following equations:
  when $x = 2$, $5 = 2D + E$
  when $x = 3$, $8 = 3D + E$

- Solve these simultaneously to get $D = 3$ and $E = -1$.
  So now the identity looks like this:
  $x^4 - 3x^3 - 3x^2 + 10x + 5 \equiv (Ax^2 + Bx + C)(x^2 - 5x + 6) + 3x - 1$

- Now substitute $x = 0$ into the identity:
  when $x = 0$, $5 = 6C - 1$

- Solving this gives $C = 1$. So now the identity looks like this:
  $x^4 - 3x^3 - 3x^2 + 10x + 5 \equiv (Ax^2 + Bx + 1)(x^2 - 5x + 6) + 3x - 1$

- Finally, **equate the coefficients** of x^4 and x^3.
  On the LHS the coefficient of x^4 is 1, and the coefficient of x^3 is –3. Expanding the brackets on the RHS lets you see that the coefficient of x^4 is A, and the coefficient of x^3 is B – 5A. Equating these gives $1 = A$ and $-3 = -5A + B$, so $B = 2$. So the identity looks like this:

  $$x^4 - 3x^3 - 3x^2 + 10x + 5 \equiv (x^2 + 2x + 1)(x^2 - 5x + 6) + 3x - 1$$

Example 2

Divide $x^3 + 5x^2 - 18x - 10$ by $x - 3$.

- f(x) has degree 3 and d(x) has degree 1, which means that q(x) has degree $3 - 1 = 2$. The remainder has degree 0 (it must be less than 1).

- Write out the division in the form f(x) $\equiv$ q(x)d(x) + r(x):
  $x^3 + 5x^2 - 18x - 10 \equiv (Ax^2 + Bx + C)(x - 3) + D$

- Putting $x = 3$ into the identity gives $D = 8$, so:
  $x^3 + 5x^2 - 18x - 10 \equiv (Ax^2 + Bx + C)(x - 3) + 8$

- Now, setting $x = 0$ gives the equation $-10 = -3C + 8$, so $C = 6$.
  $x^3 + 5x^2 - 18x - 10 \equiv (Ax^2 + Bx + 6)(x - 3) + 8$

- Equating the coefficients of x^3 and x^2 gives $A = 1$
  and $-3A + B = 5$, so $B = 8$. So:

  $$x^3 + 5x^2 - 18x - 10 \equiv (x^2 + 8x + 6)(x - 3) + 8$$

Tip: If you're not sure what the degree is, assume it's the highest it could be (in this case 1). If it turns out to be lower it just means that some coefficients will be 0.

Tip: Factorising the divisor helps you to work out the values of x you need to put in to make certain terms disappear. When you've put it in brackets, pick values of x that will make one of the brackets zero.

Tip: After you've done a few of these you'll get used to spotting what the coefficients are going to be in terms of A and B, so you won't have to expand the brackets fully each time.

Tip: If the remainder has a degree of 0 it just means that it's a constant.

Chapter 1 Algebra and Functions

Simply stating the identity at the end doesn't properly answer the question. If you've been asked to divide one thing by another, then you need to state the **quotient** and the **remainder** which you've worked out using the formula.

So for Example 1 on the previous page:

$(x^4 - 3x^3 - 3x^2 + 10x + 5) \div (x^2 - 5x + 6) = x^2 + 2x + 1$ **remainder $3x - 1$**.

For Example 2: $(x^3 + 5x^2 - 18x - 10) \div (x - 3) = x^2 + 8x + 6$ **remainder 8**.

Method 2 — algebraic long division

You can also use **long division** to divide two algebraic expressions (using the same method you'd use for numbers).

Example

Divide $(2x^3 - 7x^2 - 16x + 11)$ by $(x - 5)$.

- Start by dividing the first term in the polynomial by the first term of the divisor: $2x^3 \div x = 2x^2$. Write this answer above the polynomial:

$$\begin{array}{r} 2x^2 \\ x - 5 \overline{)2x^3 - 7x^2 - 16x + 11} \end{array}$$

Tip: Note that we only divide each term by the 'x' term, not the '$x - 5$'. The -5 bit is dealt with in the steps in between.

- Multiply the divisor $(x - 5)$ by this answer $(2x^2)$ to get $2x^3 - 10x^2$:

$$\begin{array}{r} 2x^2 \\ x - 5 \overline{)2x^3 - 7x^2 - 16x + 11} \\ 2x^3 - 10x^2 \end{array}$$

- Subtract this from the main expression to get $3x^2$. Bring down the $-16x$ term just to make things clearer for the next subtraction.

$$\begin{array}{r} 2x^2 \\ x - 5 \overline{)2x^3 - 7x^2 - 16x + 11} \\ - \ \underline{2x^3 - 10x^2} \downarrow \\ 3x^2 - 16x \end{array}$$

- Now divide the first term of the remaining polynomial $(3x^2)$ by the first term of the divisor (x) to get $3x$ (the second term in the answer).

$$\begin{array}{r} 2x^2 + 3x \\ x - 5 \overline{)2x^3 - 7x^2 - 16x + 11} \\ - \ \underline{2x^3 - 10x^2} \downarrow \\ 3x^2 - 16x \end{array}$$

- Multiply $(x - 5)$ by $3x$ to get $3x^2 - 15x$, then subtract again and bring down the $+11$ term.

$$\begin{array}{r} 2x^2 + 3x \\ x - 5 \overline{)2x^3 - 7x^2 - 16x + 11} \\ - \ \underline{2x^3 - 10x^2} \downarrow \\ 3x^2 - 16x \downarrow \\ - \ \underline{3x^2 - 15x} \downarrow \\ - x + 11 \end{array}$$

- Divide $-x$ by x to get -1 (the third term in the answer). Then multiply $(x - 5)$ by -1 to get $-x + 5$.

$$
\begin{array}{r}
2x^2 + 3x - 1 \\
x - 5 \overline{)\,2x^3 - 7x^2 - 16x + 11} \\
\underline{-\ 2x^3 - 10x^2} \quad\quad\quad \\
3x^2 - 16x \quad\quad \\
\underline{-\ 3x^2 - 15x} \quad \\
-x + 11 \\
\underline{-\ -x + 5} \\
6
\end{array}
$$

- After subtracting, this term (6) has a degree that's **less** than the degree of the divisor, $(x - 5)$, so it can't be divided. This is the **remainder**.

- So $(2x^3 - 7x^2 - 16x + 11) \div (x - 5) = \boxed{2x^2 + 3x - 1 \text{ remainder } 6.}$

This could also be written as:

$$\frac{2x^3 - 7x^2 - 16x + 11}{x - 5} = 2x^2 + 3x - 1 + \frac{6}{x - 5}.$$

Tip: You can multiply the quotient by $(x - 5)$, and then add on the remainder, 6, to check you've got it right.

Tip: In C3 you only have to deal with divisors with order 1 or 2 — i.e. linear or quadratic expressions.

You can use the long division method when the divisor has a degree bigger than 1 (e.g. a quadratic), as long as the expression you're dividing has an even higher degree. The example below shows the working out all in one go.

Example

Divide $(2x^4 - x^2 - 6x + 5)$ by $(2x^2 + 4x + 5)$.

- First make sure you write out the expressions with all terms included — put a coefficient of 0 for the 'missing' x^3 term here.

- $2x^4 \div 2x^2 = x^2$.

$$
\begin{array}{r}
x^2 - 2x + 1 \\
2x^2 + 4x + 5 \overline{)\,2x^4 + 0x^3 - x^2 - 6x + 5} \\
\underline{-\ 2x^4 + 4x^3 + 5x^2} \quad\quad\quad\quad \\
-4x^3 - 6x^2 - 6x \quad \\
\underline{-\ -4x^3 - 8x^2 - 10x} \quad \\
2x^2 + 4x + 5 \\
\underline{-\ 2x^2 + 4x + 5} \\
0
\end{array}
$$

- Multiply $2x^2 + 4x + 5$ by x^2 to get $2x^4 + 4x^3 + 5x^2$.

- Subtract this and bring down the $-6x$ term.

- $-4x^3 \div 2x^2 = -2x$ (the second term in the answer).

- Multiply $2x^2 + 4x + 5$ by $-2x$ to get $-4x^3 - 8x^2 - 10x$.

- Subtract this and bring down the $+5$ term.

- $2x^2 \div 2x^2 = +1$ (the third term in the answer).

- Multiply $2x^2 + 4x + 5$ by 1 to get $2x^2 + 4x + 5$. Subtracting this gives a remainder of 0.

- So $(2x^4 - x^2 - 6x + 5) \div (2x^2 + 4x + 5) = \boxed{x^2 - 2x + 1.}$

Tip: If the original polynomial doesn't have an x term, for example, just put $0x$ where the x term should be.

Tip: A remainder of zero means it divides exactly.

Q1 Use the formula $f(x) \equiv q(x)d(x) + r(x)$ to divide the following expressions. In each case state the quotient and remainder.

a) $(x^3 - 14x^2 + 6x + 11) \div (x + 1)$

b) $(2x^3 + 5x^2 - 8x - 17) \div (x - 2)$

c) $(2x^3 + 4x^2 - 5x + 2) \div (x^2 - 2x + 1)$

Q1 Hint: If you're told which method to use make sure you show all your working clearly to prove that you know how to use the method.

Q2 Write $6x^4 + 11x^3 + 9x^2 + 15x - 2$ in the form:
$(Ax^2 + Bx + C)(2x^2 + x + 3) + Dx + E$.

Using your answer, state the result when $6x^4 + 11x^3 + 9x^2 + 15x - 2$ is divided by $2x^2 + x + 3$.

Q2 Hint: This is just another way of asking you to use the formula.

Q3 Use long division to divide the following expressions. In each case state the quotient and remainder.

a) $(x^3 - 14x^2 + 6x + 11) \div (x + 1)$

b) $(x^3 + 10x^2 + 15x - 13) \div (x + 3)$

c) $(2x^3 + 5x^2 - 8x - 17) \div (x - 2)$

d) $(3x^3 - 78x + 9) \div (x + 5)$

e) $(x^4 - 1) \div (x - 1)$

f) $(8x^3 - 6x^2 + x + 10) \div (2x - 3)$

g) $(2x^3 + 4x^2 - 5x + 2) \div (x^2 - 2x + 1)$

h) $(6x^4 + 11x^3 + 9x^2 + 15x - 2) \div (2x^2 + x + 3)$

In the following questions you can choose which method to use.

Q4 Divide $10x^3 + 7x^2 - 5x + 21$ by $2x + 1$, stating the quotient and remainder.

Q5 Divide $3x^3 - 8x^2 + 15x - 12$ by $x^2 + x - 2$, stating the quotient and remainder.

Q6 Divide $6x^4 - 7x^2 - 3$ by $2x^2 - 3$, stating the quotient and remainder.

3. Functions and Mappings

Learning Objectives:

- Understand the definition of a function as a particular type of mapping and be able to deduce from this whether a given mapping is a function.

- Be able to use function notation.

- Be able to identify the domain and range of a given function.

- Be able to restrict the domain of a mapping to make it a function.

- Be able to identify whether a function is one-to-one or many-to-one for a given domain.

A mapping is just a set of instructions that tells you how to get from one value to another, and a function is a special kind of mapping.

Mappings and functions

Mappings

A **mapping** is an operation that takes one number and transforms it into another. For example, 'multiply by 5', 'square root' and 'divide by 7' are all mappings. The set of numbers you start with is called the **domain**, and the set of numbers they become is called the **range**.

Mappings can be drawn as **mapping diagrams**, like the one shown here for 'multiply by 5 and add 1' acting on the domain {−1, 0, 1, 2}:

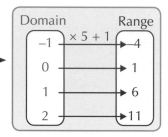

Use the notation {1, 2, ...} for the domain and range if they are a discrete list of values. If they can take any value above or below a limit, use e.g. $x \geq 0$.

The domain and / or range will often be the set of **real numbers**, $\mathbb{R}$. A real number is any positive or negative number (or 0) — fractions, decimals, integers, surds. If x can take any real value, it's usually written as: $x \in \mathbb{R}$. Other sets of numbers include $\mathbb{Z}$, the set of integers, and $\mathbb{N}$, the set of natural numbers (positive integers, not including 0).

Tip: Another set of numbers is $\mathbb{C}$, the complex numbers, made up of 'imaginary' numbers — but you don't meet these in C3 or C4.

You might have to work out the range of a mapping from the domain you're given. For example, $y = x^2$, $x \in \mathbb{R}$ has the range $y \geq 0$, as the squares of all real numbers are positive (or zero).

Functions

Some mappings take every number in the domain to exactly **one** number in the range. These mappings are called **functions**. Functions are written using the following notation:

$$f(x) = 5x + 1 \qquad \text{or} \qquad f : x \to 5x + 1$$

You can substitute values for x into a function to find the value of the function at that point, as shown in the examples below.

Tip: Functions don't always use the letter 'f' — you'll see different letters used for functions over the next few pages.

> ### Examples
>
> **a) Give the value of f(−2) for the function $f(x) = x^2 − 1$.**
>
> Just replace each x in the function with −2 and calculate the answer:
> $f(−2) = (−2)^2 − 1 = 4 − 1 = \boxed{3}$
>
> **b) Find the value of x for which f(x) = 12 for the function $f : x \to 2x − 3$.**
>
> Solve this like a normal equation:
> $2x − 3 = 12 \Rightarrow 2x = 15 \Rightarrow x = \boxed{7.5}$

Functions can also be given in **several parts** (known as '**piecewise**' functions). Each part of the function will act over a different domain. For example:

$$f(x) = \begin{cases} 2x + 3 & x \leq 0 \\ x^2 & x > 0 \end{cases}$$

So f(1) is $1^2 = 1$ (because $x > 0$), but f(−1) is 2(−1) + 3 = 1 (because $x \leq 0$).

If a mapping takes a number from the domain to **more than one** number in the range (or if it isn't mapped to any number in the range), it's **not** a function.

Examples

The mapping shown here **is a function**, because any value of x in the domain maps to **only one** value in the range.

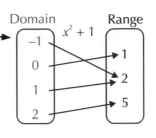
Domain   Range
$x^2 + 1$
−1
0
1
2
→ 1
→ 2
→ 5

Tip: Although each value in the domain only maps to one value in the range, the reverse is not true. This means it's a 'many to one' function — there's more about these on page 18.

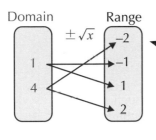
Domain   Range
$\pm\sqrt{x}$
1
4
−2
−1
1
2

The mapping shown here is **not a function**, because a value of x in the domain can map to **more than one** value in the range.

Exercise 3.1

Q1 Draw a mapping diagram for the map "multiply by 6" acting on the domain {1, 2, 3, 4}.

Q2 $y = x + 4$ is a map with domain $\{x \subset \mathbb{N}, x \leq 7\}$. Draw the mapping diagram.

Q2 Hint: $x \in \mathbb{N}$ just means that x is in the set of natural numbers (positive integers, not including 0). The $x \leq 7$ means that the domain must be the integers 1-7.

Q3 Complete the mapping diagram on the right and state the range:

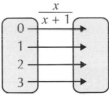
$\dfrac{x}{x + 1}$
0
1
2
3

Q4 Complete the mapping diagram below and state the domain:

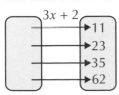
$3x + 2$
→11
→23
→35
→62

Q5 For the function $f(x) = 3x + 1$, write down the values of $f(2)$ and $f(-1)$.

Q6 For the function $g : x \rightarrow \dfrac{1}{2x + 1}$, $x > -\dfrac{1}{2}$, evaluate $g(0)$ and $g(2)$.

Q6 Hint: 'Evaluate' is just another way of asking you to 'find the value of'.

Q7 The function h is such that $h(x) = \sin x$, $-\pi \leq x \leq \pi$. Find $h\left(\dfrac{\pi}{2}\right)$ and $h\left(\dfrac{5\pi}{6}\right)$.

Q8 f defines a function $f : x \rightarrow \dfrac{1}{2 + \log_{10}x}$ for the domain $x > 0.01$. Evaluate $f(1)$ and $f(100)$.

Q9 State whether or not each of the mapping diagrams below shows a function, and if not, explain why.

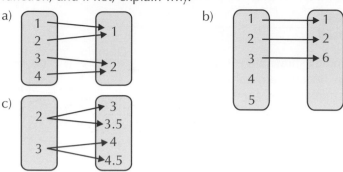

Graphs of functions

Tip: If you've got a discrete set of values that x can take (e.g. $x \in \{1,2,3\}$) then draw a mapping diagram instead of a graph.

Mappings and functions with a **continuous** domain (such as $x \in \mathbb{R}$, i.e. not a discrete set of values) can be drawn as **graphs**. Drawing a graph of, say, $f(x) = x^2$ is exactly the same as drawing a graph of $y = x^2$. For each value of x in the **domain** (which goes along the horizontal x-axis) you can plot the corresponding value of $f(x)$ in the **range** (up the vertical y-axis):

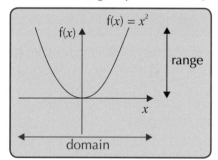

Drawing graphs can make it easier to **identify functions**, as shown below.

Examples

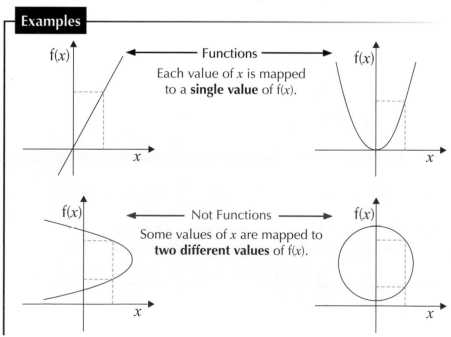

The graph on the right isn't a function because f(x) is **not defined** for $x < 0$. This just means that when x is negative there is no real value that f(x) can take.

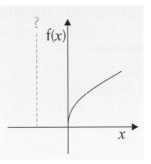

Tip: This could be turned into a function by restricting the domain to $x \geq 0$ — see page 16.

Finding ranges and domains using graphs

Sketching a graph can also be really useful when trying to find limits for the domain and range of a function.

Examples

a) **State the range for the function f(x) = x^2 – 5, $x \in \mathbb{R}$.**

The smallest possible value of x^2 is 0.

So the smallest possible value of $x^2 - 5$ must be –5.

So the range is f(x) $\geq$ –5.

This can be shown clearly by sketching a graph of the function:

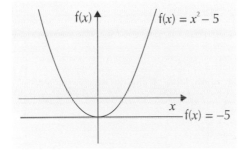

b) **State the domain for f(x) = $\sqrt{(x - 4)}$.**

There are no real solutions for the square root of a negative number.

This means there is a limit on the domain so that $x - 4 \geq 0$.

This gives a domain of $x \geq 4$.

Again, this can be demonstrated by sketching a graph of f(x) = $\sqrt{(x - 4)}$:

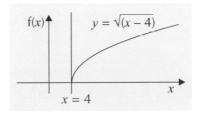

Turning mappings into functions

Some mappings that aren't functions can be turned into functions by **restricting their domain**.

For example, consider the graph of the mapping

$y = \dfrac{1}{x-1}$ for $x \in \mathbb{R}$: ──────→

The mapping $y = \dfrac{1}{x-1}$ for $x \in \mathbb{R}$ is **not** a function, because it's not defined at $x = 1$.

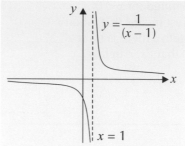

But if you change the domain to $x > 1$, the mapping is now a function, as shown: ──→

You could also restrict the domain by giving values that x can't be equal to, e.g. $x \in \mathbb{R}$, $x \neq 1$. In this case the graph would be in two parts like in the first diagram.

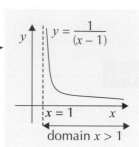

Exercise 3.2

Q1 State whether or not each of the graphs below shows a function, and if not, explain why.

a)

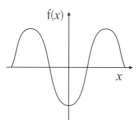

b)

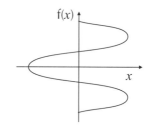

Q2 For each of the following functions, sketch the graph of the function for the given domain, marking relevant points on the axes, and state the range.

a) $f(x) = 3x + 1$ $\qquad x \geq -1$

b) $f(x) = x^2 + 2$ $\qquad -3 \leq x \leq 3$

c) $f(x) = \cos x$ $\qquad 0 \leq x \leq \pi$

d) $f(x) = \begin{cases} 5 - x & 0 \leq x \leq 5 \\ x - 5 & 5 \leq x \leq 10 \end{cases}$

Q2 d) Hint: Sketch the function $f(x) = 5 - x$ over the domain $0 \leq x < 5$, and the function $f(x) = x - 5$ over the domain $5 \leq x \leq 10$.

Q3 State the domain and range for the following functions:

a)

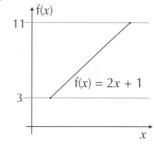

b)

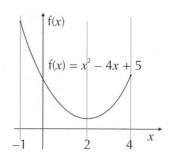

Q3 Hint: Use the given functions to work out the domain from the given range, or the range from the given domain.

Q4 The graph below shows the function $f(x) = \dfrac{x+2}{x+1}$, defined for the domain $x \geq 0$. State the range.

Q4-5 Hint: Use the functions to work out where the asymptotes lie. The range (or domain) will lie on one side of the asymptote.

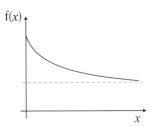

Q5 The diagram shows the function $f(x) = \dfrac{1}{x-2}$ drawn over the domain $x > a$. State the value of a.

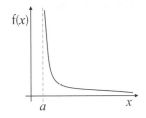

Q6 The diagram shows the function $f(x) = \sqrt{9 - x^2}$ for $x \in \mathbb{R}$, $a \leq x \leq b$. State the values of a and b.

Q6 Hint: $9 - x^2$ cannot be negative, as you can't take the square root of a negative number, so work out the values of x for which $9 - x^2 \geq 0$ and use these as the domain.

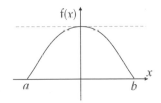

Q7 $h(x) = \sqrt{x+1}$, $x \in \mathbb{R}$.
Give a restricted domain which would make h a function.

Q8 $k : x \rightarrow \tan x$, $x \in \mathbb{R}$.
Give an example of a domain which would make k a function.

Q9 $m(x) = \dfrac{1}{x^2 - 4}$.
What is the largest continuous domain which would make m(x) a function?

Q8-9 Hint: Sketch a graph of each one first and identify where any asymptotes might be.

Q10 The diagram on the right shows the graph of $y = f(x)$.
a) Explain why f is not a function on the domain $x \in \mathbb{R}$.
b) State the largest possible domain that would make f a function.

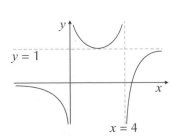

Types of function

One-to-one functions

Tip: Sketching a graph is a good way to help you identify the type of function.

> A function is **one-to-one** if each value in the **range** corresponds to **exactly one** value in the **domain**.

Example

The function $f : x \rightarrow 2x$, $x \in \mathbb{R}$ is one-to-one, as every value of x is mapped to a unique value in the range (the range is also $\mathbb{R}$).

You can see this clearly on a sketch of the function:

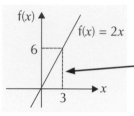

Only 3 in the domain is mapped to 6 in the range.

Many-to-one functions

Tip: There are also mappings known as 'one-to-many' and 'many-to-many', but neither of these types are functions.

> A function is **many-to-one** if some values in the **range** correspond to **more than one (many)** values in the **domain**.

Remember that no element in the domain can map to more than one element in the range, otherwise it wouldn't be a function.

Example

The function $f(x) = x^2$, $x \in \mathbb{R}$ is a many-to-one function, as two elements in the domain map to the same element in the range, as shown:

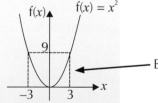

Both 3 and −3 map to 9.

Exercise 3.3

Q1   State whether each function below is one-to-one or many-to-one.

a) $f(x) = x^3$ $x \in \mathbb{R}$

b) $f : x \rightarrow \sin 2x$ $-\pi \leq x \leq \pi$

c) $f(x) = \log_{10} x$ $x > 0$

d) $f(x) = \begin{cases} x + 2 \\ 2 - x \end{cases}$ $\begin{array}{l} -2 \leq x < 0 \\ 0 \leq x \leq 2 \end{array}$

e) $f(x) = \begin{cases} 2^x \\ 1 \end{cases}$ $\begin{array}{l} x \geq 0 \\ x < 0 \end{array}$

4. Composite Functions

When one function is applied to another it makes a different function.
This is known as a composite function.

Composite functions

- If you have two functions f and g, you can combine them (do one followed by the other) to make a new function. This is called a **composite function**.
- Composite functions are written fg(x). This means 'do g first, then f'. If it helps, put brackets in until you get used to it, so fg(x) = f(g(x)).
- The order is really important — usually fg(x) ≠ gf(x). If you get a composite function that's written f²(x), it means ff(x). This just means you have to do f **twice**.

Learning Objectives:

- Be able to combine two or more functions into one composite function.
- Know that fg means 'do g first, then f'.
- Be able to solve equations involving composite functions.

Examples

If f(x) = x – 2 and g(x) = 3x, then find:

a) **fg(6):**
   First substitute 6 into g(x).
   Then substitute the value that comes out into f(x), as shown below:

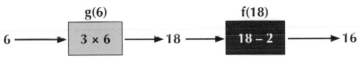

   So fg(6) – 16.

b) **gf(6):**
   This time substitute 6 into f(x) first.
   Then substitute the value that comes out into g(x):

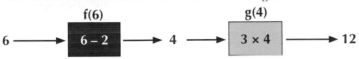

   So gf(6) = 12.

c) **fg(x):**
   This time leave everything in terms of x. Do g first, then f:

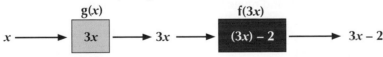

   So fg(x) = 3x – 2.

d) **gf(x):**

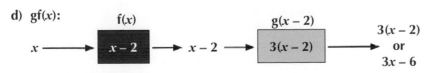

   So gf(x) = 3x – 6.

Tip: Composite functions made up of three or more functions work in exactly the same way — just make sure you get the order right.

Tip: Comparing the answers to a) and b) you can see that fg(x) ≠ gf(x).

The key to composite functions is to work things out in steps. Set out your working for composite functions as shown in the examples below.

Examples

For the functions $f : x \to 2x^3$ $\{x \in \mathbb{R}\}$ and $g : x \to x - 3$ $\{x \in \mathbb{R}\}$, find:

a) fg(4)   **b)** fg(0)   **c)** gf(0)   **d)** fg(x)   **e)** gf(x)   **f)** $f^2(x)$.

a) $fg(4) = f(g(4))$
$= f(4 - 3) = f(1)$
$= 2 \times 1^3 = \boxed{2}$

b) $fg(0) = f(g(0))$
$= f(0 - 3) = f(-3)$
$= 2 \times (-3)^3 = 2 \times -27$
$= \boxed{-54}$

c) $gf(0) = g(f(0))$
$= g(2 \times 0^3) = g(0)$
$= 0 - 3 = \boxed{-3}$

d) $fg(x) = f(g(x))$
$= f(x - 3)$
$= \boxed{2(x - 3)^3}$

e) $gf(x) = g(f(x))$
$= g(2x^3)$
$= \boxed{2x^3 - 3}$

f) $f^2(x) = f(f(x))$
$= f(2x^3)$
$= 2(2x^3)^3 = \boxed{16x^9}$

Tip: Don't forget the 2^3 when expanding $(2x^3)^3$ in part f).

Domain and range of composite functions

Two functions with given domains and ranges may form a composite function with a **different** domain and range.

Example

Give the domain and range of the composite function fg(x), where:
$f(x) = 2x^2 + 1$, domain $x \in \mathbb{R}$, range $f(x) \geq 1$
$g(x) = \dfrac{1}{x + 3}$, domain $x > -3$, range $g(x) > 0$

- First work out the composite function in terms of x:
$$fg(x) = f(g(x))$$
$$= f\left(\frac{1}{x + 3}\right) = 2\left(\frac{1}{x + 3}\right)^2 + 1$$

- Next, consider the graph of the composite function over the domain and range of the original functions:

Tip: Working out the domains and ranges of composite functions can be tricky — but sketching a graph always helps.

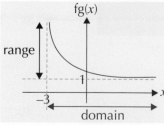

fg(x)

range

domain

As g(x) is restricted to $x > -3$, so the domain of fg(x) is also restricted to $\boxed{x > -3.}$

Since $\dfrac{1}{x + 3}$ is always > 0 for the domain $x > -3$,

$2\left(\dfrac{1}{x + 3}\right)^2 + 1$ must be > 1. So the range is $\boxed{fg(x) > 1.}$

For a composite function fg(x) the domain can also be found by putting the range of g(x) into f(x). If the domain of f(x) does not fully include the range of g(x) then the domain of g(x) will have to be restricted further.

Example

Find the domain of fg(x), where f(x) = $\sqrt{x}$, {x ≥ 0}, and g(x) = x + 5, {x ∈ ℝ}

The range of g(x) is g(x) ∈ ℝ. This is bigger than the domain of f(x), so the domain of g(x) will need to be restricted.

The input into f needs to be ≥ 0. Since for fg(x) the input into f is g(x) (i.e. x + 5):

$x + 5 \geq 0 \Rightarrow x \geq -5$.

So the largest possible domain for fg(x) is $x \geq -5.$

If the domain was not restricted, fg(x) would be undefined in places, e.g. fg(−6) = f(−6 + 5) = f(−1) = $\sqrt{-1}$ (which is undefined).

Exercise 4.1

Q1　f : x → x², {x ∈ ℝ} and g : x → 2x + 1, {x ∈ ℝ}. Find the values of:
　　a) fg(3)　　b) gf(3)　　c) f²(5)　　d) g²(2)

Q2　f(x) = sin x, {x ∈ ℝ} and g(x) − 2x, {x ∈ ℝ}.
　　Evaluate fg($\frac{\pi}{2}$) and gf($\frac{\pi}{2}$).

Q3　f : x → $\frac{3}{x + 2}$, {x > −2} and g : x → 2x, {x ∈ ℝ}.
　　a) Find the values of gf(1), fg(1) and f²(4).
　　b) Explain why fg(−1) is undefined.

Q3 b) Hint: Try to find the value of fg(−1), or consider the domains and ranges of f(x) and g(x).

Q4　f(x) = 2x − 1, {x ∈ ℝ} and g(x) = x², {x ∈ ℝ}. Find the functions:
　　a) fg(x)　　b) gf(x)　　c) f²(x)

Q5　f(x) = cos x, {x ∈ ℝ} and g(x) = 2x, {x ∈ ℝ}. Find the functions:
　　a) fg(x)　　b) gf(x)

Q6　f(x) = $\frac{2}{x - 1}$, {x > 1} and g(x) = x + 4, {x ∈ ℝ}. Find the functions
　　fg(x) and gf(x), writing them as single fractions in their simplest forms.

Q7　f(x) = $\frac{x}{1 - x}$, {x ∈ ℝ, x ≠ 1} and g(x) = x², {x ∈ ℝ}.
　　Find f²(x) and gfg(x).

Q8　f(x) = x² with domain x ∈ ℝ, and g(x) = 2x − 3 also with x ∈ ℝ.
　　a) Find fg(x) and write down its range.
　　b) Find gf(x) and write down its range.

Q8-9 Hint: Sketching the graphs of the composite functions will help you find the ranges and domains.

Q9　f(x) = $\frac{1}{x}$ with domain x > 0 and g(x) = 5x with domain x ∈ ℝ.
　　a) Find fg(x) and write down its range and largest possible domain.
　　b) Find gf(x) and write down its range and largest possible domain.

Q10　Given that f(x) = 3x + 2, g(x) = 5x − 1, and h(x) = x² + 1
　　(all with domains x ∈ ℝ), find fgh(x).

Solving composite function equations

If you're asked to solve an equation such as $fg(x) = 8$, the best way to do it is to work out what $fg(x)$ is, then rearrange $fg(x) = 8$ to make x the subject.

Example 1

For the functions $f : x \rightarrow \sqrt{x}$ with domain $\{x \geq 0\}$ and $g : x \rightarrow \dfrac{1}{x-1}$ with domain $\{x > 1\}$, solve the equation $fg(x) = \dfrac{1}{2}$. Also, state the range of $fg(x)$.

- First, find $fg(x)$: $\quad fg(x) = f\left(\dfrac{1}{x-1}\right) = \sqrt{\dfrac{1}{x-1}} = \dfrac{1}{\sqrt{x-1}}$

- So $\dfrac{1}{\sqrt{x-1}} = \dfrac{1}{2}$

- Rearrange this equation to find x:
$$\dfrac{1}{\sqrt{x-1}} = \dfrac{1}{2} \Rightarrow \sqrt{x-1} = 2 \Rightarrow x - 1 = 4 \Rightarrow \boxed{x = 5}$$

- To find the range, draw the graph of $fg(x)$.

- From the graph you can see that the domain of $fg(x)$ is $x > 1$ (though the question doesn't ask for this) and the range is $\boxed{fg(x) > 0}$.

Tip: Be careful with the domains and ranges of composite functions. Have a look back at pages 20-21 for more on how to find them.

Example 2

For the functions $f : x \rightarrow 2x + 1$ $\{x \in \mathbb{R}\}$ and $g : x \rightarrow x^2$ $\{x \in \mathbb{R}\}$, solve $gf(x) = 16$.

- Find $gf(x)$: $\qquad\qquad gf(x) = g(2x + 1) = (2x + 1)^2$

- Now solve $gf(x) = 16$: $\qquad (2x + 1)^2 = 16$
$$(2x + 1) = 4 \text{ or } -4$$
$$2x = 3 \text{ or } -5$$

- So $\boxed{x = \dfrac{3}{2} \text{ or } x = -\dfrac{5}{2}}$.

Exercise 4.2

Q1 $f(x) = 2x + 1$ and $g(x) = 3x - 4$. Solve the equation $fg(x) = 23$.

Q2 $f(x) = \dfrac{1}{x}$ and $g(x) = 2x + 5$. Solve the equation $gf(x) = 6$.

Q3 $f(x) = x^2$ and $g(x) = \dfrac{x}{x-3}$. Solve the equation $gf(x) = 4$.

Q4 $f(x) = x + 3$ and $g(x) = x^2 - 1$. Solve the equation $gf(x) = 3$.

Q5 $f(x) = x^2 + 1$ and $g(x) = 3x - 2$. Solve the equation $fg(x) = 50$.

Q6 $f(x) = 2^x$ and $g(x) = 2x + 1$. Solve the equation $fg(x) = 32$.

Q7 $f(x) = \log_{10}x$ and $g(x) = 3 - x$. Solve the equation $fg(x) = 0$.

Q8 $f(x) = 2^x$ and $g(x) = x^2 + 2x$. Solve the equation $fg(x) = 8$.

Q9 $f(x) = \dfrac{x}{x+1}$ and $g(x) = 2x - 1$. Solve the equation $fg(x) = gf(x)$.

Q10 $f(x) = 2^x$ and $g(x) = x + 1$. Solve the equation $fg(x) = gf(x)$.

5. Inverse Functions

Inverse functions 'undo' functions. So if a function tells you to do a certain thing to x, the inverse of that function tells you how to get back to the start.

Inverse functions and their graphs

Learning Objectives:

- Understand which functions will have inverses.
- Know that $f^{-1}f(x) = ff^{-1}(x) = x$.
- Be able to find the inverse of a function, and find its domain and range.
- Be able to draw and interpret graphs of functions and their inverses.

- An **inverse function** does the **opposite** to the function. So if the function was '+ 1', the inverse would be '− 1', if the function was '× 2', the inverse would be '÷ 2' etc.
- The inverse for a function f(x) is written **f⁻¹(x)**.
- An inverse function maps an element in the **range** to an element in the **domain** — the opposite of a function. This means that only **one-to-one** functions have inverses, as the inverse of a many-to-one function would be one-to-many, which isn't a function.

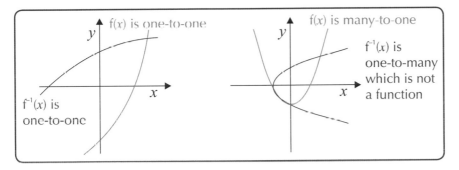

Tip: See page 18 for more on the different types of functions.

- For any inverse f⁻¹(x):

$$f^{-1}f(x) = x = ff^{-1}(x)$$

Doing the function and then the inverse...

...is the same as doing the inverse then doing the function — both just give you x.

Tip: f⁻¹f(x) is a composite function. It just means 'do f then f⁻¹' (see page 19).

- The **domain** of the inverse is the **range** of the function, and the **range** of the inverse is the **domain** of the function.

Example

A function f(x) = x + 7 has domain x ≥ 0 and range f(x) ≥ 7.
State whether the function has an inverse.
If so, find the inverse, and give its domain and range.

The function f(x) = x + 7 is one-to-one, so it does have an inverse.

The inverse of +7 is −7, so f⁻¹(x) = x − 7.

f⁻¹(x) has domain x ≥ 7 (the range of the function).

It has range f⁻¹(x) ≥ 0 (the domain of the function).

Tip: Check that this is correct by seeing if f⁻¹f(x) = x:
f⁻¹f(x) = f⁻¹(x + 7)
= (x + 7) − 7 = x
So it's correct.

For simple functions (like the one in the example above), it's easy to work out what the inverse is just by looking at it. But for more complex functions, you need to **rearrange** the original function to **change the subject**.

Finding the inverse of a function

Here's a general method for finding the inverse of a given function:

Tip: It's easier to work with y than f(x).

- Replace f(x) with y to get an equation for **y in terms of x**.
- **Rearrange** the equation to make x the subject.
- Replace x with f^{-1}(x) and y with x — this is the **inverse function**.
- **Swap** round the **domain** and **range** of the function.

Example 1

Find the inverse of the function f(x) = $\sqrt{2x - 1}$, with domain $x \geq \frac{1}{2}$ and range f(x) $\geq$ 0. State the domain and the range of the inverse.

Tip: Breaking it into steps like this means you're less likely to go wrong. It's worth doing it this way even for easier functions.

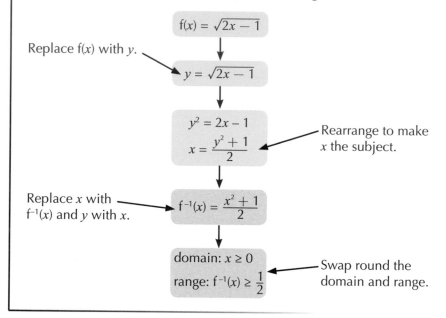

f(x) = $\sqrt{2x - 1}$

Replace f(x) with y.

$y = \sqrt{2x - 1}$

$y^2 = 2x - 1$
$x = \dfrac{y^2 + 1}{2}$

Rearrange to make x the subject.

Replace x with f^{-1}(x) and y with x.

f^{-1}(x) = $\dfrac{x^2 + 1}{2}$

domain: $x \geq 0$
range: f^{-1}(x) $\geq \dfrac{1}{2}$

Swap round the domain and range.

Example 2

Find the inverse of the function f(x) = $3x^2 + 2$ with domain $x \geq 0$, and state its domain and range.

Tip: If you're not given the domain and / or the range of the function you'll need to work this out first. In this example where x is always at least 0, f(x) must always be at least 2.

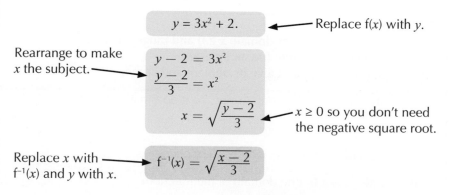

$y = 3x^2 + 2.$

Replace f(x) with y.

Rearrange to make x the subject.

$y - 2 = 3x^2$
$\dfrac{y - 2}{3} = x^2$

$x = \sqrt{\dfrac{y - 2}{3}}$

$x \geq 0$ so you don't need the negative square root.

Replace x with f^{-1}(x) and y with x.

f^{-1}(x) = $\sqrt{\dfrac{x - 2}{3}}$

The range of f(x) is f(x) $\geq$ 2, so f^{-1}(x) has domain $x \geq 2$.

The domain of f(x) is $x \geq 0$ and so the inverse has range f^{-1}(x) $\geq$ 0.

Graphs of inverse functions

The inverse of a function is its **reflection** in the line $y = x$.

Example

Sketch the graph of the inverse of the function $f(x) = x^2 - 8$ with domain $x \geq 0$.

- **Step 1:** Draw $f(x)$.

- **Step 3:** Reflect $f(x)$ in $y = x$ to get $f^{-1}(x)$.

- **Step 2:** Draw $y = x$.

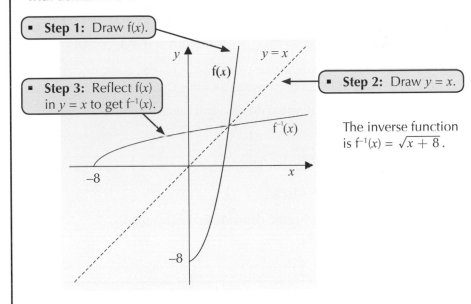

The inverse function is $f^{-1}(x) = \sqrt{x + 8}$.

Tip: Only sketch the function over the given domain and range. Otherwise you won't be able to see the correct domain and range for the graph of the inverse when you do the reflection.

It's easy to see what the domains and ranges are from the graph
— $f(x)$ has domain $x \geq 0$ and range $f(x) \geq -8$,
and $f^{-1}(x)$ has domain $x \geq -8$ and range $f^{-1}(x) \geq 0$.

Exercise 5.1

Q1 Does the function shown on the right have an inverse? Justify your answer.

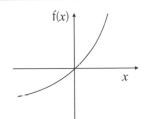

Q1-2 Hint: Work out which type of function is shown in each of the diagrams.

Q2 Does the function shown in this mapping diagram have an inverse? Justify your answer.

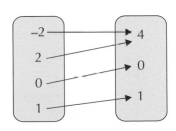

Q3 $f(x) = \sin x$ with domain $x \in \mathbb{R}$.
Does the inverse function $f^{-1}(x)$ exist? Justify your answer.

Q3 Hint: Sketch the graph of $y = \sin x$.

Q4-11 Hint: If in doubt, sketch a graph of the function to check domains and ranges.

Q4   Function f(x) is defined on the domain $x \in \mathbb{R}$, where $f(x) = x^2 + 3$. Does the inverse function $f^{-1}(x)$ exist? Justify your answer.

Q5 $f(x) = (x - 4)^2$, $\{x \geq 4\}$. Does $f^{-1}(x)$ exist? Justify your answer.

Q6   Find the inverse of each of the following functions, stating the domain and range:

a) $f(x) = 3x + 4$, $\{x \in \mathbb{R}\}$.

b) $f(x) = 5(x - 2)$, $\{x \in \mathbb{R}\}$.

c) $f(x) = \dfrac{1}{x + 2}$, $\{x > -2\}$.

d) $f(x) = x^2 + 3$, $\{x > 0\}$.

Q7-8 Hint: The range of f(x) is quite tricky to find — you might find it helpful to think about what happens to f(x) as $x \to \infty$ and sketch the graph.

Q7 $f(x) = \dfrac{3x}{x + 1}$, $\{x > -1\}$.

a) Find $f^{-1}(x)$, stating the domain and range.

b) Evaluate $f^{-1}(2)$.

c) Evaluate $f^{-1}\left(\dfrac{1}{2}\right)$.

Q8 $f(x) = \dfrac{x - 4}{x + 3}$, $\{x > -3\}$.

a) Find $f^{-1}(x)$, stating the domain and range.

b) Evaluate $f^{-1}(0)$.

c) Evaluate $f^{-1}\left(-\dfrac{2}{5}\right)$.

Q9 $f(x) = \log_{10}(x - 3)$, $\{x > 3\}$. Find the domain and range of $f^{-1}(x)$.

Q10 $f(x) = 4x - 2$, $\{1 \leq x \leq 7\}$. Find the domain and range of $f^{-1}(x)$.

Q11 $f(x) = \dfrac{x}{x - 2}$, $\{x < 2\}$. Find the domain and range of $f^{-1}(x)$.

Q12 $f(x) = 2x + 3$, $\{x \in \mathbb{R}\}$. Sketch $y = f(x)$ and $y = f^{-1}(x)$ on the same set of axes, marking the points where the functions cross the axes.

Q13 $f(x) = x^2 + 3$, $\{x > 0\}$.

a) Sketch the graphs of $f(x)$ and $f^{-1}(x)$ on the same set of axes.

b) State the domain and range of $f^{-1}(x)$.

Q14 Hint: The functions are equal where the two graphs cross.

Q14 $f(x) = \dfrac{1}{x + 1}$, $\{x > -1\}$.

a) Sketch the graphs of $f(x)$ and $f^{-1}(x)$ on the same set of axes.

b) Explain how your diagram shows that there is just one solution to the equation $f(x) = f^{-1}(x)$.

Q15 $f(x) = \dfrac{1}{x - 3}$, $\{x > 3\}$.

a) Find $f^{-1}(x)$ and state its domain and range.

b) Sketch $f(x)$ and $f^{-1}(x)$ on the same set of axes.

c) How many solutions are there to the equation $f(x) = f^{-1}(x)$?

d) Solve $f(x) = f^{-1}(x)$.

6. Modulus

Sometimes in maths you want to work with numbers or functions without having to deal with negative values. The modulus function lets you do this.

The graphs of |f(x)| and f(|x|)

Modulus of a number

The **modulus** of a number is its **size** — it doesn't matter if it's positive or negative. So for a positive number, the modulus is just the same as the number itself, but for a negative number, the modulus is its numerical value without the minus sign.

> The modulus of a number, x, is written $|x|$.
>
> In general terms, for $x \geq 0$, $|x| = x$ and for $x < 0$, $|x| = -x$.

Example

The modulus of 8 is 8, and the modulus of −8 is also 8.
This is written $|8| = |-8| = 8$.

Modulus of a function

Functions can have a modulus too — the modulus of a function $f(x)$ is just $f(x)$ but with any negative values that it can take turned positive.
Suppose $f(x) = -6$, then $|f(x)| = 6$. In general terms:

> $|f(x)| = f(x)$ when $f(x) \geq 0$ and
> $|f(x)| = -f(x)$ when $f(x) < 0$.

If the modulus is inside the brackets in the form $f(|x|)$, then you make the x-value positive **before** applying the function. So $f(|-2|) = f(2)$.

The graphs of |f(x)| and f(|x|)

- For the graph of $y = |f(x)|$, any negative values of $f(x)$ are made positive by reflecting them in the x-axis.

- This restricts the range of the modulus function to $|f(x)| \geq 0$ (or some subset within $|f(x)| \geq 0$, e.g. $|f(x)| \geq 1$).

- The easiest way to draw a graph of $y = |f(x)|$ is to initially draw $y = f(x)$, then reflect the negative part in the x-axis.

- For the graph of $y = f(|x|)$, the negative x-values produce the same result as the corresponding positive x-values. So the graph of $f(x)$ for $x \geq 0$ is reflected in the y-axis for the negative x-values.

- To draw a graph of $y = f(|x|)$, first draw the graph of $y = f(x)$ for positive values of x, then reflect this in the y-axis to form the rest of the graph.

Learning Objectives:

- Understand the meaning of the modulus, including modulus notation.

- Be able to write the modulus of a number or function.

- Be able to sketch the graph of $y = |ax + b|$, and the graph of $y = |f(x)|$ given $y = f(x)$.

- Be able to sketch the graph of $y = f(|x|)$ given $y = f(x)$.

- Be able to solve equations involving the modulus.

Tip: The modulus is sometimes called the **absolute value**.

Tip: Don't get the two types of modulus graph mixed up. For some functions $y = |f(x)|$ looks very different to $y = f(|x|)$ — as you'll see in the examples on the next two pages.

Example 1

Draw the graphs of $y = |f(x)|$ and $y = f(|x|)$ for $f(x) = 5x - 5$.

$y = |f(x)|$

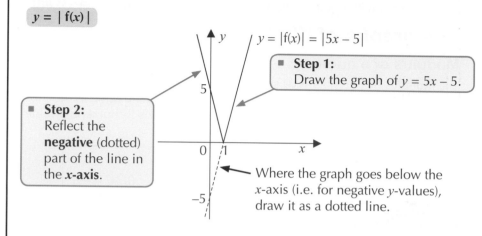

$y = |f(x)| = |5x - 5|$

- **Step 1:**
  Draw the graph of $y = 5x - 5$.

- **Step 2:**
  Reflect the **negative** (dotted) part of the line in the **x-axis**.

Where the graph goes below the x-axis (i.e. for negative y-values), draw it as a dotted line.

$y = f(|x|)$

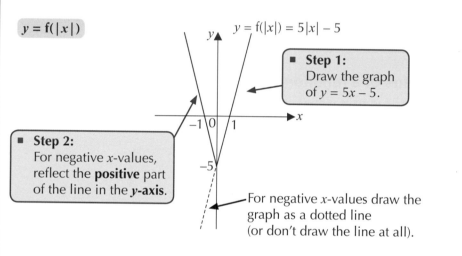

$y = f(|x|) = 5|x| - 5$

- **Step 1:**
  Draw the graph of $y = 5x - 5$.

- **Step 2:**
  For negative x-values, reflect the **positive** part of the line in the **y-axis**.

For negative x-values draw the graph as a dotted line (or don't draw the line at all).

Example 2

Draw the graphs of $y = |f(x)|$ and $y = f(|x|)$ for $f(x) = x^2 - 4x$.

$y = |f(x)|$

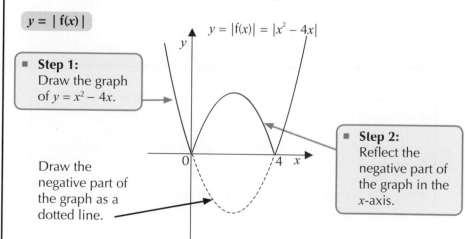

$y = |f(x)| = |x^2 - 4x|$

- **Step 1:**
  Draw the graph of $y = x^2 - 4x$.

- **Step 2:**
  Reflect the negative part of the graph in the x-axis.

Draw the negative part of the graph as a dotted line.

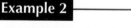

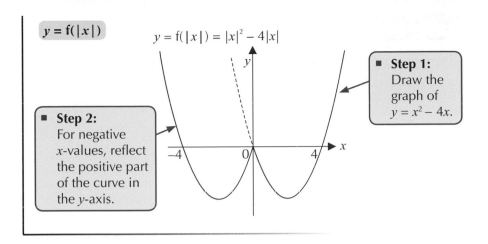

$y = f(|x|)$

$y = f(|x|) = |x|^2 - 4|x|$

Step 1: Draw the graph of $y = x^2 - 4x$.

Step 2: For negative x-values, reflect the positive part of the curve in the y-axis.

Exercise 6.1

Q1 Sketch the following graphs:

a) $y = |x + 3|$ b) $y = |5 - x|$ c) $y = |3x - 1|$

d) $y = |x^2 - 9|$ e) $y = |x^2 - 5x|$

Q1 Hint: Don't forget to label the key points such as where the graphs cross the axes.

Q2 If $f(x) = \sin x$, sketch the graph of $|f(x)|$.

Q3 If $f(x) = x^3$, sketch the graph of $|f(x)|$.

Q4 If $f(x) = (x - 2)(x + 3)$, sketch the graph of $|f(x)|$.

Q5 Sketch the graphs of $y = f(|x|)$ for the following functions:

a) $f(x) = 2x + 3$ b) $f(x) = 4 - 3x$ c) $f(x) = x^2 - 3x$

d) $f(x) = x^2 - 8x + 12$ e) $f(x) = x^3 + 1$ f) $f(x) = 2^x$

g) $f(x) = \dfrac{1}{x}$ h) $f(x) = x^2 - 7x - 18$ i) $f(x) = x^3 - 4x$

Q6 Match up each graph (1-4) with its correct equation (a-d):

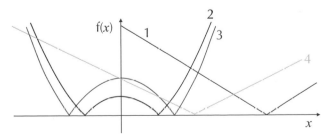

Q6 Hint: Try sketching the graphs from the given functions to see what shape they should be, then compare them in terms of where they cross the x and y axes.

a) $y = |x^2 - 1|$
b) $y = |4 - x|$
c) $y = |x - 2|$
d) $y = |2 - x^2|$

Q7 For each of the following graphs, copy the graph of $y = f(x)$ and sketch the graphs of $y = |f(x)|$ and $y = f(|x|)$:

a)

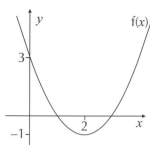

b)

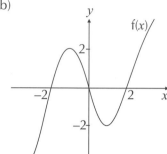

Q8 For the function $f(x) = 3x - 5$:

a) Draw, on the same axes, the graphs of $y = f(x)$ and $y = |f(x)|$.

b) How many solutions are there to the equation $|3x - 5| = 2$?

Q8 b) Hint: Read across from 2 on the y-axis to find the number of values of x for which $|3x - 5| = 2$.

Q9 Draw the graph of the function $f(x) = \begin{cases} |2x + 4| & x < 0 \\ |x - 2| & x \geq 0 \end{cases}$

Q10 For the function $f(x) = 4x + 1$:

a) Draw accurately the graph of $y = f(|x|)$.

b) Use your graph to solve the equation $f(|x|) = 3$.

Q10 b) Hint: Read across from 3 on the y-axis to find any values of x for which $4|x| + 1 = 3$.

Q11 Match up each graph (1-4) with its correct equation (a-d).

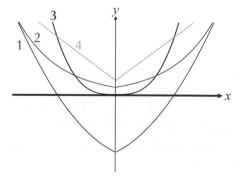

Q11 Hint: If you can't see which graph goes with which equation, try sketching some of the functions yourself and matching it to the graph it looks like.

a) $y = |x|^3$

b) $y = 2^{|x|}$

c) $y = 3|x| + 2$

d) $y = (|x| - 2)(|x| + 4)$

Solving modulus equations

|f(x)| = n and |f(x)| = g(x)

The method for solving equations of the form $|f(x)| = n$ is shown below.
Solving $|f(x)| = g(x)$ is exactly the same — just replace n with $g(x)$.

- **Step 1:** Sketch the functions $y = |f(x)|$ and $y = n$ on the same axes. The solutions you're trying to find are where they **intersect**.
- **Step 2:** From the graph, work out the ranges of x for which $f(x) \geq 0$ and $f(x) < 0$: e.g. $f(x) \geq 0$ for $x \leq a$ or $x \geq b$ and $f(x) < 0$ for $a < x < b$. These ranges should 'fit together' to cover **all** possible x-values.
- **Step 3:** Use this to write **two new equations**, one true for each range of x:

  (1) $f(x) = n$ for $x \leq a$ or $x \geq b$

  (2) $-f(x) = n$ for $a < x < b$

- **Step 4:** Solve each equation and check that any solutions are **valid**. Get rid of any solutions outside the range of x you've got for that equation.
- **Step 5:** Look at the graph and **check** that your solutions look right.

Tip: The original equation $|f(x)| = n$ becomes $f(x) = n$ in the range where $f(x) \geq 0$, and it becomes $-f(x) = n$ in the range where $f(x) < 0$.

Example 1

Solve $|x^2 - 9| = 7$. ← This is an example of $|f(x)| = n$, where $f(x) = x^2 - 9$ and n = 7.

- First off, sketch the graphs of $y = |x^2 - 9|$ and $y = 7$.

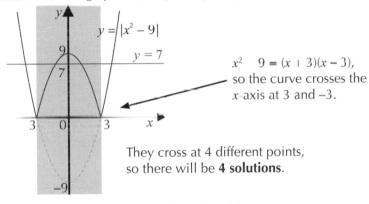

$x^2 - 9 = (x + 3)(x - 3)$, so the curve crosses the x-axis at 3 and -3.

They cross at 4 different points, so there will be **4 solutions**.

Tip: When sketching the graphs, use a big enough domain so that you can see all the places where the lines cross.

- Now use the graph to see where $f(x) \geq 0$ and $f(x) < 0$:

  $x^2 - 9 \geq 0$ for $x \leq -3$ or $x \geq 3$, and

  $x^2 - 9 < 0$ for $-3 < x < 3$ (shaded in grey on the diagram)

- Form two equations for the different ranges of x:

  (1) $x^2 - 9 = 7$ for $x \leq -3$ or $x \geq 3$

  (2) $-(x^2 - 9) = 7$ for $-3 < x < 3$

- Solving (1) gives: $x^2 = 16 \Rightarrow x = 4, x = -4$
- Check they're valid: $x = -4$ is in '$x \leq -3$' and $x = 4$ is in '$x \geq 3$' — so they're both valid.
- Solving (2) gives: $x^2 - 2 = 0 \Rightarrow x^2 = 2 \Rightarrow x = \sqrt{2}, x = -\sqrt{2}$.
- Check they're valid: $x = \sqrt{2}$ and $x = -\sqrt{2}$ are both within $-3 < x < 3$ — so they're also both valid.
- Check back against the graphs — we've found four solutions and they're in the right places. So the four solutions to $|x^2 - 9| = 7$ are:

  $$x = -4, x = -\sqrt{2}, x = \sqrt{2}, x = 4$$

Tip: It's important to work out and label the points where the graphs touch the x-axis so you can easily see where $f(x)$ changes from positive to negative.

Example 2

Tip: Remember that you can solve equations of the form $|f(x)| = g(x)$ using the method for solving $|f(x)| = n$ on the previous page.

Solve $|x^2 - 2x - 3| = 1 - x$. ◄——— This is an example of $|f(x)| = g(x)$, where $f(x) = x^2 - 2x - 3$ and $g(x) = 1 - x$.

- Sketch $y = |x^2 - 2x - 3|$ and $y = 1 - x$. The graphs cross twice.

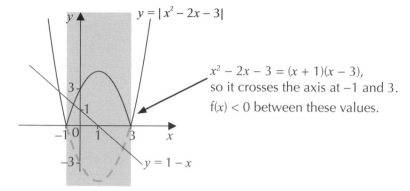

$x^2 - 2x - 3 = (x + 1)(x - 3)$, so it crosses the axis at -1 and 3.

$f(x) < 0$ between these values.

Tip: You can see from the graph that there will be one solution in the shaded area where $-f(x) = g(x)$, and one solution in the positive region ($x \leq -1$) where $f(x) = g(x)$.

- Looking at where $f(x) \geq 0$ and where $f(x) < 0$ gives:
  (1) $x^2 - 2x - 3 = 1 - x$ for $x \leq -1$ or $x \geq 3$
  (2) $-(x^2 - 2x - 3) = 1 - x$ for $-1 < x < 3$.

- Solving (1) using the quadratic formula gives:

  $x \leq -1$ or $x \geq 3$, ——► $x = 2.562$ and $x = -1.562$ ◄——— ...but this one is.
  so this solution is
  not valid...

- Solving (2) using the quadratic formula gives:

  $-1 < x < 3$, so this ——► $x = 3.562$ and $x = -0.562$ ◄——— ...but this one is.
  solution is not valid...

- Checking against the graph, there are two solutions and they're where we expected.

$|f(x)| = |g(x)|$

When using **graphs** to solve functions of the form $|f(x)| = |g(x)|$ you have to do a bit more work at the start to identify the different areas of the graph. There could be regions where:

Tip: Solving $-f(x) = -g(x)$ is the same as solving $f(x) = g(x)$, and solving $f(x) = -g(x)$ is the same as solving $-f(x) = g(x)$.

- $f(x)$ and $g(x)$ are **both** positive or **both** negative — for solutions in these regions you need to solve the equation **$f(x) = g(x)$**.
- One function is **positive** and the other is **negative** — for solutions in these regions you need to solve the equation **$-f(x) = g(x)$**.

There is also an **algebraic** method for solving equations of this type:

> If $|a| = |b|$ then $a^2 = b^2$.
> So if $|f(x)| = |g(x)|$ then $[f(x)]^2 = [g(x)]^2$.

This is true because squaring gives the same answer whether the value is positive or negative. You'll usually be left with a quadratic to solve, but in some cases this might be easier than using a graphical method.

The following example shows how you could use either method to solve the same equation.

Example

Solve $|x - 2| = |3x + 4|$. ← This is an example of $|f(x)| = |g(x)|$, where $f(x) = x - 2$ and $g(x) = 3x + 4$.

a) Solving graphically:

- Sketch $y = |x - 2|$ and $y = |3x + 4|$. The graphs cross twice.

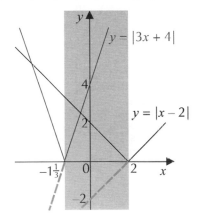

- There are two regions of the graph that contain a solution (i.e. where the graphs cross):
  - (1) where $f(x)$ is negative but $g(x)$ is positive (shaded grey)
  - (2) where $f(x)$ and $g(x)$ are both negative (where $x < -1\frac{1}{3}$).

Tip: There is a third region on the graph — where $f(x)$ and $g(x)$ are both positive (for $x \geq 2$). The graphs do not cross in this region though so there won't be a solution.

- This means we can form the following equations:
  - (1) $-(x - 2) = 3x + 4$ for $-1\frac{1}{3} \leq x < 2$
  - (2) $(x - 2) - (3x + 4)$ for $x < -1\frac{1}{3}$

- Solving (1) gives $x = -\frac{1}{2}$.

  This is valid, as it's in the region $-1\frac{1}{3} \leq x < 2$.

- Solving (2) gives $x = -3$.

  This is valid, as it's in the region $x < -1\frac{1}{3}$.

- Checking against the graph, there are two valid solutions and they're where we expected.

b) Solving algebraically:

Tip: For this example the algebraic method involves less work than using graphs.

- $|x - 2| = |3x + 4|$
  Square both sides to give:

  $(x - 2)^2 = (3x + 4)^2$
  $x^2 - 4x + 4 = 9x^2 + 24x + 16$
  $8x^2 + 28x + 12 = 0$
  $2x^2 + 7x + 3 = 0$

- Factorise and solve: $(2x + 1)(x + 3) = 0$

  $x = -\frac{1}{2}$ and $x = -3$

Tip: You can use the quadratic formula to solve it if it won't easily factorise.

Q1 The diagram below shows a function $y = |f(x)|$.
$y = f(x)$ is shown as a dotted line.

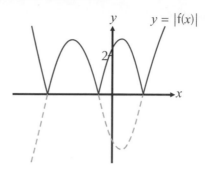

Q1 Hint: Try drawing a line across at $y = 2$, and shading in the different regions of the graph where $f(x)$ is negative.

a) How many solutions are there to the equation $|f(x)| = 2$?

b) How many of the solutions could be found by solving the equation $f(x) = 2$?

c) Explain how the other solutions could be found.

Q2 Solve the equation $|x - 2| = 6$.

Q3 Solve the equation $|4x + 2| = 10$.

Q4 Solve the equation $2 - |3x - 4| = 1$.

Q5 Solve the equation $|x^2 - 4| = 5$.

Q6 Solve the equation $|x^2 - 2x - 8| = 1$.
Leave your answers in surd form.

Q6 Hint: 'Surd form' just means keeping the roots as roots, but make sure you simplify as much as possible.

Q7 Solve the equation $|x^2 - x - 6| = 2x - 4$.
Leave your answers in surd form.

Q8 a) Sketch the graph of $y = |x^2 - 16|$.

b) Hence solve the equation $|x^2 - 16| = 3$.
Leave your answers in surd form.

Q9 a) On the same axes sketch the graphs of $|f(x)|$ and $g(x)$, where:
$f(x) = \dfrac{1}{x}$
$g(x) = x - 1$

b) Hence solve the equation $|f(x)| = g(x)$.

Q10 a) Sketch the graphs of $y = |4x - 1|$ and $y = |2x + 3|$.

b) Hence, or otherwise, solve the equation $|4x - 1| = |2x + 3|$.

Q10 b) Hint: You can solve this equation algebraically if you prefer, using the squaring method.

Q11 a) On the same axes sketch the graphs of $|f(x)|$ and $|g(x)|$, where:
$f(x) = x^2 - 5x + 6$
$g(x) = x + 1$

b) Hence solve the equation $|f(x)| = |g(x)|$.

7. Transformations of Graphs

Learning Objective:

- Be able to sketch graphs when $y = f(x)$ has been affected by a combination of these transformations:
  $y = f(x + c)$,
  $y = f(x) + c$,
  $y = af(x)$,
  and $y = f(ax)$.
- Be able to interpret transformed graphs, including finding coordinates of points.

You should be familiar with transformations from C1 and C2. For C3 you have to know how to put them all together to form combinations of transformations.

Transformations of graphs

The four transformations

The transformations you met in C1 and C2 are translations (a vertical or horizontal shift), stretches or squeezes (either vertical or horizontal) and reflections in the *x*- or *y*- axis. Here's a quick reminder of what each one does:

$y = f(x + c)$

For c > 0:
- f(x + c) is f(x) translated c **left**,
- f(x − c) is f(x) translated c **right**.

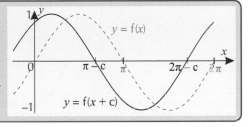

Tip: All these graphs use f(x) = sin x.

$y = f(x) + c$

For c > 0:
- f(x) + c is f(x) translated c **up**,
- f(x) − c is f(x) translated c **down**.

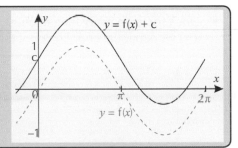

$y = af(x)$

- The graph of af(x) is f(x) **stretched vertically** by a factor of a.
- And if **a < 0**, the graph is also **reflected** in the **x-axis**.

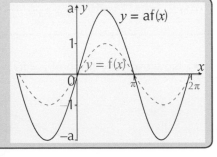

Tip: It might be easier to think of a stretch by a scale factor **0 < a < 1** as a 'squash' — but make sure you use the word stretch in the exam.

$y = f(ax)$

- The graph of f(ax) is f(x) **stretched horizontally** by a factor of $\frac{1}{a}$.
- And if **a < 0**, the graph is also **reflected** in the **y-axis**.

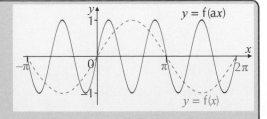

Tip: In this case, the transformation is a stretch when **0 < a < 1** and a squash when **a > 1**.

Combinations of transformations

Combinations of transformations can look a bit tricky, but if you take them one step at a time they're not too bad. Don't try and do all the transformations at once — break it up into the separate bits shown on the previous page and draw a graph for each stage.

Example 1

The graph below shows the function $y = f(x)$. Draw the graph of $y = 3f(x + 2)$, showing the coordinates of the turning points.

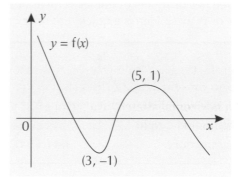

Tip: Make sure you do the transformations the right way round — you should do the bit in the brackets first.

- Don't try to do everything at once. First draw the graph of $y = f(x + 2)$ and work out the coordinates of the turning points:

Tip: Remember — $y = f(x + c)$ is $f(x)$ translated c to the left.

The graph is translated **left** by **2 units**, so **subtract 2** from the **x-coordinates**.

- Now use your graph of $y = f(x + 2)$ to draw the graph of $y = 3f(x + 2)$:

Tip: $y = af(x)$ is $f(x)$ stretched vertically by a factor of a.

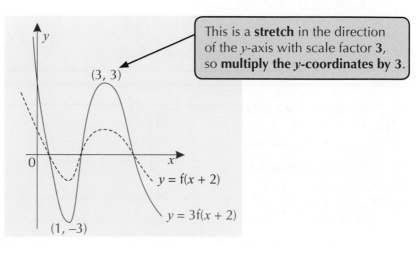

This is a **stretch** in the direction of the y-axis with scale factor **3**, so **multiply the y-coordinates by 3**.

Example 2

The graph below shows the function $y = \sin x$, $0 \leq x \leq 2\pi$.
Draw the graph of $y = 2 - \sin 2x$, $0 \leq x \leq 2\pi$.

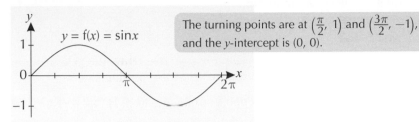

The turning points are at $\left(\frac{\pi}{2}, 1\right)$ and $\left(\frac{3\pi}{2}, -1\right)$, and the y-intercept is $(0, 0)$.

- This is a lot easier to deal with if you rearrange the function from $y = 2 - \sin 2x$ to $y = -\sin 2x + 2$. This gets it in the form $y = -f(2x) + 2$. So we need a **horizontal stretch** by a factor of $\frac{1}{2}$, followed by a **vertical stretch** by a factor of **−1**, followed by a **vertical translation** by **2 up** (in the positive y-direction).

Tip: Always try to break it down like this before you start drawing lots of graphs.

- First draw the graph of $y = \sin 2x$, by squashing the graph horizontally by a factor of 2 (i.e. a stretch by a factor of $\frac{1}{2}$).

The turning points have been squashed up in the x-direction, so halve the x-coordinates: $\left(\frac{\pi}{4}, 1\right)$ and $\left(\frac{3\pi}{4}, \quad 1\right)$. There are also now an extra two within the domain, each one occurring a further $\frac{\pi}{2}$ along the x-axis: $\left(\frac{5\pi}{4}, 1\right)$ and $\left(\frac{7\pi}{4}, -1\right)$.

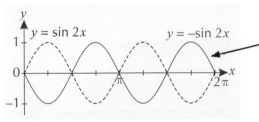

- From there, draw the graph of $y = -\sin 2x$, by reflecting in the x-axis.

Tip: A stretch with a factor of −1 doesn't change the size of the graph, you just have to reflect in the x-axis.

This transformation flips the turning points, so multiply the y-coordinates by −1. They're now at $\left(\frac{\pi}{4}, -1\right)$, $\left(\frac{3\pi}{4}, 1\right)$, $\left(\frac{5\pi}{4}, -1\right)$ and $\left(\frac{7\pi}{4}, 1\right)$.

- Finally, translate the graph of $y = -\sin 2x$ up by 2 to get the graph of $y = -\sin 2x + 2$ (or $y = 2 - \sin 2x$).

Add 2 to the y-coordinates of the turning points to give $\left(\frac{\pi}{4}, 1\right)$, $\left(\frac{3\pi}{4}, 3\right)$, $\left(\frac{5\pi}{4}, 1\right)$ and $\left(\frac{7\pi}{4}, 3\right)$.
The y-intercept is also translated up by 2: it's at $(0, 2)$.

Tip: Having clearly labelled axes makes it easier to read off key points at the end of all the transformations and check your answer.

Example 3

The graph shows the function $f(x) = |x|$. Draw the graph of $y = 4 - f(x + 1)$, and give the equation of the transformed graph.

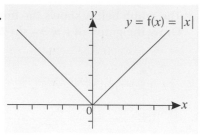

- Again, rearrange the function from $y = 4 - f(x + 1)$ to $y = -f(x + 1) + 4$. So you need to do...

- ...a **horizontal translation left** by **1**...

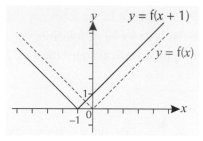

- ...followed by a **vertical stretch** by a factor of **–1** (reflection in the x-axis)...

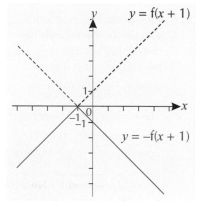

- ...followed by a **vertical translation** of **4 upwards**.

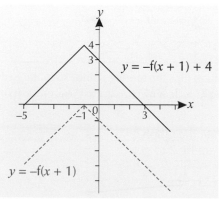

- To find the equation of the transformed graph, just replace $f(x)$ in $y = 4 - f(x + 1)$ with $|x|$. So the equation is:

$$y = 4 - |x + 1|$$

Q1 Given that $f(x) = x^2$, sketch the following graphs on the same axes:

a) $y - f(x)$ b) $y - f(x) + 3$ c) $y - f(x - 2)$ d) $y = f(x + 4) - 1$

In each case write down the coordinates of the turning point.

Q2 The graph of $f(x) = x^3$ is translated to form the graph $y = f(x - 1) + 4$.

a) Sketch the graphs of $y = f(x)$ and $y = f(x - 1) + 4$.

b) What is the equation of the graph $y = f(x - 1) + 4$?

Q2 a) Hint: Do this step by step.

Q3 Given that $f(x) = |x|$, sketch the following graphs on the same axes:

a) $y = f(x)$ b) $y = f(x) + 2$ c) $y = f(x - 4)$ d) $y = 2f(x + 1)$

In parts b) - d) describe the transformation from $y = f(x)$ in words.

Q4 Let $f(x) = |2x - 6|$. On the same axes sketch the graphs of:

a) $y = f(x)$ b) $y = f(-x)$ c) $y = f(-x) + 2$

Q5 Let $f(x) = \dfrac{1}{x}$. On the same axes sketch the graphs of:

a) $y = f(x)$ b) $y = -f(x)$ c) $y = -f(x) - 3$

Q6 a) Let $f(x) = \cos x$. Sketch the graph $y = f(x)$ for $0° \le x \le 360°$.

b) On the same axes sketch the graph of $y = f(2x)$.

c) On the same axes sketch the graph of $y = 1 + f(2x)$.

d) State the coordinates of the minimum point(s) of the graph $y = \cos 2x + 1$, in the interval $0° \le x \le 360°$.

Q7 Complete the following table for the function $f(x) = \sin x$ $(0° \le x \le 360°)$.

Transformed function	New equation	Maximum value of transformed function	Minimum value of transformed function
$f(x) + 2$			
$f(x - 90°)$			
$f(3x)$			
$4f(x)$			

Q7 Hint: Try sketching the graphs of the transformed functions first.

Q8 Complete the following table for the function $f(x) = x^3$:

Transformed function	New equation	Coordinates of point of inflection
$f(x) + 1$		
$f(x - 2)$		
$-f(x) - 3$		
$f(-x) + 4$		

Q8 Hint: The point of inflection is the stationary point. For $y = x^3$ the point of inflection is at $(0, 0)$

Q9 The graph $y = \cos x$ is translated $\dfrac{\pi}{2}$ to the right and stretched by scale factor $\dfrac{1}{2}$ parallel to the y-axis.

a) Sketch the new graph for $0 \le x \le 2\pi$.   b) Write down its equation.

Q10 Hint: You can also write g(x) as $-\frac{1}{x} + 3$.

Q10 a) Sketch the graph of $y = f(x)$ where $f(x) = \frac{1}{x}$.

b) Write down the sequence of transformations needed to map f(x) on to $g(x) = 3 - \frac{1}{x}$.

c) Sketch the graph of $y = g(x)$.

Q11 Complete the following table:

Original graph	New graph	Sequence of transformations
$y = x^3$	$y = (x - 4)^3 + 5$	
$y = 4^x$	$y = 4^{3x} - 1$	
$y = |x + 1|$	$y = 1 - |2x + 1|$	
$y = \sin x$	$y = -3\sin 2x + 1$	

Q12 Hint: Try taking out a common factor (the value of a) before completing the square.

Q12 a) Write $y = 2x^2 - 4x + 6$ in the form $y = a[(x + b)^2 + c]$.

b) Hence list the sequence of transformations which will map $y = x^2$ on to $y = 2x^2 - 4x + 6$.

c) Sketch the graph of $y = 2x^2 - 4x + 6$.

d) Write down the coordinates of the minimum point of the graph.

Q13 Starting with the curve $y = \cos x$, state the sequence of transformations which could be used to sketch the following curves:

a) $y = 4\cos 3x$

b) $y = 4 - \cos 2x$

c) $y = 2\cos (x - \frac{\pi}{3})$

Q14 The diagram shows $y = f(x)$ with a minimum point, P, at (2, –3).

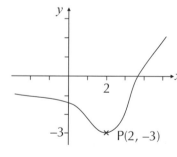

Copy the diagram and sketch each of the following graphs. In each case state the new coordinates of the point P.

a) $y = f(x) + 5$

b) $y = f(x + 4)$

c) $y = -f(x)$

Q15 The diagram shows $y = f(x)$ with a minimum point, P, at (–1, –3) and a minimum point, Q, at (–1, –3).

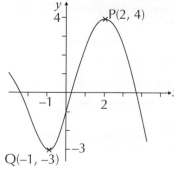

Copy the diagram and sketch each of the following graphs. In each case state the new coordinates of the points P and Q.

a) $y = f(x - 1) + 3$

b) $y = -f(2x)$

c) $y = |f(x + 2)|$

Review Exercise — Chapter 1

Q1 Simplify the following:

    a) $\dfrac{4x^2 - 25}{6x - 15}$
    b) $\dfrac{2x + 3}{x - 2} \times \dfrac{4x - 8}{2x^2 - 3x - 9}$
    c) $\dfrac{x^2 - 3x}{x + 1} \div \dfrac{x}{2}$

Q2 Write the following as a single fraction:

    a) $\dfrac{x}{2x + 1} + \dfrac{3}{x^2} + \dfrac{1}{x}$
    b) $\dfrac{2}{x^2 - 1} - \dfrac{3x}{x - 1} + \dfrac{x}{x + 1}$

Q3 Use algebraic long division to divide $x^3 + 2x^2 - x + 19$ by $x + 4$.

Q4 Write $2x^3 + 8x^2 + 7x + 8$ in the form $(Ax^2 + Bx + C)(x + 3) + D$.
    Using your answer, state the result when $2x^3 + 8x^2 + 7x + 8$ is divided by $(x + 3)$.

Q5 For the following mappings, state the range and say whether or not the mapping is a function.
    If not, explain why, and if so, say whether the function is one-to-one or many-to-one.

    a) $f(x) = x^2 - 16, \ x \geq 0$

    b) $f : x \to x^2 - 7x + 10, \ x \in \mathbb{R}$

    c) $f(x) = \sqrt{x}, \ x \in \mathbb{R}$

    d) $f : x \to \dfrac{1}{x - 2}, \ x \in \mathbb{R}$

Q6 $f(x) = \dfrac{5}{2x + 1}$ defines a map.

    a) Evaluate $f(0)$ and $f(\frac{1}{2})$.

    b) Draw the mapping diagram for the domain $\{x \in \mathbb{N}, x < 6\}$ and list the range.

    c) Is the map a function for the domain $x \in \mathbb{Z}$? If not, explain why not.

    d) Is the map a function for the domain $x \subset \mathbb{R}$? If not, explain why not.

> **Q6 Hint:** $\mathbb{Z}$ is the set of integers (positive and negative), and $\mathbb{N}$ is the set of natural numbers (positive integers, not including 0).

Q7
    a) Sketch the graph of the function

$$f(x) = \begin{cases} x^2 - 2 & -2 < x < 2 \\ 2 & \text{otherwise} \end{cases}$$

    b) State the range of the function.

Q8 For each pair of functions f and g, find $fg(2)$, $gf(1)$ and $fg(x)$.

    a) $f(x) = \dfrac{3}{x}, \ x > 0$ and $g(x) = 2x + 3, \ x \in \mathbb{R}$
    b) $f(x) = 3x^2, \ x \geq 0$ and $g(x) = x + 4, \ x \in \mathbb{R}$

Q9 $f(x) = \log_{10} x$ and $g(x) = 10^{x+1}$.
    a) Find the values of $fg(1)$, $gf(1)$, $f^2(10)$ and $g^2(-1)$.
    b) Explain why $f^2(1)$ is undefined.

Q10 $f(x) = 3x$ and $g(x) = x + 7$, both with domain $x \in \mathbb{R}$.
    Find the composite functions $fg(x)$, $gf(x)$ and $g^2(x)$.

Q11 $f(x) = 4x$ with domain $x \geq 2$, and $g(x) = x + 3$ with domain $x \leq 12$.
   a) Write down the domain and range of fg(x).
   b) Find fg(x) and sketch the graph.
   c) Write down the domain and range of gf(x).
   d) Find gf(x) and sketch the graph.

Q12 A one-to-one function f has domain $x \in \mathbb{R}$ and range $f(x) \geq 3$.
   Does this function have an inverse? If so, state its domain and range.

Q13 Using algebra, find the inverse of the function $f(x) = \sqrt{2x - 4}$, $x \geq 2$.
   State the domain and range of the inverse.

Q14 $f(x) = \cos x$, $0 \leq x \leq \frac{\pi}{2}$. Does the inverse function $f^{-1}(x)$ exist? Justify your answer.

Q15 $f(x) = \log_{10}(x + 4)$, $x > -4$. Find $f^{-1}(x)$.

Q16 $f(x) = x + 4$ and $g(x) = \dfrac{3}{x + 1}$, $x > 0$.
   a) Find $f^{-1}(x)$.
   b) Find $g^{-1}(x)$.
   c) Find $f^{-1}g^{-1}(x)$.
   d) Find gf(x).
   e) Find the inverse of gf(x). What do you notice?

Q17 For the function $f(x) = 2x - 1$ $\{x \in \mathbb{R}\}$, sketch the graphs of:
   a) $|f(x)|$ b) $f(|x|)$

Q18 Solve the equation $|3x - 1| = |4 - x|$.

Q19 $f(x) = x^2 - 2x - 8$.
   a) On the same axes sketch the graphs of $|f(x)|$ and $f(|x|)$.
   b) Use your graphs to help you solve the equation $f(|x|) = -5$.

Q19 b) Hint: You can either use the symmetry of the graph of $f(|x|)$ to find the negative solution from the positive solution, or you can use the fact that for $x \geq 0$, $f(|x|) = f(x)$ and for $x < 0$, $f(|x|) = f(-x)$.

Q20 Sketch the graphs of:
   a) $y = 3x + 2$.
   b) $y = |3x + 2|$.
   c) $y = -|3x + 2|$.

Q21 The function $y = f(x)$ is shown on the graph below.
   Draw the graph of $y = 2f(x) + 1$.

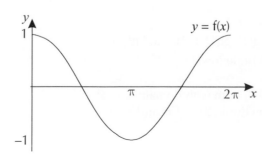

Chapter 1 Algebra and Functions

Exam-Style Questions — Chapter 1

1 Write $\frac{2x^2 - 9x - 35}{x^2 - 49}$ as a fraction in its simplest form.

(3 marks)

2 Simplify the following:

a) $\frac{x^2 - x - 20}{2x + 4} \div \frac{x^2 - 16}{x + 2}$

(3 marks)

b) $\frac{x^2 - x - 20}{2x + 4} - \frac{x^2 - 16}{x + 2}$

(3 marks)

3 In words, describe what happens to the curve $y = x^3$ to transform it into the curve $y = 2(x - 1)^3 + 4$.

(3 marks)

4 The functions f and g are given by: $\text{f}(x) = x^2 - 3,\ x \in \mathbb{R}$ and $\text{g}(x) = \frac{1}{x},\ x \in \mathbb{R}, x \neq 0$.

a) Find an expression for $\text{gf}(x)$.

(2 marks)

b) Solve $\text{gf}(x) = \frac{1}{6}$.

(3 marks)

c) The function $\text{f}^{-1}(x)$ does not exist.

(i) Explain why.

(1 mark)

(ii) Suggest a restricted domain for $\text{f}(x)$ so that the function $\text{f}^{-1}(x)$ exists.

(1 mark)

5 Write $x^3 + 15x^2 + 43x - 30$ in the form $(\text{A}x^2 + \text{B}x + \text{C})(x + 6) + \text{D}$, where A, B, C and D are constants to be found.

(3 marks)

6 For the functions f and g, where

$$\text{f}(x) = 2^x,\ x \in \mathbb{R} \quad \text{and} \quad \text{g}(x) = \sqrt{3x - 2},\ x \geq \tfrac{2}{3},$$

find:

a) $\text{fg}(6)$

(2 marks)

b) $\text{gf}(2)$

(2 marks)

c) (i) $\text{g}^{-1}(x)$

(2 marks)

(ii) $\text{fg}^{-1}(x)$

(2 marks)

7   a)   On the same axes sketch the graphs of $f(x) = |x + 1|$ and $g(x) = x^2 - 4x - 12$.

(2 marks)

   b)   Hence solve the equation $x^2 - 4x - 12 = |x + 1|$.
        Leave your answers in surd form.

(4 marks)

8   The graph of the function $f(x)$ passes through points P(1, 2) and Q(3, 6).

    $f(x)$ is first reflected in the y-axis and then translated 3 units up and 2 units right
    to form a new graph, $g(x)$.

   a)   Write down the equation of $g(x)$ in terms of $f(x)$.

(3 marks)

   b)   Write down the new coordinates of the points P and Q.

(2 marks)

9   The function $f(x)$ is defined as follows: $f : x \rightarrow \dfrac{1}{x + 5}$, domain $x > -5$.

   a)   State the range of $f(x)$.

(1 mark)

   b)   (i)   Find the inverse function, $f^{-1}(x)$.

(2 marks)

        (ii)   State the domain and range of $f^{-1}(x)$.

(2 marks)

   c)   On the same axes, sketch the graphs of $y = f(x)$ and $y = f^{-1}(x)$.

(2 marks)

10 The graph below shows the curve $y = f(x)$, and the intercepts of the curve with
    the x- and y-axes.

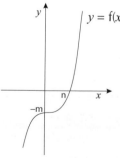

    Sketch the graphs of the following transformations on separate axes, clearly labelling the
    points of intersection with the x- and y-axes in terms of m and n.

   a) $y = |f(x)|$

(2 marks)

   b) $y = -3f(x)$

(2 marks)

   c) $y = f(|x|)$

(2 marks)

1. Inverse Trig Functions

In Chapter 1 you saw that some functions have inverses, which reverse the effect of the function. The trig functions have inverses too.

Arcsin, arccos and arctan

The inverse trig functions

- **Arcsin** is the inverse of **sin**. You might see it written as arcsine or $\sin^{-1}$.

- **Arccos** is the inverse of **cos**.
  You might see it written as arccosine or $\cos^{-1}$.

- **Arctan** is the inverse of **tan**.
  You might see it written as arctangent or $\tan^{-1}$.

The inverse trig functions **reverse** the effect of sin, cos and tan.
For example, $\sin 30° = 0.5$, so $\arcsin 0.5 = 30°$. You should
have buttons for doing arcsin, arccos and arctan on your calculator
— they'll probably be labelled $\sin^{-1}$, $\cos^{-1}$ and $\tan^{-1}$.

Graphs of the inverse trig functions

The functions sine, cosine and tangent **aren't one-to-one** mappings
(see p.18). This means that more than one value of x gives the same
value for $\sin x$, $\cos x$ or $\tan x$. For example: $\cos 0 = \cos 2\pi = \cos 4\pi = 1$,
and $\tan 0 = \tan \pi = \tan 2\pi = 0$.

If you want the inverses to be **functions**, you have to **restrict the domains**
of the trigonometric functions to make them **one-to-one**.

The graphs of the inverse functions are the **reflections**
of the sin, cos and tan graphs in the line $y = x$.

Arcsin

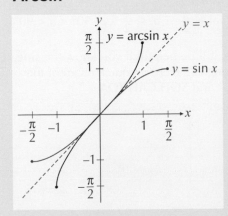

- For arcsin, limit the **domain**
  of sin x to $-\frac{\pi}{2} \leq x \leq \frac{\pi}{2}$
  (the range of sin x is still
  $-1 \leq \sin x \leq 1$).

- So, the **domain** of arcsin x
  is $-1 \leq x \leq 1$.

- The **range** of arcsin x is
  $-\frac{\pi}{2} \leq \arcsin x \leq \frac{\pi}{2}$.

- The graph of $y = \arcsin x$
  goes through the **origin**.

- The coordinates of its **endpoints**
  are $(-1, -\frac{\pi}{2})$ and $(1, \frac{\pi}{2})$.

Learning Objectives:

- Know that the inverse
  of the trig functions
  sin, cos and tan are
  arcsin, arccos and
  arctan.

- Recognise and be able
  to sketch the graphs
  of arcsin, arccos and
  arctan, including their
  restricted domains.

- Be able to evaluate
  the inverse trig
  functions.

Tip: Functions are
mappings which have
just one y value for
every x value. There's
more on functions on
pages 12-18, and on
inverse functions on
pages 23-26.

Tip: These graphs
show values in radians,
but you might have to
use angles in degrees
too. Remember that π
radians is 180°.

Tip: Learn the key features of the inverse trig graphs — you might be asked to transform them in different ways. There's more on transformations of graphs on pages 35-38.

Arccos

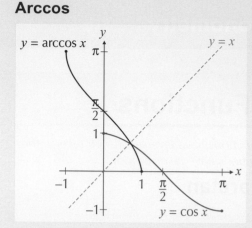

- For arccos, limit the **domain** of $\cos x$ to $0 \le x \le \pi$ (the range of $\cos x$ is still $-1 \le \cos x \le 1$.)
- So the **domain** of $\arccos x$ is $-1 \le x \le 1$.
- The **range** of $\arccos x$ is $0 \le \arccos x \le \pi$.
- The graph of $y = \arccos x$ crosses the **y-axis** at $(0, \frac{\pi}{2})$.
- The coordinates of its **endpoints** are $(-1, \pi)$ and $(1, 0)$.

Arctan

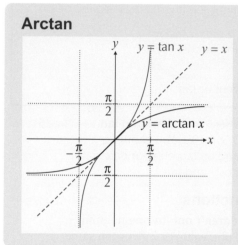

- For arctan, limit the **domain** of $\tan x$ to $-\frac{\pi}{2} < x < \frac{\pi}{2}$ (this **doesn't limit** the range of $\tan x$.)
- This means that the **domain** of $\arctan x$ **isn't** limited (it's $x \in \mathbb{R}$).
- The **range** of $\arctan x$ is $-\frac{\pi}{2} < \arctan x < \frac{\pi}{2}$.
- The graph of $y = \arctan x$ goes through the **origin**.
- It has **asymptotes** at $y = \frac{\pi}{2}$ and $y = -\frac{\pi}{2}$.

Tip: Note that there are no endpoints marked on the graph as the domain is not restricted.

Evaluating arcsin, arccos and arctan

If a is an angle within the interval $-\frac{\pi}{2} \le a \le \frac{\pi}{2}$ (or $-90° \le a \le 90°$) such that $\sin a = x$, then **arcsin $x = a$**. So to evaluate **arcsin x** you need to find the angle a in this interval such that $\sin a = x$. Using a calculator, this will be the answer you get when you enter "$\sin^{-1} x$" (for a given value of x).

Similarly, to find **arccos x**, you need to find the angle a within the interval $0 \le a \le \pi$ (or $0° \le a \le 180°$) such that $\cos a = x$.

And **arctan x** is the angle a in the interval $-\frac{\pi}{2} < a < \frac{\pi}{2}$ (or $-90° < a < 90°$) such that $\tan a = x$.

When evaluating inverse trig functions, it'll be helpful if you know the **sine**, **cosine** and **tangent** of some **common angles**. Here's a quick recap of the method of drawing triangles from C2 — and **SOH CAH TOA**.

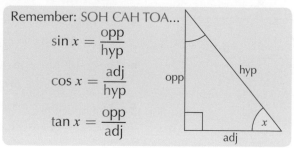

Remember: SOH CAH TOA...

$\sin x = \dfrac{\text{opp}}{\text{hyp}}$

$\cos x = \dfrac{\text{adj}}{\text{hyp}}$

$\tan x = \dfrac{\text{opp}}{\text{adj}}$

The sin, cos and tan of 30°, 45° and 60° can be found by drawing the following triangles and using **SOH CAH TOA**.

You should already know the sin, cos and tan of 90° and 180°, so you can work out all the values in this table:

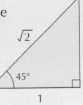

Draw an equilateral triangle with 60° angles and sides of 2 and split it to make a right-angled triangle.

Use Pythagoras to work out the length of the third side.

$x°$	x (rad)	$\sin x$	$\cos x$	$\tan x$
0	0	0	1	0
30	$\frac{\pi}{6}$	$\frac{1}{2}$	$\frac{\sqrt{3}}{2}$	$\frac{1}{\sqrt{3}}$
45	$\frac{\pi}{4}$	$\frac{1}{\sqrt{2}}$	$\frac{1}{\sqrt{2}}$	1
60	$\frac{\pi}{3}$	$\frac{\sqrt{3}}{2}$	$\frac{1}{2}$	$\sqrt{3}$
90	$\frac{\pi}{2}$	1	0	—
180	π	0	−1	0

Draw a right-angled triangle where the edges adjacent to the right angle have length 1. Use Pythagoras to work out the length of the third side.

Be careful though — the first solution you find might **not** lie within the appropriate domain for the inverse function (see the graphs on pages 45 and 46). To find a solution that **does** lie in the correct domain, you need to use the **graphs** of the functions, or the **CAST diagram** that was introduced in C2. The following examples show how to use these methods.

Tip: You might find it useful to look back at your C2 notes on solving trig equations in a given interval.

Examples

a) **Evaluate, without using a calculator, arccos 0.5.**
Give your answer in degrees.

- First, work out the angle a for which $\cos a = 0.5$.
  Since you're expected to do this without a calculator, it will be a common angle you can find using a right-angled triangle:

 0.5 is $\frac{1}{2}$ which is either sin 30° (if using $\frac{\text{opp}}{\text{hyp}}$ on the triangle) or cos 60° (if using $\frac{\text{adj}}{\text{hyp}}$).

- We are looking for the inverse of **cos**, so $a = 60°$.
- Next check that this answer lies in the appropriate domain for cos: $0 \le a \le \pi$ in radians, which is $0° \le a \le 180°$. 60° lies within this domain, so $\boxed{\text{arccos } 0.5 = 60°}$.

Tip: For all of these examples, the values that you need are in the table — it really helps to learn it.

b) **Evaluate, without using a calculator, arctan –1.**
Give your answer in radians.

- Work out the angle a for which $\tan a = -1$, over $-\frac{\pi}{2} < a < \frac{\pi}{2}$.

  - Using this triangle you can see that $\tan \frac{\pi}{4} = 1$. But you need to look at the symmetry of the tan x graph to find the solution for $\tan a = -1$:

Tip: You could also use the CAST diagram (as shown in the example on the next page) to find any negative solutions — for tan they lie in the 'S' and 'C' quadrants. You will have used the CAST diagram in C2, so check your notes if you can't remember.

- The graph shows that if $\tan \frac{\pi}{4} = 1$ then $\tan -\frac{\pi}{4} = -1$.
- So $\boxed{\arctan -1 = -\frac{\pi}{4}}$.

  This answer lies in the appropriate domain for tan, i.e. $-\frac{\pi}{2} < a < \frac{\pi}{2}$.

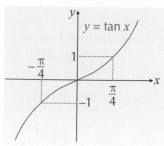

c) **Evaluate $\arcsin -\dfrac{1}{\sqrt{2}}$ without using your calculator.**
   Give your answer in radians.

- Using the triangle from the previous example: $\sin \frac{\pi}{4} = \frac{1}{\sqrt{2}}$.
- To find the angle a such that $\sin a = -\frac{1}{\sqrt{2}}$, look at the **CAST diagram**:

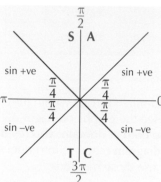

- Positive solutions for $\sin \frac{\pi}{4}$ are found in the quadrants labelled 'S' (for 'sin positive') and 'A' (for 'all positive'). This means that the desired **negative** solutions will be in the 'T' and 'C' quadrants:

  so $a = \pi + \frac{\pi}{4} = \frac{3\pi}{4}$, or $0 - \frac{\pi}{4} = -\frac{\pi}{4}$.

- Only the second of these answers lies within the appropriate domain $\left(-\frac{\pi}{2} \le a \le \frac{\pi}{2}\right)$, so $\boxed{\arcsin -\dfrac{1}{\sqrt{2}} = -\dfrac{\pi}{4}}$.

Tip: If you're not confident with using the CAST diagram you could sketch the sin graph instead and look at the symmetry (as in the previous example).

Exercise 1.1

Q1 Evaluate the following, giving your answer in radians.

   a) $\arccos 1$
   b) $\arcsin \dfrac{\sqrt{3}}{2}$
   c) $\arctan \sqrt{3}$

Q2 a) Sketch the graph of $y = 2 \arccos x$ for $-1 \le x \le 1$.

   b) Sketch the graph of $y = \dfrac{1}{2} \arctan x$ and state the range.

Q3 By drawing the graphs of $y = \dfrac{x}{2}$ and $y = \cos^{-1} x$, determine the number of real roots of the equation $\cos^{-1} x = \dfrac{x}{2}$.

Q3 Hint: Remember $\cos^{-1} x$ is just another name for $\arccos x$.

Q4 Evaluate the following, giving your answers in radians:

   a) $\sin^{-1}(-1)$
   b) $\cos^{-1}\left(-\dfrac{\sqrt{3}}{2}\right)$

Q5 Evaluate the following:

   a) $\tan(\arcsin \frac{1}{2})$
   b) $\cos^{-1}(\cos \frac{2\pi}{3})$
   c) $\cos(\arcsin \frac{1}{2})$

Q6 $f(x) = 1 + \sin 2x$. Find an expression for $f^{-1}(x)$.

2. Cosec, Sec and Cot

There are a few more trigonometric functions to learn. This time it's the reciprocals of sin, cos and tan — cosec, sec and cot.

Learning Objectives:

- Know that the reciprocals of sin, cos and tan are cosec, sec and cot.
- Recognise and be able to sketch the graphs of cosec, sec and cot.
- Be able to evaluate the reciprocal trig functions.
- Be able to simplify expressions involving the reciprocal trig functions.
- Be able to solve equations involving the reciprocal trig functions.

Graphs of cosec, sec and cot

When you take the **reciprocal** of the three main trig functions, sin, cos and tan, you get three new trig functions — **cosecant** (or **cosec**), **secant** (or **sec**) and **cotangent** (or **cot**).

$$\operatorname{cosec} \theta \equiv \frac{1}{\sin \theta}$$

$$\sec \theta \equiv \frac{1}{\cos \theta}$$

$$\cot \theta \equiv \frac{1}{\tan \theta}$$

Since $\tan \theta = \frac{\sin \theta}{\cos \theta}$, you can also think of **cot** θ as being $\frac{\cos \theta}{\sin \theta}$.

Examples

Write the following in terms of sin and cos only:

a) **cosec 20°** $\operatorname{cosec} 20° = \dfrac{1}{\sin 20°}$

b) **sec** π $\sec \pi = \dfrac{1}{\cos \pi}$

c) **cot** $\dfrac{\pi}{6}$ $\cot \dfrac{\pi}{6} = \dfrac{1}{\tan \dfrac{\pi}{6}} = \dfrac{\cos \dfrac{\pi}{6}}{\sin \dfrac{\pi}{6}}$

Tip: The trick for remembering which is which is to look at the third letter — co**s**ec (1/**s**in), se**c** (1/**c**os) and cot (1/**t**an).

Graph of cosec

This is the graph of $y = \operatorname{cosec} x$:

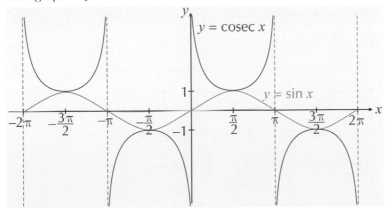

- Since $\operatorname{cosec} x = \dfrac{1}{\sin x}$, $y = \operatorname{cosec} x$ is **undefined** at any point where $\sin x = 0$.

- So $y = \operatorname{cosec} x$ has **vertical asymptotes** at $x = n\pi$ (where n is any integer).

- The graph $y = \operatorname{cosec} x$ has **minimum** points at $x = ..., -\dfrac{3\pi}{2}, \dfrac{\pi}{2}, \dfrac{5\pi}{2}, ...$ (wherever the graph $y = \sin x$ has a **maximum**). At these points, $y = 1$.

- It has **maximum** points at $x = ..., -\dfrac{\pi}{2}, \dfrac{3\pi}{2}, \dfrac{7\pi}{2}, ...$ (wherever the graph $y = \sin x$ has a **minimum**). At these points, $y = -1$.

Tip: The x-coordinates of the turning points for cosec x are the same as for sin x — but remember a maximum on sin x becomes a minimum on cosec x, and vice versa.

Graph of sec

This is the graph of $y = \sec x$:

Tip: Just like the graphs of sin x and cos x, the graphs of cosec x and sec x have a **period** of 2π radians — this just means they repeat themselves every 2π (or 360°).

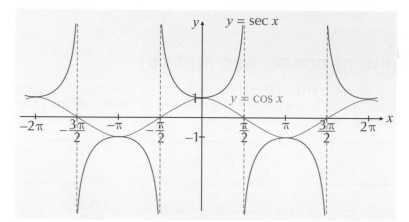

Tip: The integer n can be negative too, so the asymptotes are at $x = -\frac{\pi}{2}, -\frac{3\pi}{2}, -\frac{5\pi}{2}$ ... etc, as well as $\frac{\pi}{2}, \frac{3\pi}{2}, \frac{5\pi}{2}$ ...

- As $\sec x = \frac{1}{\cos x}$, $y = \sec x$ is **undefined** at any point where $\cos x = 0$. So $y = \sec x$ has **vertical asymptotes** at $x = \left(n\pi + \frac{\pi}{2} \right)$ (where n is any integer).

- The graph of $y = \sec x$ has **minimum** points at $x = 0, \pm 2\pi, \pm 4\pi, \ldots$ (wherever the graph of $y = \cos x$ has a **maximum**). At these points, $y = 1$.

- It has **maximum** points at $x = \pm\pi, \pm 3\pi, \ldots$ (wherever the graph of $y = \cos x$ has a **minimum**). At these points, $y = -1$.

Graph of cot

This is the graph of $y = \cot x$:

Tip: The graphs of tan x and cot x both have a period of π radians.

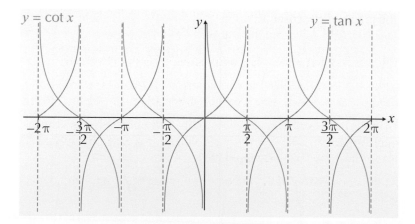

Tip: The asymptotes for cot x are the tan x asymptotes shifted horizontally by $\frac{\pi}{2}$.

- Since $\cot x = \frac{1}{\tan x}$, $y = \cot x$ is **undefined** at any point where $\tan x = 0$.
- So $y = \cot x$ has **vertical asymptotes** at $x = n\pi$ (where n is any integer).
- $y = \cot x$ **crosses the x-axis** at every place where the graph of tan x has an asymptote. This is any point with the coordinates $\left(\left(n\pi + \frac{\pi}{2} \right), 0 \right)$.

Transformations of cosec, sec and cot

The graphs of the cosec, sec and cot functions can be transformed in the same way as other functions.

a) Sketch the graph of $y = \cot 2x$ over the interval $-\pi \leq x \leq \pi$.

If $f(x) = \cot x$, then $y = f(2x)$. This transformation is a **horizontal stretch** by a factor of $\frac{1}{2}$ (i.e. the graph is squashed up in the x-direction by a factor of 2).

Tip: Look back at pages 35-38 for more on transformations of graphs.

The x coordinates of the asymptotes for $y = \cot 2x$ are **half** of those for $y = \cot x$.

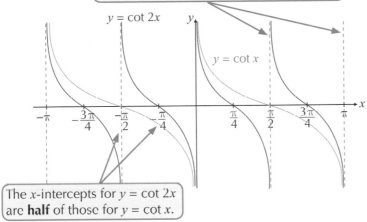

The x-intercepts for $y = \cot 2x$ are **half** of those for $y = \cot x$.

The **period** of the graph is also halved: $y = \cot 2x$ repeats itself every $\frac{\pi}{2}$ radians.

b) Give the coordinates of the maximum point on the graph of $y = \sec(x - 30°) + 1$, between 0 and 360°.

Tip: Make sure you know all the key coordinates on the graphs in both radians and degrees.

- The graph of $f(x) = \sec x$ has a maximum point at **(180°, −1)**.

- $y = f(x - 30°) + 1$. This transformation is a **horizontal translation right** by **30°**, followed by a **vertical translation up** by **1**.

- The coordinates of the maximum point will be affected by this transformation — the x-coordinate will be **increased by 30°** and the y-coordinate will be **increased by 1**.

- So the coordinates of the maximum point on the transformed graph will be: (210°, 0).

c) Describe the position of the asymptotes on the graph of $y = \operatorname{cosec}(x + \frac{\pi}{3})$.

- The graph of $f(x) = \operatorname{cosec} x$ has asymptotes at $x = n\pi$ (where n is any integer).

- $y = f(x + \frac{\pi}{3})$. This transformation is a **horizontal translation left** by $\frac{\pi}{3}$.

- Each asymptote will be translated left by $\frac{\pi}{3}$.

   So there will be asymptotes at $x = n\pi - \frac{\pi}{3}$ (where n is any integer).

Tip: The position of a vertical asymptote is only affected by transformations in the x-direction.

Q1   a) Sketch the graph of $y = \sec x$ for $-2\pi \leq x \leq 2\pi$.

        b) Give the coordinates of the minimum points within this interval.

        c) Give the coordinates of the maximum points within this interval.

Q1 d) Hint: Think about which values are **not** included in the range.

        d) State the range of $y = \sec x$.

Q2   a) Sketch the graph of $y = \csc x$ for $0 < x < 2\pi$.

        b) Give the coordinates of any maximum and minimum points within this interval.

        c) State the domain and range of $y = \csc x$.

Q3 Hint: Compare the graphs you've drawn for Q1 and Q2.

Q3   Describe the transformation that maps $y = \sec x$ onto $y = \csc x$.

Q4   a) Describe the transformation that maps $y = \cot x$ onto $y = \cot \frac{x}{4}$.

        b) What is the period, in degrees, of the graph $y = \cot \frac{x}{4}$?

        c) Sketch the graph of $y = \cot \frac{x}{4}$ for $0 < x \leq 360°$.

Q5   a) Sketch the graph of $y = 2 + \sec x$ for $-2\pi \leq x \leq 2\pi$.

        b) Give the coordinates of any maximum and minimum points within this interval.

        c) State the domain and range of $y = 2 + \sec x$.

Q6   a) Sketch the graph of $y = 2 \csc 2x$ for $0° < x < 360°$.

        b) Give the coordinates of the minimum points within this interval.

        c) Give the coordinates of the maximum points within this interval.

        d) For what values of x in this interval is $y = 2 \csc 2x$ undefined?

Q7 Hint: Work out the transformations from the graph of $y = \csc x$ first and see how they affect the graph's properties.

Q7   a) Describe the position of the asymptotes on the graph of $y = 2 + 3 \csc x$.

        b) What is the period, in degrees, of the graph $y = 2 + 3\csc x$?

        c) Sketch the graph of $y = 2 + 3\csc x$ for $-180° < x < 180°$.

        d) State the range of $y = 2 + 3\csc x$.

Evaluating cosec, sec and cot

To **evaluate** cosec, sec or cot of a number, first evaluate sin, cos or tan then work out the **reciprocal** of the answer.

Examples

a) **Evaluate 2 sec(–20°) + 5, giving your answer to 3 significant figures.**

- First write out the expression in terms of sin, cos or tan.

$$\sec x = \frac{1}{\cos x}, \text{ so } 2\sec(-20°) + 5 = \frac{2}{\cos(-20°)} + 5.$$

- Now use a calculator to find the answer:

$$\frac{2}{\cos(-20°)} + 5 = \frac{2}{0.93969...} + 5 = \boxed{7.13 \text{ to 3 sf.}}$$

b) **Evaluate cosec $\frac{\pi}{4}$ without a calculator. Give your answer in surd form.**

- $\operatorname{cosec} x = \frac{1}{\sin x}$, so $\operatorname{cosec} \frac{\pi}{4} = \frac{1}{\sin \frac{\pi}{4}}$

- Using the triangle on the right, $\sin \frac{\pi}{4} = \frac{1}{\sqrt{2}}$.

- So $\operatorname{cosec} \frac{\pi}{4} = \frac{1}{\left(\frac{1}{\sqrt{2}}\right)} = \boxed{\sqrt{2}}.$

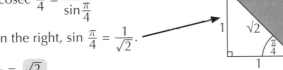

Tip: If you're asked for an answer in surd form, or to give an exact answer, it means you probably have to do it without a calculator. You should be able to solve it by considering angles of 0, $\frac{\pi}{6}$, $\frac{\pi}{4}$, $\frac{\pi}{3}$, $\frac{\pi}{2}$, π or 2π — see p.47.

c) **Give the exact value of $\cot\left(-\frac{\pi}{6}\right)$.**

- $\cot x - \frac{1}{\tan x}$, so $\cot\left(-\frac{\pi}{6}\right) = \frac{1}{\tan\left(-\frac{\pi}{6}\right)}$

- Using the triangle, you can see that $\tan \frac{\pi}{6} = \frac{1}{\sqrt{3}}$.

- The graph of $y = \tan x$ below shows that if $\tan \frac{\pi}{6} = \frac{1}{\sqrt{3}}$

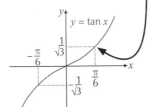

then $\tan\left(-\frac{\pi}{6}\right) = -\frac{1}{\sqrt{3}}$.

- So $\cot\left(-\frac{\pi}{6}\right) = \frac{1}{\left(-\frac{1}{\sqrt{3}}\right)} = \boxed{-\sqrt{3}}.$

Tip: You could use a CAST diagram for this too. $-\frac{\pi}{6}$ is in a negative quadrant for tan, so it is the same as $-\tan \frac{\pi}{6}$.

d) **Find cosec 300° without using a calculator.**

- $\operatorname{cosec} 300° = \frac{1}{\sin 300°} = \frac{1}{\sin(360° - 60°)}.$

- The CAST diagram shows that sin 300° is the same size as sin 60°, but it lies in a quadrant where sin is negative.

So $\sin 300° = -\sin 60° = -\frac{\sqrt{3}}{2}.$

- So $\operatorname{cosec} 300° - \frac{1}{\left(-\frac{\sqrt{3}}{2}\right)} = \boxed{-\frac{2}{\sqrt{3}}}.$

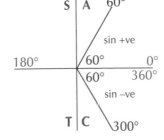

Tip: Get used to spotting angles that are 30°, 45° and 60° either side of 180° and 360° so that you can use the CAST diagram to help find them without a calculator.

Q1 Hint: If you have to give an answer rounded to a certain accuracy it means you'll have to use a calculator for part of it.

Q1   Evaluate the following, giving your answers to 2 decimal places:

a) cosec 80°   b)   sec 75°

c) cot 30°   d)   sec(–70°)

e) 3 – cot 250°   f)   2 cosec 25°

Q2 Hint: Don't forget to switch your calculator back to 'radians' for this question.

Q2   Evaluate the following, giving your answers to 3 significant figures:

a) sec 3   b)   cot 0.6

c) cosec 1.8   d)   sec(–1)

e) cosec $\frac{\pi}{8}$ f)   8 + cot $\frac{\pi}{8}$

g) $\dfrac{1}{1 + \sec\frac{\pi}{10}}$ h) $\dfrac{1}{6 + \cot\frac{\pi}{5}}$

Q3   Using the table of common angles on p.47, find the exact values of:

a) sec 60°   b)   cosec 30°

c) cot 45°   d)   cosec $\frac{\pi}{3}$

e) sec (–180°)   f)   cosec 135°

g) cot 330°   h)   sec $\frac{5\pi}{4}$

i) cosec $\frac{5\pi}{3}$ j)   cosec $\frac{2\pi}{3}$

k) 3 – cot $\frac{3\pi}{4}$ l) $\dfrac{\sqrt{3}}{\cot\frac{\pi}{6}}$

Q4 Hint: Use the table of common values on page 47 if you need to.

Q4   Find, without a calculator, the exact values of:

a) $\dfrac{1}{1 + \sec 60°}$ b) $\dfrac{2}{6 + \cot 315°}$

c) $\dfrac{1}{\sqrt{3} - \sec 30°}$ d)   1 + cot 420°

e) $\dfrac{2}{7 + \sqrt{3}\cot 150°}$

Simplifying expressions and solving equations

Simplifying expressions

You can use the cosec, sec and cot relationships to **simplify expressions**. This can make it a lot easier to **solve** trig equations.

Examples

a) Simplify $\cot^2 x \tan x$.

$\cot x = \dfrac{1}{\tan x}$, so:

$$\cot^2 x \tan x = \left(\dfrac{1}{\tan^2 x}\right) \tan x = \dfrac{1}{\tan x} = \boxed{\cot x}$$

b) Show that $\dfrac{\cot x \sec x}{\operatorname{cosec}^2 x} \equiv \sin x$.

$\cot x = \dfrac{\cos x}{\sin x}$, so:

$$\dfrac{\cot x \sec x}{\operatorname{cosec}^2 x} = \dfrac{\left(\dfrac{\cos x}{\sin x}\right)\left(\dfrac{1}{\cos x}\right)}{\left(\dfrac{1}{\sin^2 x}\right)} = \dfrac{\left(\dfrac{1}{\sin x}\right)}{\left(\dfrac{1}{\sin^2 x}\right)} = \boxed{\sin x}$$

> **Tip:** To 'show that' one thing is the same as another, you need to rearrange the expression on one side of the identity until it's the same as the other.

c) Write the expression $(\operatorname{cosec} x + 1)(\sin x - 1)$ as a single fraction in terms of $\sin x$ only.

- First expand the brackets:

$$(\operatorname{cosec} x + 1)(\sin x - 1) = \operatorname{cosec} x \sin x + \sin x - \operatorname{cosec} x - 1$$

- $\operatorname{cosec} x \sin x = \left(\dfrac{1}{\sin x}\right)\sin x = 1$, so the expression becomes:

$$1 + \sin x - \operatorname{cosec} x - 1 = \sin x - \operatorname{cosec} x$$

- Using $\operatorname{cosec} x = \dfrac{1}{\sin x}$ the expression becomes:

$$\sin x - \dfrac{1}{\sin x}$$

$$= \boxed{\dfrac{\sin^2 x - 1}{\sin x}}$$

> **Tip:** You usually need to write an expression in terms of one type of trig function in order to solve an equation.

Solving equations

You can **solve** equations involving cosec, sec and cot by **rewriting** them in terms of sin, cos or tan and solving as usual. You'll often need to write it in terms of sin, cos or tan **only**. You may also need to use the **CAST diagram** (or the graph of the trig function) to find all the solutions to an equation in a given interval.

Tip: If you've learnt the values of the sin, cos and tan of common angles on p.47, you won't need to keep drawing these triangles.

a) Solve sec $x = \sqrt{2}$ in the interval $0 \leq x \leq 2\pi$.

- sec $x = \sqrt{2}$, so cos $x = \dfrac{1}{\sqrt{2}}$ Write in terms of cos x by giving the reciprocal.

- The triangle on the right shows that one solution to cos $x = \dfrac{1}{\sqrt{2}}$ is $x = \dfrac{\pi}{4}$.

- Use the **CAST diagram** to find the **other** solution in the interval:

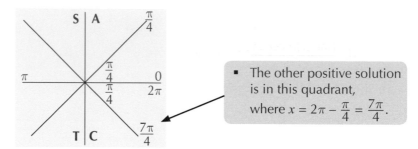

- The other positive solution is in this quadrant, where $x = 2\pi - \dfrac{\pi}{4} = \dfrac{7\pi}{4}$.

- So the two solutions are $x = \dfrac{\pi}{4}$ and $x = \dfrac{7\pi}{4}$.

b) Solve $\cosec^2 x - 3\cosec x + 2 = 0$ in the interval $-180° \leq x \leq 180°$.

Tip: Make a substitution of $y = \cosec x$ and solve as a quadratic in y if you're struggling here.

- First you need to spot that this is a **quadratic equation** in cosec x, which can be factorised as follows:

$(\cosec x - 1)(\cosec x - 2) = 0$

- This gives **two** equations to solve:

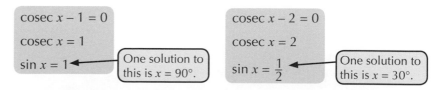

cosec $x - 1 = 0$

cosec $x = 1$

sin $x = 1$ One solution to this is $x = 90°$.

cosec $x - 2 = 0$

cosec $x = 2$

sin $x = \dfrac{1}{2}$ One solution to this is $x = 30°$.

- Look at the **graph** of $y = \sin x$ over the interval $-180° \leq x \leq 180°$:

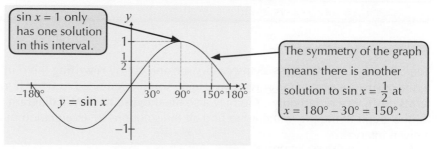

sin $x = 1$ only has one solution in this interval.

The symmetry of the graph means there is another solution to sin $x = \dfrac{1}{2}$ at $x = 180° - 30° = 150°$.

- So the three solutions are $x = 30°$, $x = 90°$ and $x = 150°$.

Q1 Simplify the following expressions:

a) $\sec x + \dfrac{1}{\cos x}$

b) $(\operatorname{cosec}^2 x)(\sin^2 x)$

c) $2 \cot x + \dfrac{1}{\tan x}$

d) $\dfrac{\sec x}{\operatorname{cosec} x}$

e) $(\cos x)(\operatorname{cosec} x)$

f) $\dfrac{\operatorname{cosec}^2 x}{\cot x}$

Q2 Show that:

a) $\sin x \cot x \equiv \cos x$

b) $\sec x - \cos x \equiv \tan x \sin x$

c) $\tan x \operatorname{cosec} x \equiv \sec x$

d) $\dfrac{(\tan^2 x)(\operatorname{cosec} x)}{\sin x} \equiv \sec^2 x$

Q2 Hint: You might find the identity $\sin^2 x + \cos^2 x \equiv 1$ useful — you should have seen it in C2.

Q3 Solve these equations for $0° < x < 360°$.
Give your answers in degrees to one decimal place.

a) $\sec x = 1.9$

b) $\cot x = 2.4$

c) $\operatorname{cosec} x = -2$

d) $\sec x = -1.3$

e) $\cot x = -2.4$

f) $4 \sec 2x = -7$

Q3 Hint: Use a calculator to find one solution, but then look at the graph or the CAST diagram to find any other solutions in the interval.

Q4 Solve these equations for $0 \le x \le 2\pi$, giving your answers in radians in terms of π.

a) $\sec x = 2$

b) $\operatorname{cosec} x = -2$

c) $\cot 2x = 1$

d) $\sec 5x = -1$

Q5 Solve the equation $\cot 2x - 4 = -5$ in the interval $0 \le x \le 2\pi$.
Give your answers in radians in terms of π.

Q3-4 Hint: For questions where you're looking for solutions for a multiple of x, such as $2x$, the interval that you'll need to look in will be different.
E.g. If $a < x < b$ then $2a \le 2x \le 2b$.

Q6 Solve for $0° \le x \le 360°$: $2 \operatorname{cosec} 2x = 3$.
Give your answers in degrees to 1 decimal place.

Q7 Find, for $0 \le x \le 2\pi$, all the solutions of the equation $-2 \sec x = 4$.
Give your answers in radians in terms of π.

Q8 Solve $\sqrt{3} \operatorname{cosec} 3x = 2$ for $0 \le x \le 2\pi$.
Give your answers in radians in terms of π.

Q9 Solve the following for $0° \le x \le 180°$.
Give your answers in degrees.

a) $\sec^2 x - 2\sqrt{2} \sec x + 2 = 0$

b) $\cot^2 x - \dfrac{4}{\sqrt{3}} \cot x + 1 = 0$

Q9 Hint: Factorise or use the quadratic formula — if it helps, make the substitution $y = \cot x$ or $y = \sec x$.

Q10 Solve the equation $(\operatorname{cosec} x - 3)(2 \tan x + 1) = 0$ for $0° \le x \le 360°$.
Give your answers to 1 decimal place.

3. Identities Involving Cosec, Sec and Cot

Learning Objective:

- Know, and be able to use, the following identities:
  $\sec^2 \theta \equiv 1 + \tan^2 \theta$
  $\csc^2 \theta \equiv 1 + \cot^2 \theta$

An identity is an equation that's true for all values of a variable. You met some trig identities in C2 — you can build on these to include cosec, sec and cot.

Deriving the identities

You should remember using the following **trig identities** in C2:

$$\cos^2 \theta + \sin^2 \theta \equiv 1 \qquad \tan\theta \equiv \frac{\sin \theta}{\cos \theta}$$

Tip: The $\equiv$ sign tells you that this is true for all values of θ, rather than just certain values.

You can use them to produce a couple of other identities:

$$\sec^2\theta \equiv 1 + \tan^2\theta \qquad \csc^2\theta \equiv 1 + \cot^2\theta$$

You'll need to know how to **derive** these identities from the C2 trig identities.

Deriving $\sec^2 \theta \equiv 1 + \tan^2 \theta$

Start with the identity $\cos^2 \theta + \sin^2 \theta \equiv 1$ and divide through by $\cos^2 \theta$.

$$\frac{\cos^2\theta}{\cos^2\theta} + \frac{\sin^2\theta}{\cos^2\theta} \equiv \frac{1}{\cos^2\theta}$$

Tip: Remember that $\cos^2 \theta = (\cos \theta)^2$.

$$\tan \theta \equiv \frac{\sin \theta}{\cos \theta}, \text{ so } \frac{\sin^2\theta}{\cos^2\theta} = \tan^2 \theta$$

$$1 + \tan^2 \theta \equiv \frac{1}{\cos^2\theta}$$

The definition of $\sec \theta = \dfrac{1}{\cos \theta}$, so replace $\dfrac{1}{\cos^2\theta}$ with $\sec^2 \theta$.

$$1 + \tan^2 \theta \equiv \sec^2 \theta$$

Rearrange slightly...

$$\sec^2 \theta \equiv 1 + \tan^2 \theta$$

Deriving $\csc^2 \theta \equiv 1 + \cot^2 \theta$

Start again with $\cos^2 \theta + \sin^2 \theta \equiv 1$ but this time **divide** through by $\sin^2 \theta$.

$$\frac{\cos^2\theta}{\sin^2\theta} + \frac{\sin^2\theta}{\sin^2\theta} \equiv \frac{1}{\sin^2\theta}$$

$$\tan \theta \equiv \frac{\sin \theta}{\cos \theta}, \text{ so } \frac{\cos^2\theta}{\sin^2\theta} = \frac{1}{\tan^2\theta}.$$

$$\frac{1}{\tan^2\theta} + 1 \equiv \frac{1}{\sin^2\theta}$$

The definition of $\cot \theta = \dfrac{1}{\tan \theta}$, so replace $\dfrac{1}{\tan^2 \theta}$ with $\cot^2 \theta$.

$$\cot^2 \theta + 1 \equiv \frac{1}{\sin^2 \theta}$$

The definition of $\mathbf{cosec}\, \theta = \dfrac{1}{\sin \theta}$, so replace $\dfrac{1}{\sin^2 \theta}$ with $\mathrm{cosec}^2 \theta$.

$$\cot^2 \theta + 1 \equiv \mathrm{cosec}^2 \theta$$

Rearrange slightly...

$$\boxed{\mathrm{cosec}^2 \theta \equiv 1 + \cot^2 \theta}$$

Tip: These derivations are examples of direct proof (see page 150), where known or accepted facts are used to prove that other relationships are true. In this case the identities from C2 are the known facts.

Using the identities

You can use identities to get rid of any trig functions that are making an equation difficult to solve.

Example 1

Simplify the expression $3 \tan x + \sec^2 x + 1$.

- Use $\sec^2 \theta \equiv 1 + \tan^2 \theta$ to swap $\sec^2 x$ for $1 + \tan^2 x$:

$$3 \tan x + 1 + \tan^2 x + 1$$

- Now rearrange:

$$\tan^2 x + 3 \tan x + 2$$

- This is a quadratic in $\tan x$ which will **factorise**:

$$(\tan x + 1)(\tan x + 2)$$

Tip: It's usually best to get the expression all in terms of one thing — in this case $\tan x$. You'll often be asked to simplify an expression in order to then solve an equation involving that expression.

Example 2

Solve the equation $\cot^2 x + 5 = 4 \,\mathrm{cosec}\, x$ in the interval $0° \leq x \leq 360°$.

- You can't solve this while it has both cot and cosec in it, so use $\mathrm{cosec}^2 \theta \equiv 1 + \cot^2 \theta$ to swap $\cot^2 x$ for $\mathrm{cosec}^2 x - 1$.

$$\mathrm{cosec}^2 x - 1 + 5 = 4 \,\mathrm{cosec}\, x$$
$$\mathrm{cosec}^2 x + 4 = 4 \,\mathrm{cosec}\, x$$
$$\mathrm{cosec}^2 x - 4 \,\mathrm{cosec}\, x + 4 = 0 \quad \longleftarrow \text{Rearrange so that one side is zero.}$$

- So you've got a quadratic in $\mathrm{cosec}\, x$ which will **factorise**.

$$(\mathrm{cosec}\, x - 2)(\mathrm{cosec}\, x - 2) = 0$$

- One of the brackets must be equal to zero — here they're both the same, so you only get one **equation**:

$$(\mathrm{cosec}\, x - 2) = 0$$
$$\Rightarrow \mathrm{cosec}\, x = 2$$

Tip: If it helps, think of this as $y^2 - 4y + 4 = 0$. Factorise it, and then replace the y with $\mathrm{cosec}\, x$.

- Now you can convert this into **sin x**, and **solve** it:

$$\sin x = \frac{1}{2}$$
$$\Rightarrow x = 30°$$

- To find the other values of x, draw a quick sketch of the sin curve:

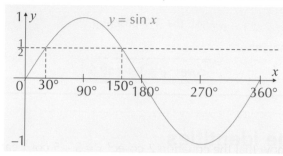

- From the graph, you can see that sin x takes the value of $\frac{1}{2}$ **twice** in the given interval, once at $x = 30°$ and once at $x = 180 - 30 = 150°$.

Tip: In this example, you're told which identity to use, but this won't always be the case. It takes practice to quickly spot which identity will work best.

Example 3

Given that cot x = $\sqrt{8}$, where $0 \leq x \leq 180°$, show how you can use the identity cosec² θ = 1 + cot² θ to find the exact value of sin x. Use Pythagoras' Theorem to confirm the result.

- If $\cot x = \sqrt{8}$, then **cot² x = 8**.

- $\cot^2 \theta = \text{cosec}^2 \theta - 1$ so: **cosec² x − 1 = 8**.

- Rearranging: $\text{cosec}^2 x = 9 \Rightarrow$ **cosec x = ±3**

- Since $\text{cosec } x = \frac{1}{\sin x}$, **sin x = ±$\frac{1}{3}$**.

  Look at the graph of sin x to see why.

- We're told that **$0 \leq x \leq 180°$**, and sin x is **positive** over this interval, so: $\sin x = \frac{1}{3}$.

- To confirm this using **Pythagoras' Theorem**:
  $\cot x = \sqrt{8} \Rightarrow \tan x = \frac{1}{\cot x} = \frac{1}{\sqrt{8}}$.
  Now draw a **right-angled triangle** for which $\tan x = \frac{1}{\sqrt{8}}$

  (i.e. the opposite has a length of 1 and the adjacent has a length of $\sqrt{8}$):

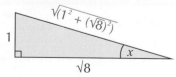

  Using Pythagoras' Theorem, the hypotenuse will have a length of $\sqrt{1^2 + (\sqrt{8})^2} = 3$.

  So $\sin x = \frac{\text{OPP}}{\text{HYP}} = \frac{1}{3}$.

Exercise 3.1

Q1 Express $\csc^2 x + 2\cot^2 x$ in terms of $\csc x$ only.

Q2 Simplify the following expression: $\tan^2 x - \dfrac{1}{\cos^2 x}$.

Q3 Given that $x = \sec\theta + \tan\theta$, show that $x + \dfrac{1}{x} = 2\sec\theta$.

Q4 a) Show that the equation $\tan^2 x = 2\sec x + 2$ can be written as:
$\sec^2 x - 2\sec x - 3 = 0$.

    b) Hence solve $\tan^2 x = 2\sec x + 2$ over the interval $0° \le x \le 360°$, giving your answers in degrees to 1 decimal place.

Q4 Hint: The 'hence' in part b) means that you should use the result of part a) and solve $\sec^2 x - 2\sec x - 3 = 0$. It's a quadratic in $\sec x$.

Q5 a) Show that the equation $2\csc^2 x = 5 - 5\cot x$ can be written as: $2\cot^2 x + 5\cot x - 3 = 0$.

    b) Hence solve $2\csc^2 x = 5 - 5\cot x$ over the interval $-\pi \le x \le \pi$, giving your answers in radians to 2 decimal places.

Q6 a) Show that the equation $2\cot^2 A + 5\csc A = 10$ can be written: $2\csc^2 A + 5\csc A - 12 = 0$.

    b) Hence solve $2\cot^2 A + 5\csc A = 10$ over the interval $0° \le x \le 360°$, giving your answers in degrees to 1 decimal place.

Q7 Solve the equation $\sec^2 x + \tan x = 1$ for $0 \le x \le 2\pi$, giving exact answers.

Q7 Hint: First write out the equation in terms of $\tan x$ only.

Q8 a) Given that $\csc^2\theta + 2\cot^2\theta = 2$, find the possible values of $\sin\theta$.

    b) Hence solve the equation $\csc^2\theta + 2\cot^2\theta = 2$ in the interval $0° \le \theta \le 180°$.

Q9 Solve the equation $\sec^2 x = 3 + \tan x$ in the interval $0° \le x \le 360°$, giving your answers in degrees to 1 decimal place.

Q10 Solve the equation $\cot^2 x + \csc^2 x = 7$, giving all the solutions in the interval $0 \le x \le 2\pi$ in radians in terms of π.

Q11 Solve the equation $\tan^2 x + 5\sec x + 7 = 0$, giving all the solutions in the interval $0 \le x \le 2\pi$ in radians to 2 decimal places.

Q12 Given that $\tan\theta = \dfrac{60}{11}$, and $180° \le \theta \le 270°$, find the value of:

    a) $\sin\theta$ b) $\sec\theta$ c) $\csc\theta$

Q13 Given that $\csc\theta = -\dfrac{17}{15}$, and $180° \le \theta \le 270°$, find the value of:

    a) $\cos\theta$ b) $\sec\theta$ c) $\cot\theta$

Q14 Hint: You're told to use this identity so you need to show your working out for this — you can't get away with stating the answer after using a different method.

Q14 Given that $\cos x = \dfrac{1}{6}$, use the identity $\sec^2\theta = 1 + \tan^2\theta$ to find the two possible values of $\tan x$.

Proving other identities

You can also use identities to prove that two trig expressions are the same, as shown in the examples below. You just need to take one side of the identity and play about with it until you get what's on the other side.

Examples

a) **Show that** $\dfrac{\tan^2 x}{\sec x} \equiv \sec x - \cos x$.

- Start by looking at the **left-hand side** of the identity: $\dfrac{\tan^2 x}{\sec x}$.
- Try replacing $\tan^2 x$ with **$\sec^2 x - 1$**:

$$\frac{\tan^2 x}{\sec x} \equiv \frac{\sec^2 x - 1}{\sec x} \equiv \frac{\sec^2 x}{\sec x} - \frac{1}{\sec x} \equiv \sec x - \cos x$$

Do some rearranging...

...until you get the **right-hand side** of the identity.

b) **Prove the identity** $\dfrac{\tan^2 x}{\sec x + 1} \equiv \sec x - \cos^2 x - \sin^2 x$.

As before, replace $\tan^2 x$ with **$\sec^2 x - 1$**...

$$\frac{\tan^2 x}{\sec x + 1} \equiv \frac{(\sec^2 x - 1)}{\sec x + 1} \equiv \frac{(\sec x + 1)(\sec x - 1)}{\sec x + 1}$$

...But factorise the $\sec^2 x - 1$ as it's the **difference of two squares**.

$$\equiv \sec x - 1$$

$$\equiv \sec x - (\cos^2 x + \sin^2 x)$$

The right-hand side of the identity has a $\cos^2 x$ and $\sin^2 x$. So use **$\cos^2 x + \sin^2 x \equiv 1$** to replace the '1' here.

$$\equiv \sec x - \cos^2 x - \sin^2 x$$

Tip: Keep checking that you're getting closer to the right-hand side of the identity. As well as using the known identities, there are lots of little tricks you can use — such as looking for the 'difference of two squares', and multiplying the top and bottom of a fraction by the same expression.

Exercise 3.2

Q1 a) Show that $\sec^2 \theta - \csc^2 \theta \equiv \tan^2 \theta - \cot^2 \theta$.

   b) Hence prove that
   $(\sec \theta + \csc \theta)(\sec \theta - \csc \theta) \equiv (\tan \theta + \cot \theta)(\tan \theta - \cot \theta)$.

Q1 b) Hint: Think about 'the difference of two squares'.

Q2 Prove the identity $(\tan x + \cot x)^2 \equiv \sec^2 x + \csc^2 x$.

Q3 Prove the identity $\cot^2 x + \sin^2 x \equiv (\csc x + \cos x)(\csc x - \cos x)$.

Q3 Hint: You'll need to use two identities here.

Q4 Prove the identity $\dfrac{(\sec x - \tan x)(\tan x + \sec x)}{\csc x - \cot x} \equiv \cot x + \csc x$.

Q5 Prove that $\dfrac{\cot x}{1 + \csc x} + \dfrac{1 + \csc x}{\cot x} \equiv 2 \sec x$.

Q6 Hint: Try multiplying the top and bottom by the same expression.

Q6 Prove the identity $\dfrac{\csc x + 1}{\csc x - 1} \equiv 2 \sec^2 x + 2 \tan x \sec x - 1$.

4. The Addition Formulas

The addition formulas are a special set of trig identities that can be used to simplify trig expressions where there are two different angles, or where there is a sum of angles.

Finding exact values

The identities shown below are known as the **addition formulas**. You can use the addition formulas to find the **sin**, **cos** or **tan** of the **sum** or **difference** of two angles, and to 'expand the brackets' in expressions such as $\sin(x + 60°)$ or $\cos(n - \frac{\pi}{2})$.

Learning Objective:

- Know, and be able to use, the formulas for $\sin(A \pm B)$, $\cos(A \pm B)$ and $\tan(A \pm B)$.

$$\sin(A \pm B) \equiv \sin A \cos B \pm \cos A \sin B$$

$$\cos(A \pm B) \equiv \cos A \cos B \mp \sin A \sin B$$

$$\tan(A \pm B) \equiv \frac{\tan A \pm \tan B}{1 \mp \tan A \tan B}$$

Tip: These formulas are given to you on the formula sheet in the exam.

Watch out for the $\pm$ and $\mp$ signs in the formulas — especially for cos and tan. If you use the sign on the **top** on the **left-hand side** of the identity, you have to use the sign on the **top** on the **right-hand side** too.
So $\cos(A + B) = \cos A \cos B - \sin A \sin B$.

Examples

a) Find the exact value of $\sin 18° \cos 12° + \cos 18° \sin 12°$.

Using the **sin** addition formula:
$\sin A \cos B + \cos A \sin B \equiv \sin(A + B)$. ◄ A is 18° and B is 12°.

$\sin 18° \cos 12° + \cos 18° \sin 12° = \sin(18° + 12°) = \boxed{\sin 30° = \frac{1}{2}}$

b) Write $\dfrac{\tan 5x - \tan 2x}{1 + \tan 5x \tan 2x}$ as a single trigonometric ratio.

Use the **tan** addition formula, with $A = 5x$ and $B = 2x$:

$$\frac{\tan 5x - \tan 2x}{1 + \tan 5x \tan 2x} = \tan(5x - 2x) = \boxed{\tan 3x}$$

Tip: Note that it's $\tan A - \tan B$ (rather than +) on the top line, which means it's the $\tan(A - B)$ formula.

c) Find $\cos(x + y)$ if $\sin x = \dfrac{4}{5}$ and $\sin y = \dfrac{15}{17}$. Both x and y are acute. Give an exact answer.

- In order to use the **cos** addition formula, first find **cos x** and **cos y**.
- Draw triangles and use **SOH CAH TOA** and Pythagoras to work out cos x and cos y...

$\cos x = \dfrac{\text{adj}}{\text{hyp}} = \dfrac{3}{5}$ → ← $\cos y = \dfrac{\text{adj}}{\text{hyp}} = \dfrac{8}{17}$

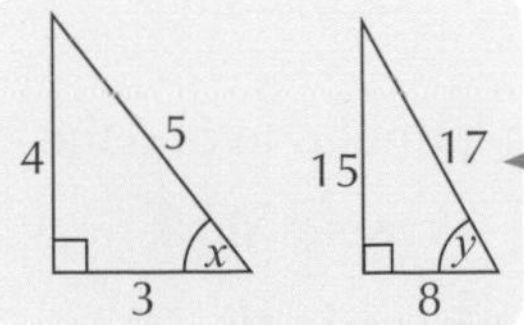

Tip: You could also use the identity $\cos^2 \theta + \sin^2 \theta \equiv 1$ to work out cos x and cos y here.

- $\cos(x + y) = \cos x \cos y - \sin x \sin y$
$= \left(\dfrac{3}{5} \times \dfrac{8}{17}\right) - \left(\dfrac{4}{5} \times \dfrac{15}{17}\right) = \boxed{-\dfrac{36}{85}}$

Tip: If you need a reminder of the sin, cos and tan of common angles — see the table on p.47.

You should know the value of sin, cos and tan for **common angles**, in degrees and radians. You can use your knowledge of these angles, along with the addition formulas, to find the **exact value** of sin, cos or tan for **other** angles.

Find a **pair** of common angles which **add or subtract** to give the angle you're after. Then plug them into the addition formula, and work it through.

Example

Using the addition formula for tangent, show that tan 15° = 2 − $\sqrt{3}$.

- Pick two angles that **add or subtract** to give **15°**, and put them into the **tan** addition formula. It's easiest to use **tan 60°** and **tan 45°** here, since neither of them are fractions:

$$\tan(A - B) = \frac{\tan A - \tan B}{1 + \tan A \tan B}$$

$$\tan 15° = \tan(60° - 45°) = \frac{\tan 60° - \tan 45°}{1 + \tan 60° \tan 45°}$$

- **Substitute** the values for tan 60° (= $\sqrt{3}$) and tan 45° (= 1) into the equation.

$$= \frac{\sqrt{3} - 1}{1 + (\sqrt{3} \times 1)} = \frac{\sqrt{3} - 1}{\sqrt{3} + 1}$$

Tip: If you can't remember how to rationalise the denominator have a look at your C1 notes.

- Now **rationalise the denominator** of the fraction to get rid of the $\sqrt{3}$.

$$= \frac{\sqrt{3} - 1}{\sqrt{3} + 1} \times \frac{\sqrt{3} - 1}{\sqrt{3} - 1} = \frac{3 - 2\sqrt{3} + 1}{3 - \sqrt{3} + \sqrt{3} - 1}$$

- Now **simplify** the expression...

$$= \frac{4 - 2\sqrt{3}}{2} = \boxed{2 - \sqrt{3}}$$

...and there's the **right-hand side**.

Exercise 4.1

Q1-2 Hint: You've been asked for exact values, which is a big clue that they'll have something to do with the common angles you should know.

Q1 Use the addition formulas to find the exact values of the following:

a) $\cos 72° \cos 12° + \sin 72° \sin 12°$

b) $\cos 13° \cos 17° - \sin 13° \sin 17°$

c) $\dfrac{\tan 12° + \tan 18°}{1 - \tan 12° \tan 18°}$

d) $\dfrac{\tan 500° - \tan 140°}{1 + \tan 500° \tan 140°}$

e) $\sin 35° \cos 10° + \cos 35° \sin 10°$

f) $\sin 69° \cos 9° - \cos 69° \sin 9°$

Q2 Use the addition formulas to find the exact values of the following:

a) $\sin \dfrac{2\pi}{3} \cos \dfrac{\pi}{2} - \cos \dfrac{2\pi}{3} \sin \dfrac{\pi}{2}$

b) $\cos 4\pi \cos 3\pi + \sin 4\pi \sin 3\pi$

c) $\dfrac{\tan \dfrac{5\pi}{12} + \tan \dfrac{5\pi}{4}}{1 - \tan \dfrac{5\pi}{12} \tan \dfrac{5\pi}{4}}$

Q3 Write the following expressions as a single trigonometric ratio:

a) $\sin 5x \cos 2x - \cos 5x \sin 2x$

b) $\cos 4x \cos 6x - \sin 4x \sin 6x$

c) $\dfrac{\tan 7x + \tan 3x}{1 - \tan 7x \tan 3x}$

d) $5 \sin 2x \cos 3x + 5 \cos 2x \sin 3x$

e) $8 \cos 7x \cos 5x + 8 \sin 7x \sin 5x$

Q4 $\sin x = \dfrac{3}{4}$ and $\cos y = \dfrac{3}{\sqrt{10}}$, where x and y are both acute angles.
Calculate the exact value of:

a) $\sin(x + y)$ b) $\cos(x - y)$

c) $\operatorname{cosec}(x + y)$ d) $\sec(x - y)$

> **Q4 Hint:** You'll need to work out cos x and sin y before you can answer parts a)-d). You can use the triangle method or the identity $\cos^2 \theta + \sin^2 \theta \equiv 1$ to work them out.

Q5 Using the addition formula for cos, show that $\cos \dfrac{\pi}{12} = \dfrac{\sqrt{6} + \sqrt{2}}{4}$.

Q6 Using the addition formula for sin, show that $\sin 75° = \dfrac{\sqrt{6} + \sqrt{2}}{4}$.

Q7 Using the addition formula for tan, show that $\tan 75° = \dfrac{\sqrt{3} + 1}{\sqrt{3} - 1}$.

Simplifying, solving equations and proving identities

You might be asked to use the addition formulas to **prove an identity**. All you need to do is put the numbers and variables from the left-hand side into the addition formulas and simplify until you get the expression you're after.

Example 1

Prove that $\cos(a + 60°) + \sin(a + 30°) = \cos a$.

- Put the numbers from the question into the addition formulas:

$$\cos(a + 60°) + \sin(a + 30°)$$
$$\equiv (\cos a \cos 60° - \sin a \sin 60°) + (\sin a \cos 30° + \cos a \sin 30°)$$

> **Tip:** Be careful with the + and − signs here.

- Now substitute in any sin and cos values that you know...

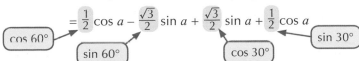

$$= \tfrac{1}{2} \cos a - \tfrac{\sqrt{3}}{2} \sin a + \tfrac{\sqrt{3}}{2} \sin a + \tfrac{1}{2} \cos a$$

cos 60°   sin 60°   cos 30°   sin 30°

- ..and simplify:

$$= \tfrac{1}{2} \cos a + \tfrac{1}{2} \cos a = \boxed{\cos a}$$

Example 2

Use the sine and cosine addition formulas to prove that
$$\tan(A + B) \equiv \frac{\tan A + \tan B}{1 - \tan A \tan B}.$$

$$\tan(A + B) \equiv \frac{\sin(A + B)}{\cos(A + B)}$$

> Start with the identity $\tan\theta \equiv \frac{\sin\theta}{\cos\theta}$.

$$\equiv \frac{\sin A \cos B + \cos A \sin B}{\cos A \cos B - \sin A \sin B}$$

> Replace $\sin(A + B)$ and $\cos(A + B)$ with the addition formulas for each.

Tip: You know that the first term on the denominator needs to be '1' — so divide through by whatever this term is and you'll get the 1 in the right place.

$$\equiv \frac{\dfrac{\sin A \cos B}{\cos A \cos B} + \dfrac{\cos A \sin B}{\cos A \cos B}}{\dfrac{\cos A \cos B}{\cos A \cos B} - \dfrac{\sin A \sin B}{\cos A \cos B}}$$

> Divide each part of the fraction by $\cos A \cos B$ and cancel where possible.

$$\equiv \frac{\dfrac{\sin A}{\cos A} + \dfrac{\sin B}{\cos B}}{1 - \left(\dfrac{\sin A}{\cos A}\right)\left(\dfrac{\sin B}{\cos B}\right)}$$

> Finally, replace each $\frac{\sin}{\cos}$ with tan.

$$\equiv \frac{\tan A + \tan B}{1 - \tan A \tan B}$$

You can also use the addition formulas to **solve** complicated trig equations.

Example 3

Solve $\sin\left(x + \frac{\pi}{2}\right) = \sin x$ in the interval $0 \le x \le 2\pi$.

- First replace $\sin\left(x + \frac{\pi}{2}\right)$ using the **sin** addition formula:

$$\sin x \cos\frac{\pi}{2} + \cos x \sin\frac{\pi}{2} = \sin x$$

$$\Rightarrow 0 + \cos x = \sin x$$

> $\cos\frac{\pi}{2} = 0$ and $\sin\frac{\pi}{2} = 1$.

Tip: Remember — to solve a trig equation you need to get it all in terms of sin, cos or tan. You can use any of the identities you've learnt so far to do this.

- **Divide** through by **cos x**:

$$\frac{\cos x}{\cos x} = \frac{\sin x}{\cos x}$$

- Replace $\frac{\sin x}{\cos x}$ with **tan x**:

$$1 = \tan x$$

$$\Rightarrow \tan x = 1$$

- Solve for $0 \le x \le 2\pi$:

$$x = \frac{\pi}{4} \text{ and } \frac{5\pi}{4}$$

Q1 Use the sine and cosine addition formulas to prove that

$$\tan(A - B) \equiv \frac{\tan A - \tan B}{1 + \tan A \tan B}.$$

Q1 Hint: Look at the proof of tan $(A + B)$ on the previous page.

Q2 Prove the following identities:

a) $\dfrac{\cos(A - B) - \cos(A + B)}{\cos A \sin B} \equiv 2 \tan A$

b) $\dfrac{1}{2}[\cos(A - B) - \cos(A + B)] \equiv \sin A \sin B$

c) $\sin(x + 90°) \equiv \cos x$

Q3 Solve $4 \sin \left(x - \frac{\pi}{3}\right) = \cos x$ in the interval $-\pi \le x \le \pi$. Give your answers in radians to 2 decimal places.

Q4 a) Show that $\tan \left(-\frac{\pi}{12}\right) = \sqrt{3} - 2$.

b) Use your answer to a) to solve the equation $\cos x = \cos \left(x + \frac{\pi}{6}\right)$ in the interval $0 \le x \le \pi$. Give your answer in terms of π.

Q5 Show that $2 \sin(x + 30°) \equiv \sqrt{3} \sin x + \cos x$.

Q6 Write an expression for $\tan \left(\frac{\pi}{3} - x\right)$ in terms of $\tan x$ only.

Q7 $\tan A = \frac{3}{8}$ and $\tan(A + B) - \frac{1}{4}$. Find the exact value of $\tan B$.

Q8 a) Given that $\sin(x + y) = 4 \cos(x - y)$, write an expression for $\tan x$ in terms of $\tan y$.

b) Use your answer to a) to solve $\sin \left(x + \frac{\pi}{4}\right) = 4 \cos \left(x - \frac{\pi}{4}\right)$ in the interval $0 \le x \le 2\pi$.

Q9 Solve the following equations in the given interval. Give your answers to 2 decimal places.

a) $\sqrt{2} \sin(\theta + 45°) = 3 \cos \theta$, $\quad 0° \le \theta \le 360°$

b) $2 \cos \left(\theta - \frac{2\pi}{3}\right) - 5 \sin \theta = 0$, $\quad 0 \le \theta \le 2\pi$

c) $\sin(\theta - 30°) - \cos(\theta + 60°) = 0$, $\quad 0° \le \theta \le 360°$

5. The Double Angle Formulas

Learning Objective:

- Know, and be able to use, the double angle formulas for sin $2A$, cos $2A$ and tan $2A$.

The double angle formulas are really just special versions of the addition formulas — using (A + A) instead of (A + B).

Deriving the double angle formulas

Double angle formulas are just a slightly different kind of **identity** — a special case of the addition formulas. They're called "double angle" formulas because they take an expression with a $2x$ term (a double angle) inside a trig function, and change it into an expression with only single x's inside the trig functions.

You need to know the double angle formulas for sin, cos and tan. Their derivations are given below.

Tip: These formulas are **not** on the formula sheet but they can be derived from the addition formulas. It helps to know them off by heart — that way you can spot them if they sneak into a question (e.g. sin x cos x is just ½ sin $2x$).

$$\sin 2A \equiv 2 \sin A \cos A$$

- Start with the **sin addition formula** (see p.63), but replace 'B' with 'A':

$$\sin (A + A) \equiv \sin A \cos A + \cos A \sin A$$

- Sin $(A + A)$ can be written as sin $2A$, and so:

$$\sin 2A \equiv \sin A \cos A + \cos A \sin A \equiv \boxed{2 \sin A \cos A}$$

$$\cos 2A \equiv \cos^2 A - \sin^2 A$$

- Start with the **cos addition formula**, but again replace 'B' with 'A':

$$\cos (A + A) \equiv \cos A \cos A - \sin A \sin A$$

$$\Rightarrow \cos 2A \equiv \cos^2 A - \sin^2 A$$

Tip: The double angle formula for cos has three different forms which are all very useful — but you can work out the second two from the general one as shown.

- You can then use $\cos^2 A + \sin^2 A \equiv 1$ to get:

$$\cos 2A \equiv \cos^2 A - (1 - \cos^2 A) \qquad \text{and} \qquad \cos 2A \equiv (1 - \sin^2 A) - \sin^2 A$$

$$\boxed{\cos 2A \equiv 2\cos^2 A - 1} \qquad \qquad \boxed{\cos 2A \equiv 1 - 2\sin^2 A}$$

$$\tan 2A \equiv \frac{2 \tan A}{1 - \tan^2 A}$$

- Start with the **tan addition formula**, and again replace 'B' with 'A':

$$\tan(A + A) \equiv \frac{\tan A + \tan A}{1 - \tan A \tan A}$$

- Simplifying this gives:

$$\tan 2A \equiv \frac{2 \tan A}{1 - \tan^2 A}.$$

Using the double angle formulas

Like the other trig identities covered in this chapter, the double angle formulas are useful when you need to find an **exact value**.

Example

a) Use a double angle formula to work out the exact value of $\sin 15° \cos 15°$.

- This looks the most like the **sin** double angle formula, $\sin 2A \equiv 2 \sin A \cos A$, but it needs to be **rearranged** slightly:

$$\sin 2A \equiv 2 \sin A \cos A \Rightarrow \sin A \cos A \equiv \tfrac{1}{2} \sin 2A$$

- Now put in the **numbers** from the question:

$$\sin 15° \cos 15° = \tfrac{1}{2} \sin 30° = \tfrac{1}{2} \times \tfrac{1}{2} = \boxed{\tfrac{1}{4}}$$

Tip: In the exam, they won't usually tell you which identity to use, so work on being able to spot the clues. If you're asked for an 'exact value' you should be thinking of your common angles. 15° is half of a common angle, so this should get you thinking about double angle formulas.

b) $\sin x = \dfrac{2}{3}$, where x is acute. Find the exact value of $\cos 2x$ and $\sin 2x$.

- For **$\cos 2x$**, use the **cos** double angle formula in terms of **sin**:

$$\cos 2A \equiv 1 - 2 \sin^2 A$$

$$\Rightarrow \cos 2x = 1 - 2\left(\tfrac{2}{3}\right)^2 = \boxed{\tfrac{1}{9}}$$

- For **$\sin 2x$**, use the **sin** double angle formula.

$$\sin 2A \equiv 2 \sin A \cos A$$

- To use this, first work out **cos x** from $\sin x$ using the triangle method:

$$\cos x = \frac{\text{adj}}{\text{hyp}} = \frac{\sqrt{5}}{3}$$

- Now put the values into the sin double angle formula as usual:

$$\sin 2x = 2 \sin x \cos x = 2 \times \tfrac{2}{3} \times \tfrac{\sqrt{5}}{3} = \boxed{\tfrac{4\sqrt{5}}{9}}$$

The double angle formulas are also handy for **simplifying expressions** in order to solve equations.

Example

Write $1 - 2\sin^2\left(\dfrac{3x}{2}\right)$ as a single trigonometric ratio.

- Look for an identity that is similar to this expression, containing a 'sin²'. The **cos** double angle formula (in terms of **sin**) looks best:

$$\cos 2A \equiv 1 - 2\sin^2 A$$

- Comparing the expression with the right-hand side of the identity, we need to use $A = \dfrac{3x}{2}$, and so $2A = 3x$.

- Putting this into the identity gives:

$$1 - 2\sin^2\frac{3x}{2} \equiv \cos 3x$$

Exercise 5.1

Q1 Hint: For some of these there are other ways to find the answer, but if you've been asked to use a certain method then show your working using that method.

Q1 Use the double angle formulas to write down the exact values of:

    a) $4\sin\dfrac{\pi}{12}\cos\dfrac{\pi}{12}$ b) $\cos\dfrac{2\pi}{3}$

    c) $\dfrac{\sin 120°}{2}$ d) $\dfrac{\tan 15°}{2 - 2\tan^2 15°}$

    e) $2\sin^2 15° - 1$

Q2 An acute angle x has $\sin x = \dfrac{1}{6}$. Find the exact values of:

    a) $\cos 2x$ b) $\sin 2x$ c) $\tan 2x$

Q3 Hint: Angle x lies in the 3rd quadrant of the CAST diagram, so $\sin x$ and $\cos x$ are negative but $\tan x$ is positive.

Q3 Angle x has $\sin x = -\dfrac{1}{4}$, and $\pi \le x \le \dfrac{3\pi}{2}$. Find the exact values of:

    a) $\cos 2x$ b) $\sin 2x$ c) $\tan 2x$

Q4 Write the following expressions as a single trigonometric ratio:

    a) $\dfrac{\sin 3\theta \cos 3\theta}{3}$ b) $\sin^2\left(\dfrac{2y}{3}\right) - \cos^2\left(\dfrac{2y}{3}\right)$

    c) $\dfrac{1 - \tan^2\left(\frac{x}{2}\right)}{2\tan\left(\frac{x}{2}\right)}$

Solving equations and proving identities

If an equation has a mixture of $\sin x$ and $\sin 2x$ terms in it, there's not much that you can do with it in that state. But you can use one of the double angle formulas to simplify it, and then solve it.

Example

Solve the equation $\cos 2x - 5 \cos x = 2$ in the interval $0 \le x \le 2\pi$.

- First use the **cos double angle formula** to get rid of $\cos 2x$:

$$\cos 2A \equiv 2 \cos^2 A - 1$$

$$\Rightarrow 2 \cos^2 x - 1 - 5 \cos x = 2$$

Tip: Use this version of the formula so that you don't end up with a mix of sin and cos terms.

- **Simplify** so you have zero on one side...

$$2 \cos^2 x - 5 \cos x - 3 = 0$$

Tip: Let $y = \cos x$ and write as a quadratic in y if it helps.

- ...then **factorise** and **solve** the **quadratic** that you've made:

$$(2 \cos x + 1)(\cos x - 3) = 0$$

$$\Rightarrow (2 \cos x + 1) = 0 \ \text{ or } \ (\cos x - 3) = 0$$

- The second bracket gives you...

$$\cos x = 3$$

...which has **no solutions** since $-1 \le \cos x \le 1$.

- So all that's left is to solve the first bracket to find x:

$$2 \cos x + 1 = 0$$

$$\cos x = -\frac{1}{2}$$

You know that $\cos x = \frac{1}{2}$ for $x = \frac{\pi}{3}$ so using the symmetry of the graph below you get:

$$x = \frac{2\pi}{3} \ \text{ or } \ x = \frac{4\pi}{3}$$

Tip: You can also use the CAST diagram.

- Remember — you can sketch the **graph** of $\cos x$ to find all values of x in the given interval:

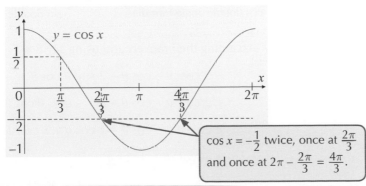

$\cos x = -\frac{1}{2}$ twice, once at $\frac{2\pi}{3}$ and once at $2\pi - \frac{2\pi}{3} = \frac{4\pi}{3}$.

The examples below show how the double angle formulas can be used to **prove** other identities.

Tip: cot is just 1 / tan, and tan is sin / cos, so cot is cos / sin. Look back at pages 49-51 if you need to refresh your memory on cot, cosec and sec.

Example 1

Prove that $2 \cot \frac{x}{2}(1 - \cos^2 \frac{x}{2}) \equiv \sin x$.

- Use the identity $\sin^2 \theta \equiv 1 - \cos^2 \theta$ to replace the $1 - \cos^2 \frac{x}{2}$ on the left-hand side, so you have:

$$\text{Left-hand side: } 2 \cot \frac{x}{2} \sin^2 \frac{x}{2}$$

- Now write $\cot \theta$ as $\frac{\cos \theta}{\sin \theta}$:

$$\frac{2 \cos \frac{x}{2} \sin^2 \frac{x}{2}}{\sin \frac{x}{2}} \equiv 2 \cos \frac{x}{2} \sin \frac{x}{2}$$

- Now use the **sin double angle formula**, using $A = \frac{x}{2}$, to write...

$$2 \cos \frac{x}{2} \sin \frac{x}{2} \equiv \boxed{\sin x}$$

...which gives you the right-hand side.

In this next example, you have to use both the addition formulas and the double angle formulas.

Example 2

Show that $\cos 3\theta \equiv 4 \cos^3 \theta - 3 \cos \theta$.

- First, write $\cos 3\theta$ as $\cos(2\theta + \theta)$.

- Now use the **cos addition formula**:

$$\cos 3\theta \equiv \cos(2\theta + \theta) \equiv \cos 2\theta \cos \theta - \sin 2\theta \sin \theta.$$

- Now use the **cos** and **sin double angle formulas** to get rid of the 2θ:

$$\cos 2\theta \cos \theta - \sin 2\theta \sin \theta \equiv (2 \cos^2 \theta - 1) \cos \theta - (2 \sin \theta \cos \theta) \sin \theta$$

cos double angle formula   sin double angle formula

- **Tidy this up** by expanding the brackets and using $\sin^2 \theta \equiv 1 - \cos^2 \theta$:

$$\equiv 2 \cos^3 \theta - \cos \theta - 2 \sin^2 \theta \cos \theta$$

$$\equiv 2 \cos^3 \theta - \cos \theta - 2(1 - \cos^2 \theta)\cos \theta$$

$$\equiv 2 \cos^3 \theta - \cos \theta - 2 \cos \theta + 2 \cos^3 \theta$$

$$\equiv \boxed{4 \cos^3 \theta - 3 \cos \theta}$$

Tip: Clever tricks like splitting up the angle so you can use the addition formulas can really help if you're stuck on a trig identity question.

Tip: You can use a similar method to show that $\sin 3\theta = 3 \sin \theta - 4 \sin^3\theta$.

The half angle formulas

The double angle formulas for cos can be **rearranged** to give another three useful identities known as the **half angle formulas**.

The examples below show how you can derive them.

Tip: These aren't on the formula sheet either. You'll need to be able to derive them for sin and cos.

Examples

a) Show that $\cos^2\left(\frac{\theta}{2}\right) \equiv \frac{1}{2}(1 + \cos\theta)$.

- Start with the **double angle** formula for **cos**: $\cos 2A \equiv 2\cos^2 A - 1$

- Replace A with $\frac{\theta}{2}$: $\cos\theta \equiv 2\cos^2\left(\frac{\theta}{2}\right) - 1$

- Now **rearrange** to get the **half angle** formula for **cos**: $\cos^2\left(\frac{\theta}{2}\right) \equiv \frac{1}{2}(1 + \cos\theta)$

b) Show that $\sin^2\left(\frac{\theta}{2}\right) \equiv \frac{1}{2}(1 - \cos\theta)$.

- This time, start with the **double angle** formula for **cos** that contains **sin**: $\cos 2A \equiv 1 - 2\sin^2 A$

- Again, replace A with $\frac{\theta}{2}$: $\cos\theta \equiv 1 - 2\sin^2\left(\frac{\theta}{2}\right)$

- Now **rearrange** to get the **half angle** formula for **sin**: $\sin^2\left(\frac{\theta}{2}\right) \equiv \frac{1}{2}(1 - \cos\theta)$

c) Hence show that $\tan^2\left(\frac{\theta}{2}\right) \equiv \frac{1 - \cos\theta}{1 + \cos\theta}$.

- Start with the identity $\tan x \equiv \frac{\sin x}{\cos x}$: $\tan\left(\frac{\theta}{2}\right) \equiv \frac{\sin\left(\frac{\theta}{2}\right)}{\cos\left(\frac{\theta}{2}\right)}$

- **Square** both sides: $\tan^2\left(\frac{\theta}{2}\right) \equiv \frac{\sin^2\left(\frac{\theta}{2}\right)}{\cos^2\left(\frac{\theta}{2}\right)}$

- Replace $\sin^2\left(\frac{\theta}{2}\right)$ and $\cos^2\left(\frac{\theta}{2}\right)$ with their **half angle formulas** from examples a) and b). $\tan^2\left(\frac{\theta}{2}\right) \equiv \frac{\frac{1}{2}(1 - \cos\theta)}{\frac{1}{2}(1 + \cos\theta)}$

- Now **simplify** to get the **half angle** formula for **tan**: $\tan^2\left(\frac{\theta}{2}\right) \equiv \frac{1 - \cos\theta}{1 + \cos\theta}$

Tip: That 'hence' in the question tells you to use your results for sin and cos. Any time you have to use sin and cos to prove something for tan you should be thinking of the identity $\tan\theta \equiv \sin\theta / \cos\theta$.

Tip: You don't need to know this derivation for your exam, but it's a good example of using identities.

Chapter 2 Trigonometry   73

Q1 Solve the equations below in the interval $0 \leq x \leq 360°$.
Give your answers in degrees to 1 decimal place.

   a) $4 \cos 2x = 14 \sin x$

   b) $5 \cos 2x + 9 \cos x = -7$

   c) $4 \cot 2x + \cot x = 5$

   d) $\tan x - 5 \sin 2x = 0$

Q1 d) Hint: There should be 7 solutions in the given interval, but two of them are easy to miss...

Q2 Solve the equations below in the interval $0 \leq x \leq 2\pi$.
Give your answers in radians to 3 significant figures.

   a) $4 \cos 2x - 10 \cos x + 1 = 0$

   b) $\dfrac{\cos 2x - 3}{2 \sin^2 x - 1} = 3$

Q3 Solve the equations below in the interval $0 \leq x \leq 2\pi$.
Give your answers in radians in terms of π.

   a) $\cos 2x + 7 \cos x = -4$

   b) $\sin x + \cos \frac{x}{2} = 0$

Q3 b) Hint: Try writing $\sin x$ as $\sin 2\left(\frac{x}{2}\right)$ and using the sin double angle formula.

Q4 Use the double angle formulas to prove each of the identities below.

   a) $\sin 2x \sec^2 x \equiv 2 \tan x$

   b) $\dfrac{2}{1 + \cos 2x} \equiv \sec^2 x$

   c) $\cot x - 2 \cot 2x \equiv \tan x$

   d) $\tan 2x + \cot 2x \equiv 2 \operatorname{cosec} 4x$

Q4 d) Hint: Write the left-hand side in terms of sin and cos first.

Q5 a) Show that $\dfrac{1 + \cos 2x}{\sin 2x} \equiv \cot x$.

   b) Use your answer to a) to solve $\dfrac{1 + \cos 4\theta}{\sin 4\theta} = 7$
in the interval $0 \leq \theta \leq 360°$.
Give your answers in degrees to 1 decimal place.

Q6 a) Show that $\operatorname{cosec} x - \cot \frac{x}{2} \equiv -\cot x$.

Q6 a) Hint: Write $\operatorname{cosec} x$ as $\frac{1}{\sin x}$ and then use $\sin x = \sin 2\left(\frac{x}{2}\right)$.

   b) Use your answer to a) to solve $\operatorname{cosec} y = \cot \frac{y}{2} - 2$
in the interval $-\pi \leq y \leq \pi$.
Give your answers in radians to 3 significant figures.

Q7 Given that $\sin \theta = \frac{5}{13}$, and that θ is acute, find

   a) (i) $\cos\left(\frac{\theta}{2}\right)$ (ii) $\sin\left(\frac{\theta}{2}\right)$

   b) Hence find $\tan\left(\frac{\theta}{2}\right)$

6. The R Addition Formulas

The R addition formulas are used to help solve equations which contain a mix of cos and sin terms.

Learning Objective:

- Know, and be able to use, expressions for $a \cos \theta + b \sin \theta$ in the equivalent forms of: $R \cos (\theta \pm \alpha)$ or $R \sin (\theta \pm \alpha)$.

Expressions of the form $a \cos \theta + b \sin \theta$

If you're solving an equation that contains both $\sin \theta$ and $\cos \theta$ terms, e.g. $3 \sin \theta + 4 \cos \theta = 1$, you need to rewrite it so that it only contains one trig function. The formulas that you use to do that are known as the **R formulas**:

One set for **sine**:
$$a \sin \theta \pm b \cos \theta \equiv R \sin (\theta \pm \alpha)$$

And one set for **cosine**:
$$a \cos \theta \pm b \sin \theta \equiv R \cos (\theta \mp \alpha)$$

where a, b and R are **positive**, and α is **acute**.

You need to be careful with the + and − signs in the cosine formula. If you have $a \cos \theta + b \sin \theta$ then use $R \cos (\theta - \alpha)$.

Using the R formulas

- You'll start with an identity like $2 \sin x + 5 \cos x \equiv R \sin (x + \alpha)$, where R and α need to be found.

- First, **expand** the right hand side using the **addition formulas** (see p.63): $2 \sin x + 5 \cos x \equiv R \sin x \cos \alpha + R \cos x \sin \alpha$.

- **Equate the coefficients** of $\sin x$ and $\cos x$.
  You'll get two equations: **(1)** $R \cos \alpha = 2$ and **(2)** $R \sin \alpha = 5$.

- To find α, **divide** equation **(2)** by equation **(1)**,
  (because $\dfrac{R \sin \alpha}{R \cos \alpha} = \tan \alpha$) then take **tan⁻¹** of the result.

- To find R, **square** equations **(1)** and **(2)** and **add** them together, then take the **square root** of the answer. This works because:
  $(R \sin \alpha)^2 + (R \cos \alpha)^2 \equiv R^2 (\sin^2 \alpha + \cos^2 \alpha) \equiv R^2$
  (using the identity $\sin^2 \alpha + \cos^2 \alpha \equiv 1$).

Tip: This method looks a bit scary, but follow through the example below and it should make more sense.

Example 1

Express $4 \cos x + 5 \sin x$ in the form $R \cos (x \pm \alpha)$.

- First you need to get the **sign** right in the formula. For this use:

$$4 \cos x + 5 \sin x \equiv R \cos (x - \alpha)$$

- Now **expand** the right hand side using the **cos addition formula**:

$$4 \cos x + 5 \sin x \equiv R \cos x \cos \alpha + R \sin x \sin \alpha.$$

Tip: The addition formula used here is:
$\cos (A - B) = \cos A \cos B + \sin A \sin B.$

- **Equating the coefficients** of cos x gives:

$$\textbf{(1)}\ R \cos \alpha = 4$$

  and equating the coefficients of sin x gives:

$$\textbf{(2)}\ R \sin \alpha = 5$$

- Dividing **(2)** by **(1)** gives:

$$\tan \alpha = \frac{5}{4} \Rightarrow \boxed{\alpha = 51.3° \text{ (to 1 d.p.)}}$$

- Squaring **(1)** and **(2)** gives:

$$\textbf{(1)}^2 : \ R^2 \cos^2 \alpha = 16$$
$$\textbf{(2)}^2 : \ R^2 \sin^2 \alpha = 25$$

$$\textbf{(1)}^2 + \textbf{(2)}^2 : \ R^2 \cos^2 \alpha + R^2 \sin^2 \alpha = 16 + 25$$
$$\Rightarrow R^2 (\cos^2 \alpha + \sin^2 \alpha) = 41$$
$$\Rightarrow R^2 = 41$$
$$\Rightarrow \boxed{R = \sqrt{41}}$$

- Finally, put the values for α and R back into the identity to give:

$$\boxed{4 \cos x + 5 \sin x \equiv \sqrt{41} \cos (x - 51.3°)}$$

Example 2

a) **Show that $5 \sin x - 5\sqrt{3} \cos x \equiv 10 \sin \left(x - \frac{\pi}{3}\right)$.**

As before, pick a formula and find values for R and α — then you can show that they are the **same** as in the right-hand side of the given identity.

- $5 \sin x - 5\sqrt{3} \cos x \equiv R \sin (x - \alpha)$ ← Expand using the **sin addition formula**.

- $5 \sin x - 5\sqrt{3} \cos x \equiv R \sin x \cos \alpha - R \cos x \sin \alpha.$

- **(1)** $R \cos \alpha = 5$ and **(2)** $R \sin \alpha = 5\sqrt{3}$ ← (by **equating coefficients**)

- $\dfrac{R \sin \alpha}{R \cos \alpha} = \tan \alpha = \dfrac{5\sqrt{3}}{5} = \sqrt{3} \Rightarrow \boxed{\alpha = \frac{\pi}{3}}$ ← **(2)** ÷ **(1)**

- $R^2 \cos^2 \alpha + R^2 \sin^2 \alpha = 5^2 + (5\sqrt{3})^2$ (by **squaring** and **adding (1)** and **(2)**)
  $\Rightarrow R^2 = 100 \Rightarrow \boxed{R = 10}$

- So, putting the values for α and R back into the identity gives...

$$\boxed{5 \sin x - 5\sqrt{3} \cos x \equiv 10 \sin \left(x - \frac{\pi}{3}\right)}$$

...which is the **right-hand side** of the identity you're trying to prove.

b) Hence sketch the graph of $y = 5 \sin x - 5\sqrt{3} \cos x$ in the interval $-\pi \leq x \leq \pi$.

Tip: Look back at pages 35-38 for a reminder about transformations of graphs.

Writing $y = 5 \sin x - 5\sqrt{3} \cos x$ as $y = \mathbf{10 \sin (x - \frac{\pi}{3})}$ makes it a lot easier to sketch the graph — just **transform** the graph of $y = \sin x$ as appropriate:

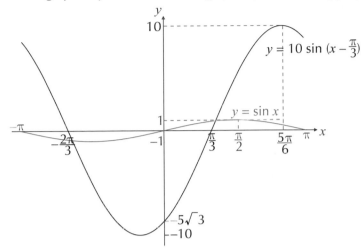

Tip: This transformation is just a translation of the graph of $y = \sin x$ horizontally right by $\frac{\pi}{3}$ followed by a stretch vertically by a scale factor of 10.

You can transform the **maximum** and **minimum** points of the graph in the same way. E.g. the maximum on $y = \sin x$ at $(\frac{\pi}{2}, 1)$, gets translated right by $\frac{\pi}{3}$ (so add $\frac{\pi}{3}$ to the x-coordinate) and stretched vertically by 10 (so multiply the y-coordinate by 10), to become $(\frac{5\pi}{6}, 10)$.

Exercise 6.1

Q1 Express $3 \sin x - 2 \cos x$ in the form $R \sin (x - \alpha)$.
Give R in surd form and α in degrees to 1 decimal place.

Q2 Express $6 \cos x - 5 \sin x$ in the form $R \cos (x + \alpha)$.
Give R in surd form and α in degrees to 1 decimal place.

Q3 Express $\sin x + \sqrt{7} \cos x$ in the form $R \sin (x + \alpha)$.
Give R in the form $m\sqrt{2}$ and α in radians to 3 significant figures.

Q4 Show that $\sqrt{2} \sin x - \cos x \equiv \sqrt{3} \sin (x - \alpha)$, where $\tan \alpha = \frac{1}{\sqrt{2}}$.

Q5 Show that $3 \cos 2x + 5 \sin 2x \equiv \sqrt{34} \cos (2x - \alpha)$, where $\tan \alpha = \frac{5}{3}$.

Q5 Hint: Treat the $2x$ just the same as an x.

Q6 a) Express $\sqrt{3} \sin x + \cos x$ in the form $R \sin (x + \alpha)$.
Give R and α as exact answers and α in radians in terms of π.

b) Hence sketch the graph of $y = \sqrt{3} \sin x + \cos x$ in the interval $-\pi \leq x \leq \pi$.

c) State the coordinates of any maximum and minimum points and intersections with the axes of the graph in b).

Q6 c) Hint: Write down their coordinates on the graph of $y = \sin x$ first, then apply the transformations to them.

Applying the R addition formulas

Tip: In exam questions they'll usually ask the question in stages anyway. You might be asked for something else too, like the maximum and minimum values of the function.

To solve equations of the form $a \sin \theta + b \cos \theta = c$, it's best to work things out in different stages — first writing out the equation in the form of one of the R formulas, then solving it. The example below shows how.

Example

a) **Solve $2 \sin x - 3 \cos x = 1$ in the interval $0 \le x \le 360°$.**

- Before you can **solve** this equation you need to get $2 \sin x - 3 \cos x$ in the form $R \sin (x - \alpha)$:

$$2 \sin x - 3 \cos x \equiv R \sin (x - \alpha)$$

$$2 \sin x - 3 \cos x \equiv R \sin x \cos \alpha - R \cos x \sin \alpha$$

- Equating coefficients gives the equations:

$$\textbf{(1) } R \cos \alpha = 2 \quad \text{and} \quad \textbf{(2) } R \sin \alpha = 3$$

- Solving for α:

$$\frac{R \sin \alpha}{R \cos \alpha} = \tan \alpha = \frac{3}{2}$$

$$\Rightarrow \alpha = \tan^{-1} 1.5 = 56.31° \text{ (to 2 d.p.)}$$

- Solving for R:

$$R^2 \cos^2 \alpha + R^2 \sin^2 \alpha = 2^2 + 3^2$$

$$\Rightarrow R^2 = 13 \Rightarrow R = \sqrt{13}$$

- So $2 \sin x - 3 \cos x = \sqrt{13} \sin (x - 56.31°)$

- Now **solve the equation**. If $2 \sin x - 3 \cos x = 1$, then:

$$\sqrt{13} \sin (x - 56.31°) = 1$$

$$\Rightarrow \sin (x - 56.31°) = \frac{1}{\sqrt{13}}$$

- Since, $0 \le x \le 360°$, you should be looking for solutions in the interval $-56.31° \le (x - 56.31°) \le 303.69°$ (just take 56.31 away from the original interval).

- Solve the equation:

$$x - 56.31° = \sin^{-1}\left(\frac{1}{\sqrt{13}}\right) = 16.10°,$$

$$\text{or } 180 - 16.10 = 163.90°.$$

Tip: The other positive solution for sin is in the second quadrant of the CAST diagram, at $180° - 16.10°$ (the angle in the first quadrant).

There are no solutions in the range $-56.31° \le (x - 56.31°) \le 0$ since $\sin x$ is negative in the range $-90° \le x \le 0$.

- So $x = 16.10 + 56.31 = 72.4°$ or $x = 163.90 + 56.31 = 220.2°$.

b) **What are the maximum and minimum values of $2 \sin x - 3 \cos x$?**

Tip: This is similar to being asked for the coordinates of the maximum and minimum points on the graph, so you can use a graph to help if you prefer.

The maximum and minimum values of the **sin** (and cos) function are ± 1, so the maximum and minimum values of $R \sin (x - \alpha)$ are $\pm R$.

As $2 \sin x - 3 \cos x = \sqrt{13} \sin (x - 56.31°)$, $R = \sqrt{13}$,

so the maximum and minimum values are $\pm \sqrt{13}$.

Q1 a) Express $5 \cos \theta - 12 \sin \theta$ in the form $R \cos (\theta + \alpha)$, where $R > 0$ and α is an acute angle (in degrees, to 1 decimal place).

    b) Hence solve $5 \cos \theta - 12 \sin \theta = 4$ in the interval $0 \leq \theta \leq 360°$.

    c) State the maximum and minimum values of $5 \cos \theta - 12 \sin \theta$.

Q2 a) Express $2 \sin 2\theta + 3 \cos 2\theta$ in the form $R \sin (2\theta + \alpha)$, where $R > 0$ (given in surd form) and $0 < \alpha < \frac{\pi}{2}$ (to 3 significant figures).

    b) Hence solve $2 \sin 2\theta + 3 \cos 2\theta = 1$ in the interval $0 \leq \theta \leq 2\pi$.

> **Q2 b) Hint:** Take care with the interval here to make sure you get all the correct solutions for θ.

Q3 a) Express $3 \sin \theta - 2\sqrt{5} \cos \theta$ in the form $R \sin (\theta - \alpha)$. Give R in surd form and α in degrees to 1 decimal place.

    b) Hence solve $3 \sin \theta - 2\sqrt{5} \cos \theta = 5$ in the interval $0 \leq \theta \leq 360°$.

    c) Find the maximum value of $f(x) = 3 \sin x - 2\sqrt{5} \cos x$ and the smallest positive value of x at which it occurs.

Q4 $f(x) = 3 \sin x + \cos x$.

    a) Express $f(x)$ in the form $R \sin (x + \alpha)$ where $R > 0$ (given in surd form) and $0 < \alpha < 90°$ (to 1 d.p.).

    b) Hence solve the equation $f(x) = 2$ in the interval $0 \leq x \leq 360°$.

    c) State the maximum and minimum values of $f(x)$.

Q5 a) Express $4 \sin x + \cos x$ in the form $R \sin (x + \alpha)$, where $R > 0$ (given in surd form) and $0 < \alpha < \frac{\pi}{2}$ (to 3 significant figures).

    b) Hence find the greatest value of $(4 \sin x + \cos x)^4$.

    c) Solve the equation $4 \sin x + \cos x = 1$ for values of x in the interval $0 \leq x \leq \pi$.

Q6 $f(x) = 8 \cos x + 15 \sin x$.

    a) Write $f(x)$ in the form $R\cos(x - \alpha)$, where $R > 0$ and $0 < \alpha < \frac{\pi}{2}$.

    b) Solve the equation $f(x) = 5$ in the interval $0 \leq x \leq 2\pi$.

    $g(x) = (8 \cos x + 15 \sin x)^2$

    c) Find the minimum value of $g(x)$ and the smallest positive value of x at which it occurs.

> **Q6 c) Hint:** Think about what happens to the negative values when you square a function.

Q7 The function g is given by $g(x) = 2 \cos x + \sin x$, $x \in \mathbb{R}$.
g(x) can be written as $R \cos (x - \alpha)$, where $R > 0$ and $0 < \alpha < 90°$.

    a) Show that $R = \sqrt{5}$, and find the value of α (to 3 s.f.).

    b) Hence state the range of $g(x)$.

> **Q7 b) Hint:** This is just another way of asking for the maximum and minimum values of the function.

Q8 Express $3 \sin \theta - \frac{3}{2}\cos \theta$ in the form $R \sin (\theta - \alpha)$, where $R > 0$ and $0 < \alpha < \frac{\pi}{2}$, and hence solve the equation $3 \sin \theta - \frac{3}{2} \cos \theta = 3$ for values of θ in the interval $0 \leq \theta \leq 2\pi$.

Q9 Solve the equation $4 \sin 2\theta + 3 \cos 2\theta = 2$ for values of θ in the interval $0 \leq \theta \leq \pi$.

7. The Factor Formulas

Learning Objective:

- Know, and be able to use, the factor formulas for: $\sin A \pm \sin B$, and $\cos A \pm \cos B$.

Here come the last lot of trig formulas for this chapter. These ones are given to you in the exam so you don't need to learn them off by heart.

Proving and using the factor formulas

The trig identities shown below are called the **factor formulas**. They follow from the **addition formulas**, as shown in the proof below. They'll come in handy for some **integrations** — it's a bit tricky to integrate $2 \cos 3\theta \cos \theta$, but integrating $\cos 4\theta + \cos 2\theta$ is much easier.

$$\sin A + \sin B \equiv 2 \sin\left(\frac{A+B}{2}\right)\cos\left(\frac{A-B}{2}\right)$$

$$\sin A - \sin B \equiv 2 \cos\left(\frac{A+B}{2}\right)\sin\left(\frac{A-B}{2}\right)$$

$$\cos A + \cos B \equiv 2 \cos\left(\frac{A+B}{2}\right)\cos\left(\frac{A-B}{2}\right)$$

$$\cos A - \cos B \equiv - 2 \sin\left(\frac{A+B}{2}\right)\sin\left(\frac{A-B}{2}\right)$$

Tip: You can derive the other formulas using the same method.

Example

Use the addition formulas to show that
$$\cos A + \cos B \equiv 2 \cos\left(\frac{A+B}{2}\right) \cos\left(\frac{A-B}{2}\right).$$

- Start with the **cos addition formulas**:

$$\cos (x + y) \equiv \cos x \cos y - \sin x \sin y$$
$$\text{and}$$
$$\cos (x - y) \equiv \cos x \cos y + \sin x \sin y.$$

- **Add them together** to get:

$$\cos (x + y) + \cos (x - y)$$
$$\equiv \cos x \cos y - \sin x \sin y + \cos x \cos y + \sin x \sin y$$
$$\equiv 2\cos x \cos y.$$

- Now **substitute** in $A = x + y$ and $B = x - y$.

   Subtracting these gives $A - B = x + y - (x - y) = 2y$, so $y = \frac{A-B}{2}$.

   Adding gives $A + B = x + y + (x - y) = 2x$, so $x = \frac{A+B}{2}$.

- So $\cos A + \cos B = 2 \cos\left(\frac{A+B}{2}\right)\cos\left(\frac{A-B}{2}\right)$.

Like the other trig identities in this chapter, the factor formulas come in useful when you need to find exact values without a calculator.

Example

Use a factor formula to write down the exact value of cos 105° + cos 15°.

- Use one of the **cos factor formulas**:

$$\cos A + \cos B = 2\cos\left(\frac{A+B}{2}\right)\cos\left(\frac{A-B}{2}\right),$$

where A = 105° and B = 15°.

- Plug in the **numbers** to get:

$$\cos 105° + \cos 15° = 2\cos\left(\frac{105° + 15°}{2}\right)\cos\left(\frac{105° - 15°}{2}\right)$$

$$\Rightarrow \cos 105° + \cos 15° = 2\cos 60° \cos 45°$$

$$\Rightarrow \cos 105° + \cos 15° = 2 \times \left(\frac{1}{2}\right) \times \left(\frac{1}{\sqrt{2}}\right) = \boxed{\frac{1}{\sqrt{2}}}$$

Tip: Always be on the lookout for those common angles when you're asked for an exact value.

Exercise 7.1

Q1 Show that $\sin A + \sin B \equiv 2\sin\left(\frac{A+B}{2}\right)\cos\left(\frac{A-B}{2}\right)$.

Q2 Show that $\sin A - \sin B \equiv 2\cos\left(\frac{A+B}{2}\right)\sin\left(\frac{A-B}{2}\right)$.

Q3 Show that $\cos A - \cos B \equiv -2\sin\left(\frac{A+B}{2}\right)\sin\left(\frac{A-B}{2}\right)$.

Q1-3 Hint: The proofs are all similar to the one for cos A + cos B on the previous page.

Q4 Use the factor formulas to show that $\sin 75° - \sin 15° = \frac{\sqrt{2}}{2}$.

Q5 Use the factor formulas to find the exact value of cos 165° – cos 75°.

Q6 Use the factor formulas to find the exact values of the following:

a) $\dfrac{\cos 140° \cos 50°}{\cos 190°}$

b) $2\sin 15° \cos 75°$

Q6 a) Hint: Simplify the numerator first — find values of A and B such that $\frac{A+B}{2} = 140°$ and $\frac{A-B}{2} = 50°$.

Q6 b) Hint: Switch round the cos and sin so that B is the smaller number.

Q7 Use the factor formulas to show that $4\sin 52.5° \cos 7.5° = \sqrt{3} + \sqrt{2}$.

Q8 Use the factor formulas to show that $\dfrac{\cos\frac{\pi}{12} - \cos\frac{5\pi}{12}}{\sin\frac{5\pi}{12} + \sin\frac{\pi}{12}} = \frac{\sqrt{3}}{3}$.

Solving equations and proving other identities

The examples below show some of the ways the factor formulas can be used to simplify expressions and solve equations.

Examples

a) Express $4 \cos \theta \cos \frac{\theta}{5}$ as the sum of two cosines.

- Start with the **factor formula** for the **sum** of two **cosines**:

$$\cos A + \cos B \equiv 2 \cos \left(\frac{A + B}{2}\right) \cos \left(\frac{A - B}{2}\right)$$

$$\Rightarrow 2 \cos A + 2 \cos B \equiv 4 \cos \left(\frac{A + B}{2}\right) \cos \left(\frac{A - B}{2}\right)$$

- Comparing the expression with the **right-hand side** of the identity gives:

$$\textbf{(1)} \ \ \theta = \left(\frac{A + B}{2}\right) \ \text{ and } \ \textbf{(2)} \ \ \frac{\theta}{5} = \left(\frac{A - B}{2}\right)$$

> **Tip:** Note that $\left(\frac{A - B}{2}\right)$ corresponds to the smaller angle.

- Rearranging **(1)** gives: $A = 2\theta - B$

- Substituting in **(2)** gives: $\frac{\theta}{5} = \left(\frac{2\theta - B - B}{2}\right) = \theta - B \Rightarrow B = \frac{4\theta}{5}$

- Substituting this back into **(1)** to find A gives: $A = 2\theta - \frac{4\theta}{5} = \frac{6\theta}{5}$

- So $4 \cos \theta \cos \frac{\theta}{5} \equiv \boxed{2 \cos \frac{6\theta}{5} + 2 \cos \frac{4\theta}{5}}$.

b) Express $\sin 2\theta - \sin \frac{\theta}{3}$ as the product of sines and cosines.

- Start with the **factor formula** for the **difference** of two **sines**:

$$\sin A - \sin B \equiv 2 \cos \left(\frac{A + B}{2}\right) \sin \left(\frac{A - B}{2}\right)$$

- Comparing the expression with the **left-hand side** of the identity gives:

$$A = 2\theta \ \text{ and } \ B = \frac{\theta}{3}$$

$$\frac{A + B}{2} = \frac{2\theta + \frac{\theta}{3}}{2} = \frac{7\theta}{6} \ \text{ and } \ \frac{A - B}{2} = \frac{2\theta - \frac{\theta}{3}}{2} = \frac{5\theta}{6}$$

> **Tip:** It's always a good idea to use the smaller angle as B so that $(A - B)$ is not negative. This might mean you have to swap things around.

- Putting this into the identity gives: $\boxed{\sin 2\theta - \sin \frac{\theta}{3} \equiv 2 \cos \frac{7\theta}{6} \sin \frac{5\theta}{6}}$

c) Use your answer to part b) to solve $\sin 2\theta - \sin \frac{\theta}{3} = 0$, for $0 \leq \theta \leq 360°$.

- This is the same as solving: $2 \cos \frac{7\theta}{6} \sin \frac{5\theta}{6} = 0$.

> **Tip:** $\frac{5\theta}{6} = 360°$ gives a solution of $\theta = 432°$, but this is outside the given range.

- Either... $\cos \frac{7\theta}{6} = 0 \Rightarrow \frac{7\theta}{6} = 90°, 270° \Rightarrow \boxed{\theta = 77.1°, 231.4° \text{ (1 d.p.)}}$

- ...or... $\sin \frac{5\theta}{6} = 0 \Rightarrow \frac{5\theta}{6} = 0°, 180°, 360° \Rightarrow \boxed{\theta = 0°, 216°}$

You can also use the factor formulas to prove other identities.

Example

Show that $\dfrac{\sin 3\theta + \sin \theta}{\sin 5\theta - \sin \theta} \equiv \cos \theta \sec 3\theta.$

$$\dfrac{\sin 3\theta + \sin \theta}{\sin 5\theta - \sin \theta} \equiv \dfrac{2\sin\left(\frac{3\theta + \theta}{2}\right)\cos\left(\frac{3\theta - \theta}{2}\right)}{2\cos\left(\frac{5\theta + \theta}{2}\right)\sin\left(\frac{5\theta - \theta}{2}\right)}$$

Using the sine factor formulas.

$$\equiv \dfrac{2\sin 2\theta \cos \theta}{2\cos 3\theta \sin 2\theta}$$

Cancel down.

$$\equiv \dfrac{\cos \theta}{\cos 3\theta} \equiv \cos \theta \sec 3\theta$$

$\sec = \dfrac{1}{\cos}$

Exercise 7.2

Q1 Express the following as the sum or difference of two sines:

a) $2 \sin 6\theta \cos 3\theta$

b) $2 \sin 8\theta \cos 4\theta$

c) $2 \sin 3\theta \cos \theta$

d) $2 \cos 5\theta \sin 2\theta$

e) $2 \cos 7\theta \sin 3\theta$

f) $2 \cos 12\theta \sin \frac{5}{2}\theta$

Q2 Express the following as the sum or difference of two cosines:

a) $2 \cos 13\theta \cos 5\theta$

b) $2 \cos \frac{7}{2}\theta \cos \frac{1}{2}\theta$

c) $2 \cos 17\theta \cos 2\theta$

d) $4 \cos 10\theta \cos 6\theta$

e) $-2 \sin 13\theta \sin 9\theta$

f) $-2 \sin 15\theta \sin \frac{1}{2}\theta$

Q3 a) Express $\cos 5x - \cos 4x$ as the product of two sines.

b) Use your answer to a) to solve $\dfrac{\cos 5x}{\cos 4x} = 1$ for $0 \le x \le 360°$.

Q4 a) Express $\cos 2x + \cos 3x$ as the product of two cosines.

b) Use your answer to a) to solve $\cos 2x + \cos 3x = 0$ for $0 \le x \le 2\pi$.

Q5 Solve $\sin (x + 15°) \cos (x - 15°) = 0.5$ in the interval $0 \le x \le 180°$.

Q6 Solve $\cos 6x + \cos 4x + \cos x = 0$ in the interval $0 \le x \le \pi$.

Q6 Hint: Use the factor formula on $\cos 6x + \cos 4x$, then factorise.

Q7 Prove the following identities:

a) $\dfrac{\sin 9x + \sin x}{\sin 8x + \sin 2x} \equiv \dfrac{\cos 4x}{\cos 3x}$

b) $\dfrac{\sin 5x - \sin x}{\cos 5x + \cos x} \equiv \tan 2x$

c) $\dfrac{\sin x + \sin y}{\cos x + \cos y} \equiv \tan\left(\dfrac{x + y}{2}\right)$

Review Exercise — Chapter 2

Q1 Using trig values for common angles, evaluate the following in radians, between 0 and $\frac{\pi}{2}$:

a) $\sin^{-1}\frac{1}{\sqrt{2}}$ b) $\cos^{-1}(0)$ c) $\tan^{-1}\sqrt{3}$

Q2 Sketch the graphs of arcsin, arccos and arctan showing their domains and ranges.

Q3 The following diagram shows the curve $y = \dfrac{1}{1+\cos x}$ for $0 \leq x \leq \frac{\pi}{2}$:

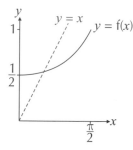

a) If $y = f(x)$, show that $f^{-1}(x) = \arccos\left(\frac{1}{x} - 1\right)$.

b) State the domain and range of this inverse function.

c) Sketch $y = f^{-1}(x)$ on the same axes as $y = f(x)$.

Q3 a) Hint: To find the inverse of a function, rearrange to make x the subject then replace x with $f^{-1}(x)$, and f(x) with x (see page 24).

Q4 Given that $f(x) = \sin^{-1} x + \cos^{-1} x + \tan^{-1} x$, find the value, in radians, of:

a) f(1)   b) f(−1)

Q5 For $\theta = 30°$, find the exact values of:

a) $\operatorname{cosec} \theta$ b) $\sec \theta$ c) $\cot \theta$

Q6 Sketch the graphs of cosecant, secant and cotangent for $-2\pi \leq x \leq 2\pi$.

Q7 a) Describe the transformation that maps $y = \sec x$ onto $y = \sec 4x$.

b) What is the period, in radians, of the graph $y = \sec 4x$?

c) Sketch the graph of $y = \sec 4x$ for $0 \leq x \leq \pi$.

d) For what values of x in this interval is sec $4x$ undefined?

Q7 d) Hint: Look at the positions of the asymptotes on the transformed graph.

Q8 Use the identity $\cos^2 \theta + \sin^2 \theta \equiv 1$ to produce the identity $\sec^2 \theta \equiv 1 + \tan^2 \theta$.

Q9 Use the trig identities to show that $\cot^2 \theta + \sin^2 \theta \equiv \operatorname{cosec}^2 \theta - \cos^2 \theta$.

Q10 Given that $x = \operatorname{cosec} \theta$ and $y = \cot^2 \theta$, show that $y = x^2 - 1$.

Q11 If $x = \sec \theta$ and $y = 2 \tan \theta$, express y in terms of x only.

Q12 a) Show that the equation $\csc^2 x = \dfrac{3\cot x + 4}{2}$ can be written as:
$2\cot^2 x - 3\cot x - 2 = 0$.

b) Hence solve the equation $\csc^2 x = \dfrac{3\cot x + 4}{2}$.
Give all the values of x in the interval $0 \le x \le 2\pi$ in radians to 2 decimal places.

Q13 Given that θ is acute and $\cos\theta = \dfrac{1}{2}$:
a) Give the exact value of $\sec\theta$.
b) Use Pythagoras' Theorem to find the value of $\tan\theta$.
c) Use the identity $\sec^2\theta \equiv 1 + \tan^2\theta$ to find the value of $\tan\theta$ and confirm that it is the same as in part b).
d) Give the exact value of $\cot\theta$.
e) Using the identity $\csc^2\theta \equiv 1 + \cot^2\theta$, give the exact value of $\sin\theta$.

Q13 b) Hint: Draw a right-angled triangle and label the lengths of any sides that you can deduce from $\cos\theta$.

Q14 Using the addition formula for cos, find the exact value of $\cos\dfrac{\pi}{12}$.

Q15 Find $\sin(A + B)$, given that $\sin A = \dfrac{4}{5}$ and $\sin B = \dfrac{7}{25}$ and that both A and B are acute angles.
You might find these triangles useful:

Q16 State the three different versions of the double angle formula for cos.

Q17 Use the double angle formula to solve the equation: $\sin 2\theta = -\sqrt{3}\sin\theta,\ 0 \le \theta \le 360°$.

Q18 Solve the equations below in the interval $0 \le x \le 2\pi$.
Give your answers in radians to 3 significant figures.

a) $4\sin x = \sin\dfrac{x}{2}$
b) $\tan\dfrac{x}{2}\tan x = 2$

Q18 Hint: x is the 'double angle' here.

Q19 Solve the equations below in the interval $0 \le x \le 2\pi$.
Give your answers in radians in terms of π.

a) $2\tan 2x = \tan x$
b) $\sin 6x - \cos 3x = 0$

Q19 b) Hint: There are 12 solutions for this one.

Q20 Which two R formulas could you use to write $a\cos\theta + b\sin\theta\ (a, b > 0)$ in terms of just sin or just cos?

Q21 Write $5\sin\theta - 6\cos\theta$ in the form $R\sin(\theta - \alpha)$, where $R > 0$ and $0 \le \alpha \le 90°$.

Q22 Show that $\dfrac{\cos\theta}{\sin\theta} + \dfrac{\sin\theta}{\cos\theta} \equiv 2\csc 2\theta$.

1   a)   Sketch the graph of $y = \operatorname{cosec} x$ for $-\pi \leq x \leq \pi$.

(3 marks)

     b)   Solve the equation $\operatorname{cosec} x = \dfrac{5}{4}$ for $-\pi \leq x \leq \pi$.

         Give your answers correct to 3 significant figures.

(3 marks)

     c)   Solve the equation $\operatorname{cosec} x = 3 \sec x$ for $-\pi \leq x \leq \pi$.
         Give your answers correct to 3 significant figures.

(3 marks)

2   a)   Write $9 \sin \theta + 12 \cos \theta$ in the form $R \sin (\theta + \alpha)$,
         where $R > 0$ and $0 \leq \alpha \leq \dfrac{\pi}{2}$.

(3 marks)

     b)   Using the result from part a), solve $9 \sin \theta + 12 \cos \theta = 3$,
         giving all solutions for θ in the range $0 \leq \theta \leq 2\pi$.

(5 marks)

3   Using the double angle and addition identities for sin and cos,
     find an expression for $\sin 3x$ in terms of $\sin x$ only.

(4 marks)

4   **Figure 1** shows an isosceles triangle ABC with $AB = AC = 2\sqrt{2}$ cm and $\angle BAC = 2\theta$.
     The mid-points of AB and AC are D and E respectively. A rectangle $DEFG$ is drawn
     inscribed in the triangle, with F and G on BC. The perimeter of rectangle $DEFG$ is P cm.

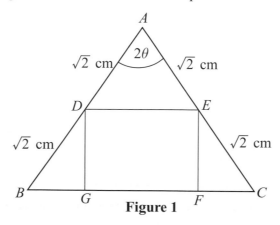

Figure 1

     a)   Using the cosine rule, $DE^2 = 4 - 4 \cos 2\theta$.
         Use a trigonometric identity to show that $DE = 2\sqrt{2} \sin \theta$.

(2 marks)

     b)   Show that $P = 4\sqrt{2} \sin \theta + 2\sqrt{2} \cos \theta$.

(2 marks)

     c)   Express P in the form $R \sin (\theta + \alpha)$ where $R > 0$ and $0 < \alpha < \dfrac{\pi}{2}$.

(3 marks)

5   **Figure 2** shows the graph of $y = \arccos x$, where y is in radians.
    A and B are the end points of the graph.

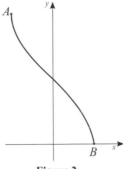

Figure 2

a)   Write down the coordinates of A and B. *(2 marks)*

b)   Express x in terms of y. *(1 mark)*

c)   Solve, to 3 significant figures, the equation $\arccos x = 2$
     for the interval shown on the graph.

(2 marks)

6   a)   Show that $\dfrac{2 \sin x}{1 - \cos x} - \dfrac{2 \cos x}{\sin x} \equiv 2 \operatorname{cosec} x$. *(4 marks)*

b)   Use this result to find all the solutions for which

     $\dfrac{2 \sin x}{1 - \cos x} - \dfrac{2 \cos x}{\sin x} = 4 \qquad 0 < x < 2\pi.$ *(3 marks)*

7   a)   Write $5 \cos \theta + 12 \sin \theta$ in the form $R \cos (\theta - \alpha)$,
         where $R > 0$ and $0 \le \alpha \le 90°$. *(4 marks)*

b)   Hence solve $5 \cos \theta + 12 \sin \theta = 2$ for $0 \le \theta \le 360°$,
     giving your answers to 2 decimal places. *(5 marks)*

c)   Use your results from part a) above to find the minimum value of
     $(5 \cos \theta + 12 \sin \theta)^3$. *(2 marks)*

8   a)   (i)   Using an appropriate identity, show that $3 \tan^2 \theta - 2 \sec \theta = 5$
              can be written as $3 \sec^2 \theta - 2 \sec \theta - 8 = 0$.

         (2 marks)

    (ii)   Hence or otherwise show that $\cos \theta = -\frac{3}{4}$ or $\cos \theta = \frac{1}{2}$.
           (3 marks)

b)   Use your results from part a) above to solve the equation $3 \tan^2 2x - 2 \sec 2x = 5$
     for $0 \le x \le 180°$. Give your answers to 2 decimal places.
     (3 marks)

1. Exponential and Logarithmic Graphs

Learning Objectives:

- Be able to sketch graphs of the functions e^x and $\ln x$.

- Be able to sketch transformations of the functions e^x and $\ln x$.

- Be able to identify functions of e^x and $\ln x$ from a graph.

Exponentials and logarithms are just types of functions. You've already seen them in C2, but for C3 you'll need to know about a special case of each — the exponential function and the natural logarithm.

Exponential functions

You should be familiar with these from C2 — but we'll begin with a short recap. The main feature of **exponential growth / decay** is that the **rate of increase / decrease** of the function is **proportional** to the function itself.

So if you plotted the **gradient** of an exponential function $y = a^x$, it would have the **same shape** as $y = a^x$.

The main points to remember for $y = a^x$ functions (a > 1) are:

- As $x \to \infty$, $y \to \infty$ (and the gradient also $\to \infty$).

- As $x \to -\infty$, $y \to 0$ (which means that a^x is **always positive**).

- When $x = 0$, $y = 1$ (so all exponential graphs go through **(0, 1)** on the y-axis).

Tip: For $0 < a < 1$, the graph does the opposite — so as $x \to \infty$, $y \to 0$ and as $x \to -\infty$, $y \to \infty$.

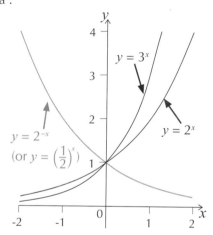

For C3, you need to know about a value of 'a' for which the **gradient** of $y = a^x$ is **exactly the same** as a^x. That value is known as **e**, an **irrational number** around 2.7183 (it's stored in your calculator just like π). This **special case** of an exponential function, $y = e^x$, is called **'the' exponential function**.

Tip: An **irrational number** is a real number which can't be written as a fraction $\frac{a}{b}$ (where a and b are both integers and $b \neq 0$).

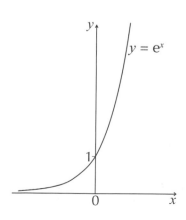

Because e is just a number, the graph of $y = e^x$ has all the properties of $y = a^x$:

- $y = e^x$ cuts the y-axis at **(0, 1)**.

- As $x \to \infty$, $e^x \to \infty$ and as $x \to -\infty$, $e^x \to 0$.

- $y = e^x$ **does not exist** for $y \leq 0$ (i.e. $e^x > 0$ — it can't be zero or negative).

- The **domain** of $f(x) = e^x$ is $x \in \mathbb{R}$ (the set of all real numbers).

- The **range** is $f(x) > 0$ (see page 12).

Tip: e^x gets infinitely close to 0 but never reaches it. $y = 0$ is called an **asymptote** of the graph.

Logarithmic functions

ln x (also known as $\log_e x$, or 'natural log') is the **inverse function** of e^x.

- $y = \ln x$ is the **reflection** of $y = e^x$ in the line $y = x$.
- It cuts the x-axis at **(1, 0)** (so **ln 1 = 0**).
- As $x \to \infty$, $\ln x \to \infty$, but it happens very slowly.
- As $x \to 0$, $\ln x \to -\infty$.
- ln x **does not exist** for $x \leq 0$ (i.e. x can't be zero or negative).
- The **domain** of $f(x) = \ln x$ is $x > 0$.
- The **range** is $f(x) \in \mathbb{R}$.

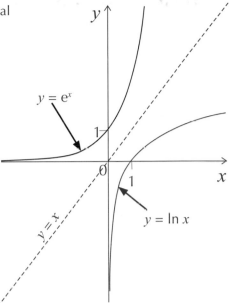

Tip: For more on functions and their inverses see p. 23-25.

Just like any other set of inverse functions, doing one function to the other gets you **back to x** on its own.

You get the following very useful formulas which will help you to solve equations later in the chapter:

$$e^{\ln x} = x$$
$$\ln(e^x) = x$$

Transformations

You can **transform** the graphs of **exponential** and **logarithmic** functions using the methods from Chapter 1. Just let $f(x) = e^x$ or $\ln x$ and apply transformations to $f(x)$ in the same way as any other function (see pages 35-38).

The graph of e^{-x} comes up quite often. It's just the graph of e^x **reflected** in the **y-axis**. You can see this by letting $f(x) = e^x$ and $g(x) = e^{-x}$.
Then $g(x) = e^{-x} = e^{(-x)} = f(-x)$. So $g(x)$ is a reflection of $f(x)$ in the y-axis.

Tip: Remember, $f(-x)$ is just a reflection of $f(x)$ in the y-axis.

$y = e^{-x}$ $y = e^x$

Just like **the exponential function**, the graph of $y = \ln(-x)$ is the graph of $y = \ln x$ reflected in the y-axis. It passes through **(-1, 0)** and still has an asymptote at **$x = 0$**.

Example 1

a) Draw the graph of $y = \ln(-x)$ on the same axes as $y = \ln x$.

- Let $f(x) = \ln x$.
- Then $\ln(-x) = f(-x)$.
- So $y = \ln(-x)$ is the graph of $y = \ln x$ reflected in the y-axis.
- The intersection with the x-axis is also reflected in the y-axis to become $(-1, 0)$.

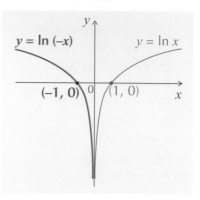

b) Sketch $y = 3e^{0.5x}$ on the same axes as $y = e^x$.

- Let $f(x) = e^x$.
- Then $3e^{0.5x} = 3(e^{(0.5x)}) = 3f(0.5x) = 3f\left(\frac{x}{2}\right)$.
- So we 'stretch' the graph of $y = e^x$ by a factor of 2 along the x-axis and a factor of 3 along the y-axis to get $y = 3e^{0.5x}$.
- The graph goes through $(0, 3)$ instead of $(0, 1)$ due to the y-axis stretch.

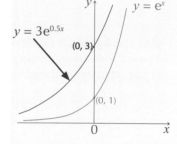

Tip: Remember that the function $f\left(\frac{1}{a}x\right)$ is $f(x)$ stretched along the x-axis by a factor of a.

Example 2

Draw the graph of $y = 5 + \ln(x + 2)$

- Let $f(x) = \ln x$.
- Then $\ln(x + 2) = f(x + 2)$
- So first draw the graph of $y = \ln(x + 2)$ by translating the graph of $y = \ln x$ left along the x-axis by 2 units.
- Then draw the graph of $y = 5 + \ln(x + 2)$ by translating the graph of $y = \ln(x + 2)$ up the y-axis by 5 units.
- The graph has an asymptote at $x = -2$ and intersects the y-axis at $5 + \ln 2$. (Put $x = 0$ into the function to get this value.)

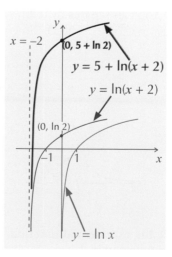

Q1 On the same axes, sketch the graphs of:

a) $y = 2^x$ b) $y = 3^{-x}$ c) $y = e^x$

Q2 Sketch each of the following functions on the same axes as $y = \ln x$ labelling any asymptotes:

a) $y = 2\ln x$ b) $y = \ln (x - 2)$

c) $y = 0.5\ln (-x)$ d) $y = 1 + \ln (x + 1)$

Q3 Sketch each graph on the same axes as $y = e^x$ labelling any asymptotes:

a) $y = 2e^x - 4$ b) $y = 0.5e^{-x}$

c) $y = e^{(0.5x + 2)}$ d) $y = 1 + e^{(x + 1)}$

Q4 Find the missing coordinates A, B and C on the following graphs:

a) $y = 3\ln\left(\frac{x}{2}\right)$ b) $y = \ln(-3x) + 2$ c) $y = 3 - \ln(-x)$

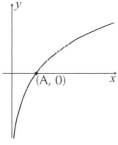
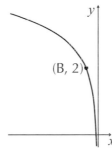
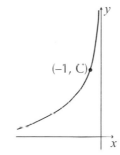

Q4 Hint: If you can't work it out by looking at the graph, try putting the x or y coordinate into the equation to work out what the missing coordinate is.

Q5 Write down the coordinates of the marked points A, B and C and the equations of the asymptotes D, E and F on these graphs:

a) $y = 3e^{\frac{x}{2}}$ b) $y = 2 + e^{-3x}$ c) $y = 3 - e^{-x}$

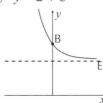
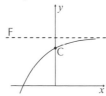

Q6 What functions are shown in the following graphs?

a) $y = f(x)$ b) $y = g(x)$ c) $y = h(x)$

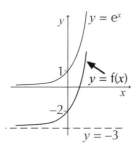
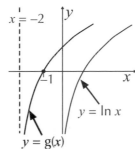
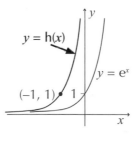

Q6 Hint: Look where intercept and asymptotes have moved to, and whether the gradient has changed to work out how the graph of $y = \ln x$ or $y = e^x$ has been transformed.

2. Using Exponentials and Logarithms

Learning Objectives:

- Be able to solve equations containing functions of $\ln x$ and e^x.

- Be able to solve exponential growth and decay problems in real life settings.

In this section you'll see how to solve equations containing $\ln x$ and e^x. You'll also see how these equations can be used to model real life situations, such as population growth and decay.

Solving equations

You can use the **log laws** from C2 as well as the **formulas** from the previous topic to **solve equations**.

Formulas

$e^{\ln x} = x$

$\ln (e^x) = x$

Log Laws

$\ln x + \ln y = \ln (xy)$

$\ln x - \ln y = \ln \left(\dfrac{x}{y}\right)$

$\ln x^k = k \ln x$

Tip: If the question asks you to give an exact solution, leave the answer as a logarithm or exponential.

Example 1

Solve the following equations, giving your answers as exact solutions.

a) $e^x = 10$

Apply $\ln$ to both sides to remove the e function.

$$e^x = 10$$

$\ln e^x = x$.

$$\ln e^x = \ln 10$$

$$x = \ln 10$$

b) $e^{(0.5x + 1)} = 20$

Apply $\ln$ to both sides to remove the e function.

$$e^{(0.5x + 1)} = 20$$

$$\ln e^{(0.5x + 1)} = \ln 20$$

$$0.5x + 1 = \ln 20$$

$$0.5x = \ln 20 - 1$$

$$x = \frac{\ln 20 - 1}{0.5}$$

$$x = 2\ln 20 - 2 \qquad \longleftarrow \text{Dividing by a half is the same as multiplying by 2.}$$

c) $\ln (2x - 1) = 2$

Apply e to both sides to remove the $\ln$ function.

$$\ln (2x - 1) = 2$$

$$e^{\ln(2x - 1)} = e^2$$

$e^{\ln x} = x$

$$2x - 1 = e^2$$

$$2x = e^2 + 1$$

$$x = \frac{e^2 + 1}{2}$$

---

d) $\ln(x^4) = 1$

$4\ln x = 1$ ← $\ln x^k = k\ln x$

$\ln x = \dfrac{1}{4}$

$e^{\ln x} = e^{\frac{1}{4}}$

$x = e^{\frac{1}{4}}$ ← $e^{\ln x} = x$

Example 2

a) **Solve the equation $2\ln x - \ln 2x = 6$, giving your answer as an exact value of x.**

Use log laws to simplify the left hand side.

$$2\ln x - \ln 2x = 6$$

$$\ln x^2 - \ln 2x = 6$$

$\ln x^k = k\ln x$

$$\ln\left(\frac{x^2}{2x}\right) = 6$$ ← $\ln x - \ln y = \ln\left(\frac{x}{y}\right)$

$$\ln\left(\frac{x}{2}\right) = 6$$

Apply the inverse function e^x to both sides to find x.

$$e^{\ln\left(\frac{x}{2}\right)} = e^6$$

$e^{\ln x} = x$

$$\frac{x}{2} = e^6$$

$$x = 2e^6$$

Since you need an exact value, leave it in exponential form.

b) **Find the two exact solutions of the equation $e^x + 5e^{-x} = 6$.**

A big clue here is that you're asked for more than one solution. Think quadratics...

Multiply each part of the equation by e^x to get rid of e^{-x}.

$$e^x + 5e^{-x} = 6$$

$$e^{2x} + 5 = 6e^x$$

$$e^{2x} - 6e^x + 5 = 0$$

Substitute y for e^x to get a quadratic in y. Since you're asked for exact solutions, it will probably factorise.

$$y^2 - 6y + 5 = 0$$

$$(y - 1)(y - 5) = 0$$

$$y = 1 \quad \text{and} \quad y = 5.$$

Put e^x back in and apply the inverse function $\ln x$ to both sides.

$$e^x = 1 \quad \text{and} \quad e^x = 5.$$

$$\ln e^x = \ln 1 \quad \text{and} \quad \ln e^x = \ln 5$$

$\ln e^x = x.$

$$x = \ln 1 = 0 \quad \text{and} \quad x = \ln 5$$

Again, you're asked for an exact answer so leave it in this form.

Tip: Remember basic powers laws:
$$(e^x)^2 = e^{2x}$$
$$e^{-x} \times e^x = e^0 = 1.$$

Q1 a) Find x in terms of y if $y = e^x$.   b) Find b in terms of a if $a = \ln b$.

Q2 Solve these equations, giving your answers as exact solutions.

a) $e^x = 7$ b) $5e^{3t} = 11$ c) $2e^{(-2x)} = 6$

d) $e^{(0.5x + 3)} = 9$ e) $10 - 3e^{(1 - 2x)} = 8$

Q3 Solve these equations, giving
(i) an exact solution   (ii) a solution correct to 3 s.f.

a) $\ln x = -2$ b) $3\ln (2x) = 7$ c) $\ln (5t - 3) = 4$

d) $6\ln (8 - 2t) = 10$ e) $6 - \ln (0.5x) = 3$

Q4 Hint: Remember the log law $\ln x^k = k \ln x$.

Q4 Solve these equations, giving your answers in terms of $\ln 3$.

a) $e^{3x} = 27$ b) $e^{-4x} = 9$ c) $e^{(6x - 1)} = \dfrac{1}{3}$

d) $3e^{(2x + 3)} = \dfrac{1}{27}$ e) $\dfrac{1}{3}e^{(1 - x)} - 3 = 0$

Q5 Hint: Try making a substitution. Also, 'where possible' gives you a hint that there might not be any solutions.

Q5 Solve, where possible, giving
(i) an exact answer   (ii) a solution correct to 3 s.f.

a) $e^{2x} - 7e^x + 12 = 0$ b) $e^{7x} - 3e^{5x} = 0$ c) $3e^{2x} + 10e^x + 3 = 0$

d) $e^{4x} + 4e^{2x} + 5 = 0$ e) $e^x + e^{-x} = 6$

Q6 Solve these equations, giving exact answers.

a) $\ln 5 + \ln x = 7$ b) $\ln (2x) + \ln (3x) = 15$

c) $\ln (x^2 - 4) - \ln (2x) = 0$ d) $3\ln (x^2) + 5\ln x = 2$

Modelling growth and decay

Modelling growth and decay means using a formula to **predict** how something will increase or decrease. This formula is called a **model**.

In an exam you'll often be given a background **story** to an exponential equation. There's nothing here you haven't seen before, you just need to know how to deal with all the **wordy** bits.

Example 1

The exponential growth of a colony of bacteria can be modelled by the equation $B = 60e^{0.03t}$, where B is the number of bacteria and t is the time in hours from the point at which the colony is first monitored ($t \geq 0$). Use the model to:

a) **Work out the initial population of bacteria.**

The initial population of bacteria is given by the formula when $t = 0$.

$$B = 60e^{0.03t}$$
$$= 60e^{(0.03 \times 0)}$$
$$= 60e^0$$
$$= 60 \times 1$$
$$\boxed{B = 60}$$

Tip: Don't forget that $e^0 = 1$.

b)   Predict the number of bacteria after 4 hours.

- Substitute $t = 4$ into the equation to find B after 4 hours. $\longrightarrow$ $B = 60 \times e^{(0.03 \times 4)}$
  $$= 60 \times 1.1274...$$
  $$= 67.6498...$$
- Round down because you want to know the number of whole bacteria. $\longrightarrow$ So $B = 67$ bacteria.

c)   Predict the time taken for the colony to grow to 1000.

- You need to find the time, t, when the population is 1000. $\longrightarrow$ $B = 1000$
  $$1000 = 60e^{0.03t}$$
- Substitute in the value of B. $\longrightarrow$ $e^{0.03t} = 1000 \div 60 - 16.6666...$
- Take 'ln' of both sides as usual. $\longrightarrow$ $\ln e^{0.03t} = \ln(16.6666...)$
  $$0.03t = 2.8134...$$
  $$t = 2.8134... \div 0.03$$
  $$= 93.8 \text{ hours to 3 s.f.}$$

Example 2

The concentration (C) of a drug in the bloodstream, t hours after taking an initial dose, decreases exponentially according to $C = Ae^{-kt}$, where A and k are constants. If the initial concentration is 0.72, and this halves after 5 hours, find the values of A and k and sketch a graph of C against t.

Tip: This is an example of exponential decay — the gradient of the curve is negative.

0.72 is the initial concentration — so start by putting this information into the equation and solving for A.

$$\text{When } t = 0, \ C = 0.72$$
$$\text{So } 0.72 = A \times e^0$$
$$0.72 = A \times 1$$
$$A = 0.72$$

After 5 hours the initial concentration has halved — so you can put in the value of C at $t = 5$, and then solve for k.

$$\text{When } t = 5, \ C = 0.72 \div 2 = 0.36$$
$$0.36 = 0.72 \times e^{-5k}$$
$$0.36 = \frac{0.72}{e^{5k}}$$
$$e^{5k} - \frac{0.72}{0.36} = 2$$
$$\ln e^{5k} = \ln 2 \longleftarrow \text{Apply ln to solve for } k.$$
$$5k = \ln 2$$
$$k = \ln 2 \div 5$$
$$k = 0.139 \text{ to 3 s.f.}$$

So the equation is $C = 0.72e^{-0.139t}$.

OK — the last thing left to do is to sketch the graph. Now whenever you're asked to draw a sketch of an exponential or logarithmic function, the key is to find any intercepts and asymptotes.

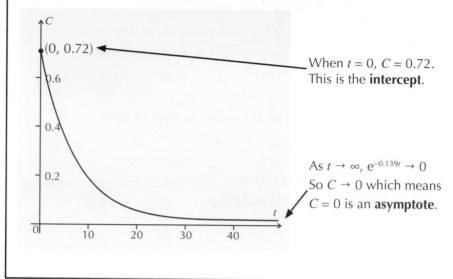

When $t = 0$, $C = 0.72$. This is the **intercept**.

As $t \to \infty$, $e^{-0.139t} \to 0$
So $C \to 0$ which means $C = 0$ is an **asymptote**.

Tip: You only need to draw the graph for $t \geq 0$, since time is always positive.

Exercise 2.2

Q1 Hint: This question gives you lots of information that you don't really need. Make sure you work out the important information before you start.

Give your answers correct to 3 significant figures.

Q1   In 1953, at the time of the coronation of Queen Elizabeth II, the population of Great Britain was approximately 52 million. In 1993 it was approximately 60 million.

Assuming that the population grows according to the formula $P = P_0 e^{nt}$, where P is the population after t years and P_0 and n are constants, and assuming there are no major wars, plagues etc., estimate the population of Great Britain in:

a) 2020   b) 2050   c) 2100

Q2 Hint: Radioactive half life means the time it takes for half of its mass to decay.

Q2   A radioactive substance has a half-life of 10 years. Its decay is modelled by the equation $M = M_0 e^{-kt}$, where M is the mass in grams after t years and M_0 and k are constants.

a) After how many years will the substance be reduced to a quarter of its original mass?

b) What was the original mass if the mass after 5 years is 200 grams?

c) Find the mass remaining after 15 years.

Q3 An oven is turned on at 12:00. After t minutes its temperature, $T\,°C$, is given by the formula:
$$T = 225 - 207e^{-\frac{t}{8}}$$

a) What was the initial temperature of the oven?

b) What temperature would the oven approach if it was left on indefinitely?

c) What was the temperature after 5 minutes?

d) At what time does the oven reach a temperature of 190 °C?

e) Sketch the graph of T against t.

Q4 A fungus is being grown under controlled conditions in a laboratory. Initially, it covers an area of 4 mm². After t hours, its area is F mm², where $F = F_0 e^{gt}$. (F_0 and g are constants).
After 6 hours its area is 10 mm².

a) Find the values of F_0 and g.

b) Predict the area of the fungus after 12 hours.

c) How long will it take for the fungus to grow to 15 mm²?

Q5 A woman is prescribed a medicine, and the concentration of the medicine in her bloodstream is monitored. Initially the concentration in her bloodstream is 3 mg per litre of blood (mg/l). After t hours, the concentration of the drug is N mg/l, where $N = Ae^{-t}$.

a) What is the concentration after 30 minutes?

b) How long does it take for the level to reduce to 0.1 mg/l?

c) Sketch the graph of N against t.

Q6 The value of a car (£V) t years after purchase can be modelled by the formula:
$$V = 1500 + 9000\,e^{-\frac{t}{3}}.$$

a) What was its price when new?

b) What was its value after 5 years?

c) After how many whole years will it be worth less than £2500?

d) Sketch the graph of V against t.

Q7 A forest fire spreads in such a way that the burnt area (H hectares) after t hours is given by the relation $H = 20\,e^{bt}$. Assume that the fire burns unchecked.

a) If $e^b = 1.8$, find b.

b) Find the area burnt after 3 hours.

c) How long would it take to burn an area of 500 hectares?

d) What constant factor is the burnt area multiplied by every hour? What percentage does the burnt area increase by each hour?

Q8   A scientist uses software to produce a series of curves using data from an experiment. He expects all of the curves to have equations of the form $y = pe^{qt}$.

   a) If the first curve passes through the points (3, 20) and (0, 5), find p and q.

   b) Another curve passes through (9, 20) and (6, 5). Find its equation.

Q9   A bowl of soup is cooling so that its temperature, θ °C after t seconds, can be predicted from the formula $\theta = 65\, e^{-ct} + 18$.

   a) What was the initial temperature of the heated soup?

   b) After the first minute, the soup has cooled by 8 °C. Find the value of c.

   c) Find the temperature of the soup after a total of 3 minutes.

   d) How long will it take for the soup to cool down to 40 °C?

   e) Sketch the graph of θ against t.

Q10   The formula $p = \dfrac{1}{(1 + Re^{-qt})}$ models the spread of information through a population, where p is the proportion of the population aware of some information after t hours.

   At 8:00, 5% of the population of Illyria have heard about the death of the King. By 10:00, 30% know of it.

   a) Find the constants R and q.

   b) What proportion of the population of Illyria will the model predict to have heard the news by 14:00?

   c) At what time will the model predict that 70% of the population know about the King's death?

Q10 Hint: Don't forget to convert the percentages into proportions (decimals or fractions).

Review Exercise — Chapter 3

Q1 Write down the exponential functions with base e shown in the following graphs.

a)

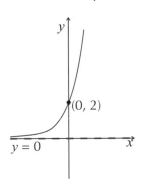

b)

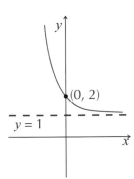

Q1 Hint: Where the question says base e, it just means that the function you are looking for has an e in it — instead of an exponential of the form a^x where a can be anything.

Q2 Find the missing coordinates A and B, and lines C and D for the following functions.

a) $y = \ln(x + 2)$

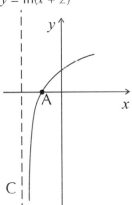

b) $y = 3 + \ln x$

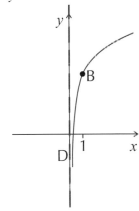

Q3 Plot the following graphs on the same axes, for $-2 \le x \le 2$:

a) $y = 4e^x$

b) $y = 4e^{-x}$

c) $y = 4\ln x$

d) $y = \ln 4x$.

Q4 Plot the following graphs on separate axes. In each case, draw the graph of $y = e^x$ on the same axes. Describe the series of transformations from $y = e^x$ to the new function.

a) $y = 2 + e^x$

b) $y = e^{\frac{x}{2}} - 1$

c) $y = e^{3x} - 0.5$

d) $y = 5 - 3e^x$

Q5 Plot the following graphs on separate axes. In each case, draw the graph of $y = \ln x$ on the same axes. Describe the series of transformations from $y = \ln x$ to the new function.

a) $y = 1 + \ln x$

b) $y = \ln(2x)$

c) $y = 3\ln x - 1$

d) $y = 5\ln(-x)$

Q6 Find the value of x, to 4 decimal places, when:

    a) $e^{2x} = 6$ b) $\ln(x + 3) = 0.75$

    c) $3e^{-4x+1} = 5$ d) $\ln x + \ln 5 = \ln 4$.

Q7 Solve the following equations, giving your solutions as exact values:

    a) $2\ln x - \ln(2x) = 2$ b) $\ln(2x - 7) + \ln 4 = -3$

Q8 Sketch graphs of the following, labelling key points and asymptotes:

    a) $y = 2 - e^{x+1}$ b) $y = 5e^{0.5x} + 5$

    c) $y = \ln(2x) + 1$ d) $y = \ln(x + 5)$

Q9 Solve the following equations giving your solutions as exact values:

    a) $2e^{2x} + e^x = 3$.   b) $e^{8x} - e^{4x} - 6 = 0$

Q10 The value of a motorbike ($£V$) varies with age (in t years from new) according to $V = 7500e^{-0.2t}$.

    a) How much did it originally cost?

    b) What is its value after 10 years (to the nearest £)?

    c) After how many years will the motorbike's value have fallen below £500?

    d) Sketch a graph showing how the value of the motorbike varies with age, labelling all key points.

Q11 A nature reserve has a population of 20 leopards in 2010. The number of leopards in the nature reserve can be modelled by the formula $L = L_0 e^{\frac{t}{12}}$ where L is the number of leopards in the population, L_0 is the initial population size and t is the time in years.

    a) How many leopards does the model predict the nature reserve will have after 10 years?

    b) The reserve has enough space for 60 leopards.
       How long will it be until the reserve runs out of space?

When a number of leopards are released into the wild, the wild population can be modelled by the formula $W = W_0 e^{-\frac{t}{3}}$ where W is the population, t is the time in years and W_0 is the initial population.

    c) If the zoo releases a population of 15 leopards into the wild, predict how many will be in this population after 5 years in the wild.

Q12 The spread of a zombie apocalypse through a population can be modelled by the exponential formula:

$$Z = 10 + 20e^t$$

where Z is the number of zombies and t is the time in weeks.

    a) How many zombies were there initially?

    b) Predict how many people will have become zombies after 2 weeks if it spreads according to the model.

    c) How many weeks will it be before there are 60 million zombies?

    d) Sketch a graph of Z against t, labelling any key points.

1   (a) Given that $6e^x = 3$, find the exact value of x.

        (2 marks)

   (b) Find the exact solutions to the equation:
$$e^{2x} - 8e^x + 7 = 0.$$

        (4 marks)

   (c) Given that $4 \ln x = 3$, find the exact value of x.

        (2 marks)

   (d) Solve the equation:
$$\ln x + \frac{24}{\ln x} = 10$$

      giving your answers as exact values of x.

        (4 marks)

2   The sketch below shows the function $y = e^{ax} + b$, where a and b are constants.

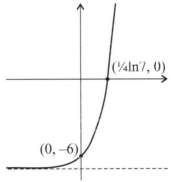

Find the values of a and b, and the equation of the asymptote shown on the sketch.

        (5 marks)

3   A breed of mink is introduced to a new habitat.
The number of mink, M, after t years in the habitat, is modelled by:
$$M = 74e^{0.6t} \qquad (t \geq 0)$$

   (a) State the number of mink that were introduced to the new habitat originally.

        (1 mark)

   (b) Predict the number of mink after 3 years in the habitat.

        (2 marks)

   (c) Predict the number of complete years it would take for the
population of mink to exceed 10 000.

        (2 marks)

   (d) Sketch a graph to show how the mink population varies with time
in the new habitat.

        (2 marks)

4   A curve has the equation $y = \ln(4x - 3)$.

   (a)   The point A with coordinate $(a, 1)$ lies on the curve.
         Find a to 2 decimal places.

                                                                    (2 marks)

   (b)   The curve only exists for $x > b$. State the value of b.

                                                                    (2 marks)

   (c)   Sketch the curve, labelling the asymptote and x-intercept.

                                                                    (2 marks)

5   Solve the following equations, giving your answers as exact values of x.

   (a) $2e^x + 18e^{-x} = 20$

                                                                    (4 marks)

   (b) $2\ln x - \ln 3 = \ln 12$

                                                                    (3 marks)

6   A radioactive substance decays exponentially so that its activity, A, can be modelled by
$$A = Be^{-kt}$$
   where t is the time in days, and $t \geq 0$. Some experimental data is shown below.

t	0	5	10
A	50	42	

   (a)   State the value of B.

                                                                    (1 mark)

   (b)   Find the value of k, to 3 significant figures.

                                                                    (2 marks)

   (c)   Find the missing value from the table, to the nearest whole number.

                                                                    (2 marks)

   (d)   The half-life of a substance is the time it takes for the activity to halve.
         Find the half-life of this substance, in days.
         Give your answer to the nearest day.

                                                                    (3 marks)

7   A point P lies on a curve C with equation:
$$y = 3e^{2 - 2x}$$
   The y-coordinate of P is 27.

   (a)   Find the x-coordinate of P in terms of $\ln 3$.

                                                                    (3 marks)

   (b)   Sketch the curve C, labelling the asymptote and the y-intercept.

                                                                    (3 marks)

   (c)   Rearrange the equation for C to make x the subject.

                                                                    (2 marks)

1. Chovin Rule

You covered differentiation in AS Maths, and now you'll see it again — but with new rules for more complicated functions. The first of the new rules is the chain rule, which you use for differentiating functions of functions, like sin x^2.

The chain rule

The **chain rule** helps you **differentiate** complicated functions by **splitting them up** into functions that are easier to differentiate. The trick is spotting **how** to split them up, and choosing the right bit to **substitute**. Once you've worked out how to split up the function, you can differentiate it using this **formula**:

$$\text{If } y = f(u) \text{ and } u = g(x)$$
$$\text{then:}$$
$$\frac{dy}{dx} = \frac{dy}{du} \times \frac{du}{dx}$$

To differentiate a function using the chain rule, just follow these steps:

- Pick a suitable function of x for 'u' and rewrite y in terms of u.

- Differentiate u (with respect to x) to get $\frac{du}{dx}$ and differentiate y (with respect to u) to get $\frac{dy}{du}$.

- Stick it all in the formula and write everything in terms of x.

The important part is **choosing** which bit to make into u. The aim is to split it into **two separate functions** that you can **easily differentiate**.

- If you have a function inside **brackets**, then the part **inside** the brackets is normally u:

    $y = (x + 1)^2$ can be written as $y = u^2$ where $u = x + 1$.

    Now both u^2 and $x + 1$ are **easy to differentiate**, and the chain rule formula does the hard work for you.

- If there's a **trig function** or **log** involved, it's usually the part **inside** the trig function or log:

    $y = \sin x^2$ can be written as $y = \sin u$ where $u = x^2$

    Again, you end up with 2 functions that are **easy to differentiate**, so you just differentiate each one **separately** then put it all in the **formula**.

Learning Objectives:

- Be able to identify which part of a function to use as u in the chain rule.
- Be able to use the chain rule to differentiate functions of functions.
- Be able to use the chain rule to convert dx/dy into dy/dx.

Tip: It may help you to think of the derivatives as fractions (they're not, but it's a good way to think of it).

Then the du's cancel:

$$\frac{dy}{du} \times \frac{du}{dx} = \frac{dy}{dx}$$

If you remember this you'll never get the order wrong.

Tip: Don't worry if you don't know how to differentiate trig functions yet — it's covered later in this chapter.

Example 1

Find $\dfrac{dy}{dx}$ if $y = (6x - 3)^5$.

- First of all, decide which part of the function to replace with u. In this case, the bit inside the brackets is easy to differentiate, so that's u.

$$y = (6x - 3)^5, \text{ so let } y = u^5 \text{ where } u = 6x - 3$$

- Next, differentiate the two parts separately:

$$\frac{dy}{du} = 5u^4 \quad \text{and} \quad \frac{du}{dx} = 6$$

- Finally, put everything back into the chain rule formula.

$$\frac{dy}{dx} = \frac{dy}{du} \times \frac{du}{dx} = 5u^4 \times 6 = 30u^4 = \boxed{30(6x - 3)^4}$$

Tip: Make sure you always substitute the function back in for u. It'll cost you marks if you don't.

Now that you can differentiate **functions of functions** using the chain rule, you can find the equation of a **tangent** or **normal** to a curve that has an equation given by a function of a function.

Example 2

Find the equation of the tangent to the curve $y = \dfrac{1}{\sqrt{x^2 + 3x}}$ at $(1, \frac{1}{2})$.

- This function's a little more complicated than the previous one, so it will help to first rewrite it in terms of powers:

$$y = \frac{1}{\sqrt{x^2 + 3x}} = (x^2 + 3x)^{-\frac{1}{2}}$$

- Then identify which part to turn into u.

$$y = (x^2 + 3x)^{-\frac{1}{2}}, \text{ so let } y = u^{-\frac{1}{2}} \text{ where } u = (x^2 + 3x)$$

Tip: When you get a question with a root or fraction, always rewrite it in terms of powers. Remember, $1/x$ is the same as x^{-1} and $\sqrt{x}$ is the same as $x^{\frac{1}{2}}$.

- Once again you now have two functions you can differentiate:

$$y = u^{-\frac{1}{2}} \Rightarrow \frac{dy}{du} = (-\frac{1}{2})u^{-\frac{3}{2}} = -\frac{1}{2(\sqrt{x^2 + 3x})^3}$$

$$u = x^2 + 3x \Rightarrow \frac{du}{dx} = 2x + 3$$

- Now put it all back into the chain rule formula:

$$\frac{dy}{dx} = \frac{dy}{du} \times \frac{du}{dx} = (-\frac{1}{2(\sqrt{x^2 + 3x})^3}) \times (2x + 3) = -\frac{2x + 3}{2(\sqrt{x^2 + 3x})^3}$$

- To find the equation of the tangent, you first need to know the gradient at the point $(1, \frac{1}{2})$, so put the x-value into your equation for $\dfrac{dy}{dx}$:

$$\frac{dy}{dx} = -\frac{(2 \times 1) + 3}{2(\sqrt{1^2 + (3 \times 1)})^3} = -\frac{5}{16}$$

- Then use your gradient and the values you're given to find c:

$$y = mx + c \Rightarrow \frac{1}{2} = (-\frac{5}{16} \times 1) + c \Rightarrow c = \frac{13}{16}$$

- So the equation of the tangent at $(1, \frac{1}{2})$ is $\boxed{y = -\dfrac{5}{16}x + \dfrac{13}{16}}$

104 Chapter 4 Differentiation

Q1 Differentiate with respect to x:

    a) $y = (x + 7)^2$ b) $y = (2x - 1)^5$

    c) $y = 3(4 - x)^8$ d) $y = (3 - 2x)^7$

    e) $y = (x^2 + 3)^5$ f) $y = (5x^2 + 3)^2$

Q2 Find $f'(x)$ for the following:

    a) $f(x) = (4x^3 - 9)^8$ b) $f(x) = (6 - 7x^2)^4$

    c) $f(x) = (x^2 + 5x + 7)^6$ d) $f(x) = (x + 4)^{-3}$

    e) $f(x) = (5 - 3x)^{-2}$ f) $f(x) = \dfrac{1}{(5 - 3x)^4}$

    g) $f(x) = (3x^2 + 4)^{\frac{3}{2}}$ h) $f(x) = \dfrac{1}{\sqrt{5 - 3x}}$

> **Q2 Hint:** Remember $f'(x)$ is just another way of writing dy/dx.

Q3 Find the exact value of $\dfrac{dy}{dx}$ when $x = 1$ for:

    a) $y = \dfrac{1}{\sqrt{5x - 3x^2}}$ b) $y = \dfrac{12}{\sqrt[3]{x + 6}}$

Q4 Differentiate $(\sqrt{x} + \dfrac{1}{\sqrt{x}})^2$ with respect to x by:

    a) Multiplying the brackets out and differentiating term by term.

    b) Using the chain rule.

Q5 Find the equation of the tangent to the curve $y = (x - 3)^5$ at $(1, -32)$

Q6 Find the equation of the tangent to the curve $y = (2x - 3)^7$ at the point $(2, 1)$.

Q7 Find the equation of the normal to the curve $y = \dfrac{1}{4}(x - 7)^4$ when $x = 6$.

> **Q7 Hint:** Remember, the gradient of the normal to a curve is just $-1 \div$ gradient of the tangent (this was in C1 if you need a refresher).

Q8 Find the equation of the normal to the curve $y = \left(\dfrac{x}{4} - 2\right)^3$ at the point $(4, -1)$, in the form $ax + by + c = 0$ where a, b and c are integers.

Q9 Find the value of $\dfrac{dy}{dx}$ when $x = 1$ for $y = (7x^2 - 3)^{-4}$.

Q10 Find $f'(x)$ if $f(x) = \dfrac{7}{\sqrt[3]{3 - 2x}}$.

Q11 Find the equation of the tangent to the curve $y = \sqrt{5x - 1}$ when $x = 2$, in the form $ax + by + c = 0$, $a, b, c \in \mathbb{Z}$.

> **Q11 Hint:** Remember that a, b, c $\in \mathbb{Z}$ means that a, b and c are integers.

Q12 Find the equation of the normal to the curve $y = \sqrt[3]{3x - 7}$ when $x = 5$.

Q13 Find the equation of the tangent to the curve $y = (x^4 + x^3 + x^2)^2$ when $x = -1$.

Finding $\frac{dy}{dx}$ when $x = f(y)$

The principle of the chain rule can also be used where x is given in terms of y (i.e. $x = f(y)$). This comes from a little mathematical rearranging, and you'll find it's often quite useful:

Tip: As with the chain rule, treat the derivatives as fractions to make this result easier to follow (they're not actually fractions though).

$$\frac{dy}{dx} \times \frac{dx}{dy} = \frac{dy}{dy} = 1, \text{ so rearranging gives } \frac{dy}{dx} = \frac{1}{\left(\frac{dx}{dy}\right)}.$$

So to differentiate $x = f(y)$, use:

$$\frac{dy}{dx} = \frac{1}{\left(\frac{dx}{dy}\right)}$$

Example

A curve has the equation $x = y^3 + 2y - 7$. Find $\frac{dy}{dx}$ at the point $(-4, 1)$.

- Forget that the x's and y's are in the 'wrong' place and differentiate as usual:

$$x = y^3 + 2y - 7 \Rightarrow \frac{dx}{dy} = 3y^2 + 2.$$

- Use $\frac{dy}{dx} = \frac{1}{\left(\frac{dx}{dy}\right)}$ to find $\frac{dy}{dx}$: $\qquad \frac{dy}{dx} = \frac{1}{3y^2 + 2}$

- $y = 1$ at the point $(-4, 1)$, so put this in the equation:

$$\frac{dy}{dx} = \frac{1}{3(1)^2 + 2} = \frac{1}{5} = 0.2, \text{ so } \frac{dy}{dx} = 0.2 \text{ at the point } (-4, 1).$$

Exercise 1.2

Q1 Find $\frac{dy}{dx}$ for each of the following functions at the given point. In each case, express $\frac{dy}{dx}$ in terms of y.

a) $x = 3y^2 + 5y + 7$ at $(5, -1)$ b) $x = y^3 - 2y$ at $(-4, -2)$

c) $x = (2y + 1)(y - 2)$ at $(3, -1)$ d) $x = \frac{4 + y^2}{y}$ at $(5, 4)$

Q2 Find $\frac{dy}{dx}$ if $x = (2y^3 - 5)^3$.

Q3 Find $\frac{dy}{dx}$ if $x = \sqrt{4 + y}$ by:

a) Finding $\frac{dx}{dy}$ first.

b) Rearranging into the form $y = f(x)$.

2. Differentiation of e^x and $\ln x$

Differentiating exponentials and logarithms is actually a lot easier than you might think because each one follows certain rules.

Differentiating e^x

In the last chapter (see p.88) you saw that 'e' was just a number for which the **gradient of e^x was e^x**, which makes it pretty simple to **differentiate**:

$$y = e^x$$
$$\frac{dy}{dx} = e^x$$

You can use the chain rule to show another useful relation involving exponentials. If you replace x with $f(x)$, you have a **function of a function**:

$$y = e^{f(x)}, \quad \text{so let } y = e^u \text{ where } u = f(x)$$

So $\dfrac{dy}{du} = e^u = e^{f(x)}$ (see above) and $\dfrac{du}{dx} = f'(x)$

Putting it into the chain rule formula you get:

$$\frac{dy}{dx} = \frac{dy}{du} \times \frac{du}{dx} = e^{f(x)} \times f'(x) = f'(x)e^{f(x)}$$

- This works because $e^{f(x)}$ is a special case — the 'e' part stays the same when you differentiate, so you only have to worry about the $f(x)$ part. You can just learn the formula:

$$y = e^{f(x)}$$
$$\frac{dy}{dx} = f'(x)e^{f(x)}$$

- You can use this formula to differentiate difficult exponentials.

Example 1

Find $\dfrac{dy}{dx}$ **if** $y = e^{(3x-2)}$

- Using the formula above, you can see that y is in the form $e^{f(x)}$ where $f(x) = 3x - 2$.

- Differentiating $f(x)$ is very easy: $f'(x) = 3$

- Now just put the right parts back into the formula for $\dfrac{dy}{dx}$.

$$y = e^{(3x-2)} \quad \Rightarrow \quad \frac{dy}{dx} = f'(x)e^{f(x)} = 3e^{(3x-2)}$$

Learning Objectives:

- Be able to differentiate e^x and $\ln x$.

- Be able to use the rules of differentiation for e^x and $\ln x$ to differentiate more complex functions using the chain rule.

- Be able to use these methods to answer questions on tangents, normals and turning points.

Example 2

If $f(x) = e^{x^2} + 2e^x$, find $f'(x)$ for $x = 0$.

- The function is in 2 parts, so let's break it down into its two bits and differentiate them separately:

- The second bit's easy: If $f(x) = 2e^x$ then $f'(x) = 2e^x$ too.

- For the first bit, you could just use the formula you used on the previous examples, but let's use the chain rule here just to show how it works.

$$y = e^{x^2}, \text{ so let } y = e^u \text{ where } u = x^2$$

- Both u and y are now easy to differentiate:

$$\frac{dy}{du} = e^u \text{ and } \frac{du}{dx} = 2x$$

$$\frac{dy}{dx} = \frac{dy}{du} \times \frac{du}{dx} = e^u \times 2x = 2xe^{x^2}$$

- Now put the bits back together:

$$f'(x) = 2xe^{x^2} + 2e^x$$

- And finally, work out the value of $f'(x)$ at $x = 0$

$$f'(0) = (2 \times 0 \times e^{0^2}) + 2e^0$$

$$f'(0) = 0 + 2$$

$$f'(0) = 2$$

Tip: Remember that $e^0 = 1$.

Example 3

Differentiate $y = e^{2x} - 6x$. Find the exact coordinates of the turning point of the curve $y = e^{2x} - 6x$ and determine the nature of this point.

- To find the coordinates of turning points, you need to find where $\frac{dy}{dx}$ is equal to zero.

- Like in example 2, split the function up into two parts and differentiate the parts separately.

- The second bit's easy: $y = -6x \Rightarrow \frac{dy}{dx} = -6$

- For the first bit, use the formula given at the start of this section.

$$y = e^{2x} = e^{f(x)}$$

$$f(x) = 2x \text{ so } f'(x) = 2$$

$$\frac{dy}{dx} = f'(x)e^{f(x)} = 2e^{2x}$$

- Now just put the two parts back together:

$$\frac{dy}{dx} = 2e^{2x} - 6$$

- Now to find any turning points, set $\frac{dy}{dx} = 0$ and rearrange to find x and y.

$$0 = 2e^{2x} - 6 \quad \Rightarrow \quad e^{2x} = 3 \quad \Rightarrow \quad 2x = \ln 3 \quad \Rightarrow \quad x = 0.5\ln 3$$

$$y = e^{2x} - 6x \quad \Rightarrow \quad y = e^{\ln 3} - 3\ln 3 \quad \Rightarrow \quad y = 3 - 3\ln 3$$

So the turning point is at $(0.5\ln 3, 3 - 3\ln 3)$

Tip: Remember that $e^{\ln x} = x$.

- To determine the nature of the turning point, differentiate again and put the coordinates of the turning point in $\frac{d^2y}{dx^2}$.

$$\frac{dy}{dx} = 2e^{2x} - 6 = 2e^{f(x)} - 6$$

$$\frac{d^2y}{dx^2} = 2f'(x)e^{f(x)} = 2(2 \times e^{2x}) = 4e^{2x}$$

So when $x = 0.5\ln 3$, $\frac{d^2y}{dx^2} = 4e^{\ln 3} = 12$

Tip: Remember that d^2y/dx^2 is positive for minimums and negative for maximums.

- $\frac{d^2y}{dx^2}$ is positive so the turning point is a minimum.

Exercise 2.1

Q1   Differentiate with respect to x:

a) $y = e^{3x}$ b) $y = e^{2x-5}$ c) $y = e^{x+7}$

d) $y = e^{3x+9}$ e) $y = e^{7-2x}$ f) $y = e^{x^3}$

Q2   Find $f'(x)$ if $f(x) = e^{x^3 + 3x}$

Q3   Find $f'(x)$ if $f(x) = e^{x^3 - 3x - 5}$

Q4   Find $f'(x)$ if $f(x) = e^{x(2x+1)}$

Q5   Find $f'(x)$ if $f(x) = \frac{1}{2}(e^x - e^{-x})$

Q7   Find f'(x) if $f(x) = e^{x^4 + 3x^2} + 2e^{2x}$

Q8   Find the equation of the tangent to the curve $y = e^{2x}$ at the point (0, 1).

Q9   Find the equation of the tangent to the curve $y = e^{3(x-2)}$ at the point (2, 1).

Q10   Find the equation of the tangent to the curve $y = e^{2x^2}$ when $x = 1$. Leave the numbers in your answer in exact form.

Q11   Find the equation of the normal to the curve $y = e^{2x-4}$ at the point (2, 1).

Q12   Find the equation of the normal to the curve $y = e^{3x} + 3$ where it cuts the y-axis.

Q13   Find the equation of the normal to the curve $y = e^{3(x-1)}$ when $x = 2$. Leave the numbers in your answer in exact form.

Q14   Show that the curve $y = e^{x^3 - 3x - 5}$ has turning points at $x = \pm 1$.

Q15   Find the x-coordinate of the turning point for the curve $y = e^{3x} - 6x$ and determine the nature of this point. Leave the numbers in your answer in exact form.

Differentiating ln x

The natural logarithm of a function is the logarithm with base e, written as ln x. Differentiating natural logarithms also uses the chain rule:

- If $y = \ln x$, then $x = e^y$ (see page 89).

- Differentiating gives $\frac{dx}{dy} = e^y$, and $\frac{dy}{dx} = \frac{1}{\left(\frac{dx}{dy}\right)} = \frac{1}{e^y} = \frac{1}{x}$ (since $x = e^y$).

- This gives the result:

$$y = \ln x$$
$$\frac{dy}{dx} = \frac{1}{x}$$

Examples

Find $\dfrac{dy}{dx}$ if $y = \ln (2x + 3)$.

- It's a function of a function, so use the **chain rule**:

$$y = \ln (2x + 3), \text{ so let } y = \ln u \text{ where } u = 2x + 3$$

$$\Rightarrow \frac{dy}{du} = \frac{1}{u} \text{ (p.110)} = \frac{1}{2x + 3} \quad \text{and} \quad \frac{du}{dx} = 2$$

- Now put all the parts into the chain rule formula:

$$\frac{dy}{dx} = \frac{dy}{du} \times \frac{du}{dx} = \frac{1}{2x + 3} \times 2 = \boxed{\frac{2}{2x + 3}}$$

Find $\dfrac{dy}{dx}$ if $y = \ln (x^2 + 3)$.

- Use the **chain rule** again for this one: $y = \ln u$ and $u = x^2 + 3$.

$$\frac{dy}{du} = \frac{1}{u} = \frac{1}{x^2 + 3} \quad \text{and} \quad \frac{du}{dx} = 2x.$$

$$\Rightarrow \frac{dy}{dx} = \frac{dy}{du} \times \frac{du}{dx} - \frac{1}{x^2 + 3} \times 2x - \boxed{\frac{2x}{x^2 + 3}}$$

- Look at the final answer from those examples. It comes out to $\dfrac{f'(x)}{f(x)}$.

- This isn't a coincidence — it will always be the case for $y = \ln (f(x))$, so you can just learn the result:

$$\boxed{\begin{array}{c} y = \ln (f(x)) \\[2mm] \dfrac{dy}{dx} = \dfrac{f'(x)}{f(x)} \end{array}}$$

Example

Find $f'(x)$ if $f(x) = \ln (x^3 - 4x)$.

- $f(x)$ is in the form $\ln (g(x))$, so use the formula above:

$$f'(x) = \frac{g'(x)}{g(x)}$$

$$g(x) = x^3 - 4x \quad \Rightarrow \quad g'(x) = 3x^2 - 4$$

- Put this into the formula:

$$f(x) = \ln (x^3 - 4x) \quad \Rightarrow \quad f'(x) = \frac{g'(x)}{g(x)} = \frac{3x^2 - 4}{x^3 - 4x}$$

Tip: You can check this answer using the chain rule, like in the previous example.

Q1 Differentiate with respect to x:

    a) $y = \ln(3x)$ b) $y = 3\ln x$ c) $y = \ln(1 + x)$

    d) $y = \ln(5 + x)$ e) $y = \ln(1 + 5x)$ f) $y = 4\ln(4x - 2)$

Q2 Differentiate with respect to x:

    a) $y = \ln(1 + x^2)$ b) $y = \ln(4 - 2x^2)$ c) $y = \ln(2 + x)^2$

    d) $y = 3\ln x^3$ e) $y = 2\ln(3x^2 + 3x)$ f) $y = \ln(x^3 + x^2)$

> **Q2 Hint:** It might help to simplify the logs before differentiating them.

Q3 Find $f'(x)$ if $f(x) = \ln\dfrac{1}{x}$.

Q4 Find $f'(x)$ if $f(x) = \ln\sqrt{x}$.

Q5 Find $f'(x)$ if $f(x) = \ln\left(\sqrt{\dfrac{1 - x}{1 + x}}\right)$.

> **Q5-9 Hint:** You'll need to rewrite some of these questions as the sum or difference of two logarithms before differentiating them. Log rules were covered in Chapter 3 if you need a reminder.

Q6 Find $f'(x)$ if $f(x) = \ln\left((2x + 1)^2\sqrt{x - 4}\right)$.

Q7 Find $f'(x)$ if $f(x) = \ln(x - \sqrt{x - 4})$.

Q8 Find $f'(x)$ if $f(x) = \ln\left(\dfrac{(3x + 1)^2}{\sqrt{2x + 1}}\right)$.

Q9 Differentiate $y = \ln(x\sqrt{x + 4})$.

Q10 Find the equation of the tangent to the curve $y = \ln(3x)$ at the point $(\frac{1}{3}, 0)$.

Q11 Find the equation of the tangent to the curve $y = \ln(3x)^2$:

    a) when $x = -2$ b) when $x = 2$

> **Q11, 12 Hint:** Rewrite $\ln(f(x))^k$ as $k\ln(f(x))$ to make differentiation simpler.

Q12 Find the equation of the normal to the curve $y = \ln(x + 6)^2$:

    a) when $x = -3$ b) when $x = 0$

Q13 Find any turning points for the curve $y = \ln(x^3 - 3x^2 + 3x)$.

3. Differentiation of Trig Functions

Trig functions are also pretty easy to differentiate once you learn the rules for sin, cos and tan. In this section you'll see how to differentiate trig functions and then use the chain rule to differentiate the more tricky ones.

Learning Objectives:

- Be able to differentiate sin, cos and tan.
- Be able to use the rules for differentiating trig functions in more complicated functions that require the chain rule.

Differentiating sin, cos and tan

- For **trigonometric functions** where the angle is measured in **radians** the following rules apply:

If $y =$	$\dfrac{dy}{dx} =$
$\sin x$	$\cos x$
$\cos x$	$-\sin x$
$\tan x$	$\sec^2 x$

- These equations can be combined with the **chain rule** to differentiate **more complicated** functions.

Tip: Remember that $\sec x = 1/\cos x$ — there's more about this on page 49.

Examples

Differentiate the following with respect to x:

a) $y = \cos (2x)$.

- Rewrite the function in 'chain rule notation':

$$y = \cos (2x), \quad \text{so let} \quad y = \cos u \quad \text{where} \quad u = 2x$$

So $\dfrac{dy}{du} = -\sin u = -\sin (2x)$ and $\dfrac{du}{dx} = 2$

$$\dfrac{dy}{dx} = \dfrac{dy}{du} \times \dfrac{du}{dx} = \boxed{-2 \sin (2x)}$$

b) $y = 4 \sin (x^2 + 1)$.

- As before, work out which part needs to be u for the chain rule:

$$y = 4 \sin (x^2 + 1), \quad \text{so let} \quad y = 4 \sin u \quad \text{where} \quad u = x^2 + 1$$

So $\dfrac{dy}{du} = 4 \cos u = 4 \cos (x^2 + 1)$ and $\dfrac{du}{dx} = 2x$

$$\dfrac{dy}{dx} = \dfrac{dy}{du} \times \dfrac{du}{dx} = 4 \cos (x^2 + 1) \times 2x = \boxed{8x \cos (x^2 + 1)}$$

c) **Find** $\dfrac{dy}{dx}$ **when** $x = \tan (3y)$.

- First find $\dfrac{dx}{dy}$ with, you guessed it, the chain rule:

$$x = \tan u, \, u = 3y \quad \Rightarrow \quad \dfrac{dx}{du} = \sec^2 u = \sec^2 (3y) \text{ and } \dfrac{du}{dy} = 3$$

$$\dfrac{dx}{dy} = \dfrac{dx}{du} \times \dfrac{du}{dy} = 3 \sec^2 (3y)$$

Tip: Have a look back at page 106 for more on $1 / \mathrm{d}x/\mathrm{d}y$.

- Then use $\dfrac{\mathrm{d}y}{\mathrm{d}x} = \dfrac{1}{\left(\dfrac{\mathrm{d}x}{\mathrm{d}y}\right)}$ to get the final answer:

$$\frac{\mathrm{d}y}{\mathrm{d}x} = \frac{1}{3\sec^2(3y)} = \frac{1}{3}\cos^2(3y)$$

Once you get the hang of it, you don't need to use the chain rule every time. If it's a **simple function** inside, e.g. sin (kx), it just differentiates to $k\cos(kx)$. If it's more **complicated** though, like sin (x^3), it's worth using the **chain rule**.

When differentiating trig functions it's important to know **which part of the function** to turn into u.

- It's **not** always the part **inside the brackets.**

Tip: Remember $\cos^2 x$ is another way of writing $(\cos x)^2$.

- When you have a trig function multiplied by itself, like $\cos^2 x$, it's often easiest to turn the **trig function itself** into u.

Example

Find $\dfrac{\mathrm{d}y}{\mathrm{d}x}$ if $y = \sin^3 x$

- Start off by rewriting the function as $y = (\sin x)^3$

- Now you have a function of a function and can carry out the chain rule in exactly the same way as before:

$$y = (\sin x)^3, \quad \text{so let} \quad y = u^3 \text{ where } u = \sin x$$

Tip: Don't get $(\sin x)^3$ confused with $\sin x^3$ — for this, you'd take $u = x^3$, so end up with $3x^2\cos x^3$ when you differentiate.

- Differentiate y and u:

$$y = u^3 \Rightarrow \frac{\mathrm{d}y}{\mathrm{d}u} = 3u^2 = 3\sin^2 x \quad \text{and} \quad \frac{\mathrm{d}u}{\mathrm{d}x} = \cos x$$

- Then put it all into the chain rule formula:

$$\frac{\mathrm{d}y}{\mathrm{d}x} = \frac{\mathrm{d}y}{\mathrm{d}u} \times \frac{\mathrm{d}u}{\mathrm{d}x} = 3\sin^2 x \cos x$$

When you're differentiating trig functions, you'll sometimes be asked to **rearrange** your answer to show it's equal to a **different** trig function. It's worth making sure you're familiar with **trig identities** (see pages 58–83) so you can spot which ones to use and when to use them.

Example

For $y = 2\cos^2 x + \sin(2x)$, show that $\dfrac{\mathrm{d}y}{\mathrm{d}x} = 2(\cos(2x) - \sin(2x))$

- First rewrite the equation to make the chain rule easier to use:
$$y = 2\cos^2 x + \sin(2x) \Rightarrow y = 2(\cos x)^2 + \sin(2x)$$

- Then differentiate the parts separately. For the first bit:

$$y = 2u^2 \text{ where } u = \cos x \quad \Rightarrow \quad \frac{\mathrm{d}y}{\mathrm{d}u} = 4u, \frac{\mathrm{d}u}{\mathrm{d}x} = -\sin x$$

- For the second bit:

$$y = \sin u \text{ where } u = 2x \quad \Rightarrow \quad \frac{dy}{du} = \cos u, \frac{du}{dx} = 2$$

- Putting it all back into the chain rule formula:

$$\frac{dy}{dx} = [(4 \cos x) \times (-\sin x)] + [(\cos (2x)) \times 2]$$

$$= 2 \cos (2x) - 4 \sin x \cos x$$

- From the target answer in the question it looks like you need a sin (2x) from somewhere, so use the double angle formula for sin (page 68):

$$\sin (2x) \equiv 2 \sin x \cos x \Rightarrow 4 \sin x \cos x \equiv 2 \sin (2x)$$

$$\Rightarrow \frac{dy}{dx} = 2 \cos (2x) - 2 \sin (2x)$$

$$= 2(\cos (2x) - \sin (2x)) \text{ as required.}$$

Exercise 3.1

Q1 Differentiate with respect to x:

a) $y = \sin (3x)$

b) $y = \cos (-2x)$

c) $y = \cos \frac{x}{2}$

d) $y = \sin \left(x + \frac{\pi}{4}\right)$

e) $y = 6 \tan \frac{x}{2}$

f) $y = 3 \tan (5x)$

Q2 Find $f'(x)$ if $f(x) = 3 \tan (2x - 1)$.

Q3 Find $f'(x)$ if $f(x) = 3 \tan x + \tan (3x)$.

Q4 Find $f'(x)$ if $f(x) = \sin (x^2 + \frac{\pi}{3})$.

Q5 Find $f'(x)$ if $f(x) = \sin^2 x$.

Q6 Find $f'(x)$ if $f(x) = 2 \sin^3 x$.

Q7 a) Find $f'(x)$ if $f(x) = 3 \sin x + 2 \cos x$.

b) Find the value of x for which $f'(x) = 0$ and $0 \le x \le \frac{\pi}{2}$.

Q8 Find $\frac{dy}{dx}$ if $y = \frac{1}{\cos x}$.

Q9 Differentiate $y = \cos^2 x$ by:

a) Using the chain rule directly.

b) Expressing y in terms of $\cos (2x)$ and differentiating the result.

Q10 For $y = 6 \cos^2 x - 2 \sin (2x)$ show that $\frac{dy}{dx} = -6 \sin (2x) - 4 \cos (2x)$.

Q11 Find the gradient of the curve $y = \sin x$ when $x = \frac{\pi}{4}$.

Q12 Find the equation of the normal to the curve $y = \cos (2x)$ when $x = \frac{\pi}{4}$.

Q13 For the curve $x = \sin(2y)$:

    a) Find the equation of the tangent at the point $\left(\frac{\sqrt{3}}{2}, \frac{\pi}{6}\right)$.

    b) Find the equation of the normal at the point $\left(\frac{\sqrt{3}}{2}, \frac{\pi}{6}\right)$.

Q14 a) If $y = 2\sin(2x)\cos x$, express y as a difference of two expressions involving $\sin x$ and $\sin^3 x$.

    b) Hence find $\frac{dy}{dx}$.

Differentiating by using the chain rule twice

Sometimes you'll have to use the chain rule **twice** when you have a function of a function of a function, like $\sin^3(x^2)$.

Example

Find $\frac{dy}{dx}$ if $y = \sin^2(2x + 1)$

- Start by setting up the first stage of differentiation with the **chain rule**, remembering to rewrite the $\sin^2$ part to make differentiating easier:

$$y = \sin^2(2x + 1) = [\sin(2x+1)]^2 \Rightarrow y = u^2, u = \sin(2x+1)$$

- Finding $\frac{dy}{du}$ is easy, so start with that:

$$\frac{dy}{du} = 2u = 2\sin(2x+1)$$

- To find $\frac{du}{dx}$ you're going to need the **chain rule again**, so just set it up with u in terms of v instead of y in terms of u.

$$u = \sin(2x+1) \quad \text{so let} \quad u = \sin v \quad \text{where} \quad v = 2x + 1$$

Tip: Calling it v just means you don't end up with a load of u's floating around.

- Then go through the usual stages:

$$u = \sin v \Rightarrow \frac{du}{dv} = \cos v = \cos(2x+1)$$

$$v = 2x + 1 \Rightarrow \frac{dv}{dx} = 2$$

$$\frac{du}{dx} = \frac{du}{dv} \times \frac{dv}{dx} = 2\cos(2x+1)$$

- Now you have the value of $\frac{du}{dx}$ needed to complete the question:

$$\frac{dy}{dx} = \frac{dy}{du} \times \frac{du}{dx} = [2\sin(2x+1)] \times [2\cos(2x+1)]$$

$$= 4\sin(2x+1)\cos(2x+1)$$

Exercise 3.2

Q1 Hint: Differentiating e was covered on page 107 and differentiating ln was covered on page 110.

Q1 Find $\frac{dy}{dx}$ if:

    a) $y = \sin(\cos(2x))$ b) $y = 2\ln(\cos(3x))$

    c) $y = \ln(\tan^2(x))$ d) $y = e^{\tan(2x)}$

    e) $y = \sin^4(x^2)$ f) $y = e^{\sin^2 x}$

    g) $y = \tan^2(3x) + \sin x$ h) $y = e^{2\cos(2x)} + \cos^2(2x)$

4. Product Rule

*The product rule is a way of differentiating two functions multiplied together.
It's fairly simple to use, but can get tricky when put together with other rules.*

Differentiating functions multiplied together

To differentiate two functions multiplied together, use the **product rule**:

$$\text{If } y = uv$$

$$\frac{dy}{dx} = u\frac{dv}{dx} + v\frac{du}{dx}$$

Where u and v
are functions of x,
i.e. $u(x)$ and $v(x)$.

Proving this rule is a lot trickier than anything covered in this section (and you
won't need to know how to do it in the exam), but it goes like this:

When you first met differentiation, it might have been shown
in terms of limits:

$$f'(x) = \lim_{h \to 0} \frac{f(x+h) - f(x)}{h}$$

So when you have a product to differentiate, this can be written as:

$$(fg)'(x) = \lim_{h \to 0} \frac{fg(x+h) - fg(x)}{h} = \lim_{h \to 0} \frac{f(x+h)g(x+h) - f(x)g(x)}{h}$$

The numerator of this fraction can
be seen as the area of a **rectangle
f(x + h) by g(x + h)** minus the area
of a **rectangle f(x) by g(x)**.
It can therefore be rewritten as a
sum of the areas of the "extra bits"
on the diagram:

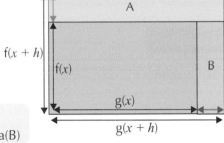

$$f(x+h)g(x+h) - f(x)g(x)$$
$$= \text{Area(A)} + \text{Area(B)}$$

$$\text{Area(A)} = g(x+h)[f(x+h) - f(x)] \qquad \text{Area(B)} = f(x)[g(x+h) - g(x)]$$

$$(fg)'(x) = \lim_{h \to 0} \left(\frac{g(x+h)[f(x+h) - f(x)] + f(x)[g(x+h) - g(x)]}{h} \right)$$

$$= \lim_{h \to 0} \left(\frac{g(x+h)[f(x+h) - f(x)]}{h} \right) + \lim_{h \to 0} \left(\frac{f(x)[g(x+h) - g(x)]}{h} \right)$$

As $h \to 0$, $x + h \to x$
so this bit is just $g(x)$.

This bit has no h's in it, so
the limit as $h \to 0$ is just $f(x)$.

$$= \lim_{h \to 0} (g(x+h)) \lim_{h \to 0} \left(\frac{f(x+h) - f(x)}{h} \right) + \lim_{h \to 0} (f(x)) \lim_{h \to 0} \left(\frac{g(x+h) - g(x)}{h} \right)$$

$$= g(x)f'(x) + f(x)g'(x)$$

These are the definitions
of $f'(x)$ and $g'(x)$.

Tip: The 'lim' notation
means you take the
value that the function
approaches as h gets
closer and closer to 0
— you might have seen
it before in C1.

Tip: The length of
the green arrow is
$f(x + h) - f(x)$ and the
length of the orange
arrow is $g(x + h) - g(x)$.

Tip: $g(x)f'(x) + f(x)g'(x)$
is just another way of
writing $u\frac{dv}{dx} + v\frac{du}{dx}$.

Example 1

Differentiate $x^3 \tan x$ with respect to x.

- The crucial thing is to write down everything in **steps**. Start by identifying 'u' and 'v':

$$u = x^3 \text{ and } v = \tan x.$$

- Now differentiate these two **separately**, with respect to x:

$$\frac{du}{dx} = 3x^2 \text{ and } \frac{dv}{dx} = \sec^2 x.$$

- Very **carefully** put all the bits into the formula:

$$\frac{dy}{dx} = u\frac{dv}{dx} + v\frac{du}{dx} = (x^3 \times \sec^2 x) + (\tan x \times 3x^2)$$

- Finally, **rearrange** to make it look nicer:

$$\frac{dy}{dx} = x^3 \sec^2 x + 3x^2 \tan x$$

Tip: See page 113 for how to differentiate $\tan x$.

You might have to differentiate functions using a mixture of the **product rule** and the **chain rule** (as well as the rules for e, ln and trig functions). In a question you might be told which rules to use, but it's not guaranteed, so make sure you get used to spotting when the different rules are needed.

Example 2

Differentiate $e^{2x}\sqrt{2x - 3}$ with respect to x.

- It's a **product** of two functions, so start by identifying 'u' and 'v':

$$u = e^{2x} \text{ and } v = \sqrt{2x - 3}.$$

- Each of these needs the **chain rule** to differentiate:

$$\frac{du}{dx} = 2e^{2x} \text{ and } \frac{dv}{dx} = \frac{1}{\sqrt{2x - 3}}$$

- Put it all into the **product rule** formula:

$$\frac{dy}{dx} = u\frac{dv}{dx} + v\frac{du}{dx} = (e^{2x} \times \frac{1}{\sqrt{2x - 3}}) + (\sqrt{2x - 3} \times 2e^{2x})$$

- As before, **rearrange** it and then **simplify**:

$$\frac{dy}{dx} = e^{2x}\left(\frac{1}{\sqrt{2x - 3}} + 2(\sqrt{2x - 3})\right) = e^{2x}\left(\frac{1 + 2(2x - 3)}{\sqrt{2x - 3}}\right)$$

$$= \frac{e^{2x}(4x - 5)}{\sqrt{2x - 3}}$$

Tip: The chain rule bit has been done all in one go here to save time, but if you need to, do it in steps just to make sure nothing goes wrong.

You'll also see questions that ask you to rearrange the final answer to 'show that' it's equal to something, or to solve an equation by differentiating.

Example 3

Show that the derivative of $x^2(2x - 1)^3$ is $2x(2x - 1)^2(5x - 1)$.

- As usual, **identify** u and v then differentiate them **separately**:

$$u = x^2 \text{ and } v = (2x - 1)^3$$

$$\Rightarrow \frac{du}{dx} = 2x \text{ and } \frac{dv}{dx} = 2 \times 3(2x - 1)^2 \text{ (using the chain rule for } \frac{dv}{dx})$$

- Then put it all into the **product rule formula**:

$$\frac{dy}{dx} = u\frac{dv}{dx} + v\frac{du}{dx} = [x^2 \times 6(2x - 1)^2] + [(2x - 1)^3 \times 2x] = 6x^2(2x - 1)^2 + 2x(2x - 1)^3$$

- This isn't exactly how the question wants the answer, so it needs a little more **rearranging**:

$$6x^2(2x - 1)^2 + 2x(2x - 1)^3 = 2x(2x - 1)^2(3x + (2x - 1))$$

$$= 2x(2x - 1)^2(5x - 1)$$

Tip: In a 'show that' question it's good to look at the final answer so that you know you're on the right track. Here you can see you need to take out $2x(2x - 1)^2$ at some point, so it's worth starting with that.

Example 4

Solve the equation $\frac{d}{dx}[(x^3 + 3x^2)\ln x] = 2x^2 + 5x$, leaving your answer as an exact value of x.

- The $\frac{d}{dx}$ just tells you to differentiate the bit in brackets first. Since $(x^3 + 3x^2)\ln x$ is a **product** of two functions, use the **product rule**:

$$u = x^3 + 3x^2 \Rightarrow \frac{du}{dx} = 3x^2 + 6x \quad \text{and} \quad v = \ln x \Rightarrow \frac{dv}{dx} = \frac{1}{x} \text{ (see p.110)}$$

$$\text{So } \frac{d}{dx}((x^3 + 3x^2)\ln x) = [(x^3 + 3x^2) \times \frac{1}{x}] + [\ln x \times (3x^2 + 6x)]$$

$$= x^2 + 3x + (3x^2 + 6x)\ln x.$$

- Now put this into the equation from the question in place of $\frac{d}{dx}((x^3 + 3x^2)\ln x)$:

$$x^2 + 3x + (3x^2 + 6x)\ln x = 2x^2 + 5x$$

- Finally, rearrange and **solve** as follows:

$$(3x^2 + 6x)\ln x = 2x^2 + 5x - x^2 - 3x \Rightarrow (3x^2 + 6x)\ln x = x^2 + 2x$$

$$\Rightarrow \ln x = \frac{x^2 + 2x}{3(x^2 + 2x)} = \frac{1}{3}$$

$$\Rightarrow x = e^{\frac{1}{3}}$$

Tip: The question asks for an exact value of x, so leave it in terms of e rather than a rounded decimal from your calculator.

Q1 Differentiate $y = x(x + 2)$ with respect to x by:

a) Multiplying the brackets out and differentiating directly.

b) Using the product rule.

Q2 Differentiate with respect to x:

a) $y = x^2(x + 6)^3$　　　　b) $y = x^3(5x + 2)^4$　　　　c) $y = x^3e^x$

d) $y = xe^{4x}$　　　　　　　e) $y = xe^{x^2}$　　　　　　　f) $y = e^{2x}\sin x$

Q3 b) Hint: Remember that $\frac{1}{\sqrt{x}} = x^{-\frac{1}{2}}$.

Q3 Find $f'(x)$ if:

a) $f(x) = x^3(x + 3)^{\frac{1}{2}}$　　b) $f(x) = \dfrac{x^2}{\sqrt{x - 7}}$　　c) $f(x) = x^4\ln x.$

d) $f(x) = 4x \ln x^2.$　　　e) $f(x) = 2x^3 \cos x$　　f) $f(x) = x^2\cos(2x).$

Q4 For parts a) and b), multiply out the brackets in your answer and simplify.

a) Differentiate $y = (x + 1)^2(x^2 - 1)$.

b) Differentiate $y = (x + 1)^3(x - 1)$.

c) Your answers to part a) and part b) should be the same. Show by rearranging that the expressions for y in parts a) and b) are the same.

Q5 For the curve $y = xe^x$:

a) Find the equation of the tangent to the curve at the point $(0, 0)$.

b) Find the equation of the normal to the curve at the point $(0, 0)$.

Q6 Hint: Rewriting roots as powers can often help.

Q6 Find the equation of the tangent to the curve $y = (\sqrt{x + 2})(\sqrt{x + 7})$ at the point $(2, 6)$. Write your answer in the form $ax + by + c = 0$, where a, b and c are integers.

Q7 Hint: To use the product rule here you'll need to rewrite the function at the bottom as a negative power.

Q7 For the curve $y = \dfrac{\sqrt{x - 1}}{\sqrt{x + 4}}$

a) Find the equation of the tangent to the curve when $x = 5$ in the form $ax + by + c = 0$ where a, b and c are integers.

b) Find the equation of the normal to the curve when $x = 5$ in the form $ax + by + c = 0$ where a, b and c are integers.

Q8 Find any stationary points of the curve $y = (x - 2)^2(x + 4)^3$.

Q9 Hint: You'll need to use the chain rule before using the product rule.

Q9 Differentiate $y = e^{x^2\sqrt{x + 3}}$.

Q10 Find any turning points for the curve $y = xe^{x - x^2}$.

5. Quotient Rule

You've seen how to differentiate products with the product rule, and now you'll see how to differentiate quotients (divisions) with the quotient rule.

Differentiating a function divided by a function

In maths a **quotient** is one thing **divided** by another. As with the product rule, there's a rule that lets you differentiate quotients easily — the **quotient rule**:

Learning Objectives:

- Be able to use the quotient rule for differentiation and understand when it's needed.

- Be able to use the quotient rule alongside other methods for differentiating complex functions.

$$\text{If } y = \frac{u}{v}$$

$$\frac{dy}{dx} = \frac{v\dfrac{du}{dx} - u\dfrac{dv}{dx}}{v^2}$$

Where u and v are functions of x, i.e. $u(x)$ and $v(x)$.

There's also a proof for the quotient rule — again you won't need to know it for the exam, but you might find it helpful in understanding how it works.

Tip: The quotient rule is basically just the product rule on $y = uv^{-1}$ — try it on two simple functions and see for yourself. The quotient rule is quicker to use though, and it's provided on the formula sheet.

- As before, start with the definition of differentiation.

$$\frac{d}{dx}f(x) = \lim_{h \to 0}\frac{f(x+h) - f(x)}{h}$$

- And so for the quotient $\dfrac{f(x)}{g(x)}$, this becomes

$$\frac{d}{dx}\left(\frac{f(x)}{g(x)}\right) = \lim_{h \to 0}\frac{\dfrac{f(x+h)}{g(x+h)} - \dfrac{f(x)}{g(x)}}{h}$$

- To neaten this up, put the top of the fraction over a common denominator $(g(x+h)g(x))$ and multiply this common denominator by the h.

$$\frac{d}{dx}\left(\frac{f(x)}{g(x)}\right) = \lim_{h \to 0}\frac{f(x+h)g(x) - f(x)g(x+h)}{g(x+h)g(x)h}$$

- The next stage is to add and subtract $f(x)g(x)$ and then factorise.

$$\frac{d}{dx}\left(\frac{f(x)}{g(x)}\right) = \lim_{h \to 0}\frac{f(x+h)g(x) - f(x)g(x) + f(x)g(x) - f(x)g(x+h)}{g(x+h)g(x)h}$$

$$\frac{d}{dx}\left(\frac{f(x)}{g(x)}\right) = \lim_{h \to 0}\frac{g(x)[f(x+h) - f(x)] - f(x)[g(x+h) - g(x)]}{g(x+h)g(x)h}$$

Tip: Adding and subtracting the same thing is a classic trick in algebra. It's just like adding zero, and it can get you from algebraic mess to perfectly formed equations.

- You might start to recognise the top row here. Just to make it a little clearer, divide both the top and bottom by h, keeping $f(x)$ and $g(x)$ aside.

$$\frac{d}{dx}\left(\frac{f(x)}{g(x)}\right) = \lim_{h \to 0}\frac{g(x)\dfrac{f(x+h) - f(x)}{h} - f(x)\dfrac{g(x+h) - g(x)}{h}}{g(x+h)g(x)}$$

- The green bits on top are the definition of $f'(x)$ and $g'(x)$ from the start of this proof. As h tends to zero, the blue bit at the bottom becomes $g(x)g(x)$, or $(g(x))^2$:

$$\frac{d}{dx}\left(\frac{f(x)}{g(x)}\right) = \frac{g(x)f'(x) - f(x)g'(x)}{(g(x))^2}$$

Tip: The expression
$$\frac{g(x)f'(x) - f(x)g'(x)}{(g(x))^2}$$
is just another way of writing the quotient rule
$$\frac{v\dfrac{du}{dx} - u\dfrac{dv}{dx}}{v^2}.$$

Example 1

Find $\dfrac{dy}{dx}$ if $y = \dfrac{\sin x}{2x + 1}$.

- You can see that y is a **quotient** in the form of $\dfrac{u}{v}$.
  First identify u and v and differentiate them **separately**:

$$u = \sin x \;\Rightarrow\; \frac{du}{dx} = \cos x \quad \text{and} \quad v = 2x + 1 \;\Rightarrow\; \frac{dv}{dx} = 2$$

Tip: This is quite similar to the product rule from the last section — the first stage is to identify u and v and differentiate them separately.

- Then just put the correct bits into the quotient rule. It's important that you get things in the right order, so concentrate on what's going where:

$$\frac{dy}{dx} = \frac{v\dfrac{du}{dx} - u\dfrac{dv}{dx}}{v^2} = \frac{(2x + 1)(\cos x) - (\sin x)(2)}{(2x + 1)^2}$$

- Now just neaten it up:

$$\frac{dy}{dx} = \frac{(2x + 1)\cos x - 2\sin x}{(2x + 1)^2}$$

Example 2

Find the gradient of the tangent to the curve with equation $y = \dfrac{2x^2 - 1}{3x^2 + 1}$ at the point (1, 0.25).

- 'Find the gradient of the tangent' means you have to **differentiate**.

- First identify u and v for the **quotient** rule, and differentiate **separately**:

$$u = 2x^2 - 1 \;\Rightarrow\; \frac{du}{dx} = 4x \quad \text{and} \quad v = 3x^2 + 1 \;\Rightarrow\; \frac{dv}{dx} = 6x$$

Tip: Don't try and simplify straight away or you're more likely to get things mixed up.

- Then put everything into the quotient rule:

$$\frac{dy}{dx} = \frac{v\dfrac{du}{dx} - u\dfrac{dv}{dx}}{v^2} = \frac{(3x^2 + 1)(4x) - (2x^2 - 1)(6x)}{(3x^2 + 1)^2}$$

- To make the expression **easier** to work with, **simplify** it where possible:

$$\frac{dy}{dx} = \frac{2x[2(3x^2 + 1) - 3(2x^2 - 1)]}{(3x^2 + 1)^2} = \frac{2x[6x^2 + 2 - 6x^2 + 3]}{(3x^2 + 1)^2}$$

$$= \frac{10x}{(3x^2 + 1)^2}$$

Tip: If it's a normal rather than a tangent, do $-1 \div$ gradient.

- Finally, put in $x = 1$ to find the gradient at (1, 0.25):

$$\frac{dy}{dx} = \frac{10}{(3 + 1)^2} = \boxed{0.625}$$

Example 3

Determine the nature of the stationary point of the curve $y = \frac{\ln x}{x^2}$ ($x > 0$).

- First use the quotient rule to find $\frac{dy}{dx}$:

$$u = \ln x \;\Rightarrow\; \frac{du}{dx} = \frac{1}{x} \quad \text{and} \quad v = x^2 \;\Rightarrow\; \frac{dv}{dx} = 2x.$$

So $\dfrac{dy}{dx} = \dfrac{(x^2)(\frac{1}{x}) - (\ln x)(2x)}{x^4} = \dfrac{x - 2x\ln x}{x^4} = \dfrac{1 - 2\ln x}{x^3}.$

- The stationary points occur where $\frac{dy}{dx} = 0$ (i.e. zero gradient), so this is when:

$$\frac{1 - 2\ln x}{x^3} = 0 \;\Rightarrow\; \ln x = \frac{1}{2} \;\Rightarrow\; x = e^{\frac{1}{2}}.$$

- To find out whether it's a maximum or minimum, differentiate $\frac{1 - 2\ln x}{x^3}$ using the quotient rule to get $\frac{d^2y}{dx^2}$.

$$u = 1 - 2\ln x \;\Rightarrow\; \frac{du}{dx} = -\frac{2}{x} \quad \text{and} \quad v = x^3 \;\Rightarrow\; \frac{dv}{dx} = 3x^2.$$

So $\dfrac{d^2y}{dx^2} = \dfrac{(x^3)(-\frac{2}{x}) - (1 - 2\ln x)(3x^2)}{x^6} = \dfrac{6x^2\ln x - 5x^2}{x^6} = \dfrac{6\ln x - 5}{x^4}$

- Now put in the x-value of your stationary point:

$$\frac{d^2y}{dx^2} = \frac{6\ln e^{\frac{1}{2}} - 5}{(e^{\frac{1}{2}})^4} = \frac{3 - 5}{e^2} = -0.27\ldots$$

- $\frac{d^2y}{dx^2}$ is negative, so it's a maximum turning point.

Tip: To determine the nature of the stationary points you're going to have to differentiate twice.

Tip: Negative second derivative means maximum and positive means minimum — it's covered in C2 if you can't quite remember.

As you saw on page 113, the derivative of $\tan x$ is $\sec^2 x$.
Because $\tan x = \frac{\sin x}{\cos x}$, you can prove this using the quotient rule.

Example 4

Differentiate $y = \tan x$ with respect to x.

- First write it out as a quotient and set up u and v for the quotient rule:

$$y = \frac{\sin x}{\cos x} = \frac{u}{v}, \quad \text{so} \quad u = \sin x, \; \frac{du}{dx} = \cos x \quad \text{and} \quad v = \cos x, \; \frac{dv}{dx} = -\sin x$$

- Then just put all the right bits into the quotient rule:

$$\frac{dy}{dx} = \frac{v\frac{du}{dx} - u\frac{dv}{dx}}{v^2} = \frac{\cos x \cos x - \sin x(-\sin x)}{\cos^2 x} = \frac{\cos^2 x + \sin^2 x}{\cos^2 x}$$

$$= \frac{1}{\cos^2 x} = \sec^2 x$$

Tip: The identity $\cos^2 x + \sin^2 x \equiv 1$ was used here to simplify.

Q1 Differentiate with respect to x:

a) $y = \frac{(x + 5)}{(x - 3)}$

b) $y = \frac{(x - 7)^4}{(5 - x)^3}$

c) $y = \frac{e^x}{x^2}$

d) $y = \frac{3x}{(x - 1)^2}$

Q2 Find $f'(x)$ if $f(x) = \frac{x^3}{(x + 3)^3}$

Q3 Find $f'(x)$ if $f(x) = \frac{x^2}{\sqrt{x - 7}}$

Q4 Find $f'(x)$ if $f(x) = \frac{e^{2x}}{e^{2x} + e^{-2x}}$

Q5 Find $f'(x)$ if $f(x) = \frac{x}{\sin x}$

Q6 Find $f'(x)$ if $f(x) = \frac{\sin x}{x}$

Q7 Find $f'(x)$ if $f(x) = \frac{x^2}{\tan x}$,
giving your answer in terms of $\cot x$ and $\mathrm{cosec}\, x$.

Q8 a) Differentiate $y = \frac{x}{\cos (2x)}$

b) Show that $\frac{dy}{dx} = 0$ when $x = -\frac{1}{2}\cot (2x)$
(don't try to solve this equation).

Q9 For the curve $y = \frac{1}{1 + 4\cos x}$:

a) Find the equation of the tangent to the curve when $x = \frac{\pi}{2}$.

b) Find the equation of the normal to the curve when $x = \frac{\pi}{2}$.

Q10 For the curve $y = \frac{2x}{\cos x}$, find the exact value of $\frac{dy}{dx}$ when $x = \frac{\pi}{3}$.

Q11 Show that if $y = \frac{x - \sin x}{1 + \cos x}$ then $\frac{dy}{dx} = \frac{x\sin x}{(1 + \cos x)^2}$.

Q12 Find any turning points on the curve $y = \frac{\cos x}{4 - 3\cos x}$ in the range $0 \leq x \leq 2\pi$.

Q13 Differentiate $y = e^{\frac{1+x}{1-x}}$

6. More Differentiation

In this section you'll see how to differentiate reciprocals of trig functions —
sec x, cosec x and cot x. All of these can be derived from the quotient rule.

Learning Objectives:

- Be able to differentiate cosec, sec and cot.
- Be able to use these results to differentiate more complicated functions.

Differentiating cosec, sec and cot

Remember from page 49 the definitions of these trig functions:

$$\operatorname{cosec} x \equiv \frac{1}{\sin x} \qquad \sec x \equiv \frac{1}{\cos x} \qquad \cot x \equiv \frac{1}{\tan x} \equiv \frac{\cos x}{\sin x}$$

- Since **cosec**, **sec** and **cot** are just **reciprocals** of **sin**, **cos** and **tan**, the quotient rule can be used to differentiate them.

- These results are on the **formula sheet**, but it will help a lot if you can show where they come from.

If $y =$	$\dfrac{dy}{dx} =$
$\operatorname{cosec} x$	$-\operatorname{cosec} x \cot x$
$\sec x$	$\sec x \tan x$
$\cot x$	$-\operatorname{cosec}^2 x$

Tip: If you can't remember which trig functions give a negative result when you differentiate them, just remember it's all the ones that begin with c — cos, cosec and cot.

Examples

Use the quotient rule to differentiate $y = \dfrac{\cos x}{\sin x}$, and hence show that for $y = \cot x$, $\dfrac{dy}{dx} = -\operatorname{cosec}^2 x$.

- Start off by identifying $u = \cos x$ and $v = \sin x$.

- Differentiating separately gives:

$$\frac{du}{dx} = -\sin x \quad \text{and} \quad \frac{dv}{dx} = \cos x \text{ (see page 113)}$$

$$\frac{dy}{dx} = \frac{(\sin x \times -\sin x) - (\cos x \times \cos x)}{(\sin x)^2} = \frac{-\sin^2 x - \cos^2 x}{\sin^2 x}$$

- Simplify using a trig identity: $\sin^2 x + \cos^2 x \equiv 1$ seems fitting.

$$\frac{dy}{dx} = \frac{-(\sin^2 x + \cos^2 x)}{\sin^2 x} = \frac{-1}{\sin^2 x}.$$

Tip: 'Show that' questions on trig functions often involve using a common identity, so make sure you know them — see pages 58–83.

- Linking this back to the question, since $\tan x = \dfrac{\sin x}{\cos x}$, and $\cot x = \dfrac{1}{\tan x}$, then $y = \dfrac{\cos x}{\sin x} = \cot x$.

- And as $\operatorname{cosec} x \equiv \dfrac{1}{\sin x}$, then:

$$\frac{dy}{dx} = \frac{-1}{\sin^2 x} = -\operatorname{cosec}^2 x.$$

Show that $\frac{d}{dx}\text{cosec }x = -\text{cosec }x \cot x.$

- $\text{cosec }x \equiv \frac{1}{\sin x}$, so use the **quotient rule**:

$$u = 1 \implies \frac{du}{dx} = 0 \text{ and } v = \sin x \implies \frac{dv}{dx} = \cos x$$

$$\frac{dy}{dx} = \frac{v\frac{du}{dx} - u\frac{dv}{dx}}{v^2} = \frac{(\sin x \times 0) - (1 \times \cos x)}{\sin^2 x} = -\frac{\cos x}{\sin^2 x}$$

- Since $\cot x \equiv \frac{\cos x}{\sin x}$, and $\text{cosec }x \equiv \frac{1}{\sin x}$:

$$\frac{dy}{dx} = \frac{1}{\sin x} \times (-\frac{\cos x}{\sin x}) = -\text{cosec }x \cot x.$$

Show that $\frac{d}{dx}\sec x = \sec x \tan x.$

- Using the quotient rule for $\sec x \equiv \frac{1}{\cos x}$:

$$u = 1 \implies \frac{du}{dx} = 0 \text{ and } v = \cos x \implies \frac{dv}{dx} = -\sin x$$

$$\frac{dy}{dx} = \frac{v\frac{du}{dx} - u\frac{dv}{dx}}{v^2} = \frac{(\cos x \times 0) - (1 \times -\sin x)}{\cos^2 x} = \frac{\sin x}{\cos^2 x}$$

- Since $\tan x \equiv \frac{\sin x}{\cos x}$, and $\sec x \equiv \frac{1}{\cos x}$,

$$\frac{dy}{dx} = \frac{1}{\cos x} \times \frac{\sin x}{\cos x} = \sec x \tan x.$$

As with other rules covered in this chapter, the rules for sec x, cosec x and cot x can be used with the **chain**, **product** and **quotient rules** and in combination with all the other functions you've seen so far.

Examples

Find $\frac{dy}{dx}$ **if** $y = \cot \frac{x}{2}.$

- This is a function (cot) of a function ($\frac{x}{2}$), so you're going to need the chain rule.

- Although $\cot x \equiv \frac{\cos x}{\sin x}$, you don't need the quotient rule as you know that cot x differentiates to give $-\text{cosec}^2 x$.

- You can go straight to identifying u to use in the chain rule:

$$y = \cot u \implies \frac{dy}{du} = -\text{cosec}^2 u = -\text{cosec}^2 \frac{x}{2}$$

$$u = \frac{x}{2} \implies \frac{du}{dx} = \frac{1}{2}$$

$$\implies \frac{dy}{dx} = \frac{dy}{du} \times \frac{du}{dx} = -\frac{1}{2}\text{cosec}^2\frac{x}{2}$$

Find $\dfrac{dy}{dx}$ if $y = \sec (2x^2)$.

This is another **function of a function**, so more chain rule:

$$y = \sec u \quad \text{and} \quad u = 2x^2$$

$$\frac{dy}{du} = \sec u \tan u \text{ (from page 125)} = \sec (2x^2) \tan (2x^2)$$

$$\frac{du}{dx} = 4x$$

$$\text{So } \frac{dy}{dx} = \frac{dy}{du} \times \frac{du}{dx} = \boxed{4x \sec (2x^2) \tan (2x^2)}$$

Find $\dfrac{dy}{dx}$ if $y = e^x \cot x$.

This is a **product** of two functions, so think 'product rule':

$$u = e^x \quad \text{and} \quad v = \cot x$$

$$\Rightarrow \frac{du}{dx} = e^x \text{ and } \frac{dv}{dx} = -\text{cosec}^2 x \text{ (see page 125)}$$

$$\Rightarrow \frac{dy}{dx} = u\frac{dv}{dx} + v\frac{du}{dx} = (e^x \times -\text{cosec}^2 x) + (\cot x \times e^x)$$

$$= \boxed{e^x(\cot x - \text{cosec}^2 x).}$$

Tip: If it was a more difficult function than x inside the 'cot', you'd do this in exactly the same way but use the chain rule for working out $\dfrac{dv}{dx}$.

Exercise 6.1

Q1   Differentiate with respect to x:

   a) $y = \text{cosec} (2x)$ b) $y = \text{cosec}^2 x$ c) $y = \cot (7x)$

   d) $y = \cot^7 x$ e) $y = x^4 \cot x$ f) $y = (x + \sec x)^2$

   g) $y = \text{cosec} (x^2 + 5)$ h) $y = e^{3x} \sec x$ i) $y = (2x + \cot x)^3$

Q2   Find $f'(x)$ if $f(x) = \dfrac{\sec x}{x + 3}$.

Q3   Find $f'(x)$ if $f(x) = \sec \dfrac{1}{x}$.

Q4   Find $f'(x)$ if $f(x) = \sec \sqrt{x}$.

Q5   Find $f'(x)$ if $f(x) = (\sec x + \text{cosec} x)^2$.

Q6   Find $f'(x)$ if $f(x) = \dfrac{1}{x \cot x}$.

Q7 Find $f'(x)$ if $f(x) = e^x \operatorname{cosec} x$.

Q8 Find $f'(x)$ if $f(x) = e^{3x} \sec x$.

Q9 Find $f'(x)$ if $f(x) = e^{3x} \cot (4x)$.

Q10 Find $f'(x)$ if $f(x) = e^{-2x} \operatorname{cosec} (4x)$.

Q11 Find $f'(x)$ if $f(x) = \ln (x) \operatorname{cosec} x$.

Q12 Find $f'(x)$ if $f(x) = \sqrt{\sec x}$.

Q13 Find $f'(x)$ if $f(x) = e^{\sec x}$.

Q14 Hint: Remember the log laws from p92.

Q14 a) Find $f'(x)$ if $f(x) = \ln (\operatorname{cosec} x)$.

     b) Show that the function in part a) can be written as $-\ln (\sin x)$ and differentiate it — you should get the same answer as in part a).

Q15 Find $f'(x)$ if $f(x) = \ln (x + \sec x)$.

Q16 Differentiate $y = \sec (\sqrt{x^2 + 5})$.

Review Exercise — Chapter 4

Q1 State which (if any) of the chain, product and quotient rules could be used to differentiate the following functions (don't actually differentiate them):

a) $f(x) = e^{2x}$

b) $f(x) = \sin x \cos x$

c) $f(x) = \sin x \cos x^2$

d) $f(x) = \dfrac{\ln(8x)}{(x+1)^2}$

e) $f(x) = \dfrac{e^x}{x^2 \cos^2 x}$

f) $f(x) = \dfrac{\sin x^2}{\cos(2x)\ln x^3}$

Q1 Hint: Some of these functions could be differentiated using more than one rule — write down all the rules that could be used.

Q2 Differentiate with respect to x:

a) $y = \sqrt{x^3 + 2x^2}$

b) $y = \dfrac{1}{\sqrt{x^3 + 2x^2}}$

c) $y = e^{5x^2}$

d) $y = \ln(6 - x^2)$

Q3 Find $\dfrac{dy}{dx}$ as a function of x when:

a) $x = 2e^{2y}$

b) $x = \ln(2y + 3)$

Q3 b) Hint: Remember, if $x = \ln a$ then $a = e^x$.

Q4 Find $f'(x)$ for the following functions:

a) $f(x) = \sin^2(x + 2)$

b) $f(x) = 2\cos(3x)$

c) $f(x) = \sqrt{\tan x}$

Q5 Find the value of the gradient for:

a) $y = e^{2x}(x^2 - 3)$ when $x = 0$

b) $y = (\ln x)(\sin x)$ when $x = 1$

Q6 Find the equation of the tangent to the curve $y = \dfrac{6x^2 + 3}{4x^2 - 1}$ at the point $(1, 3)$.

Q7 Differentiate with respect to x:

a) $y = \sqrt{\operatorname{cosec} x}$

b) $y = \cot(x^2 + 5)$

c) $y = \dfrac{\sec x}{x^2}$

d) $y = e^{2x} \operatorname{cosec}(5x)$

Q8 Find $\dfrac{dy}{dx}$ when $x = 0$ for $y = \operatorname{cosec}(3x - 2)$.

Q9 Find the coordinates of the stationary point on the curve $y = \dfrac{e^x}{\sqrt{x}}$.

Q10 Find the equation of the normal to the curve for:

$y = 3\cos ec\,\frac{x}{4}$ when $x = \pi$ (x is in radians)

Q11 Find $f'(x)$ if $f(x) = e^{\cos\,(3x)}$.

Q12 Find $f'(x)$ if $f(x) = \dfrac{\cos x^2}{\ln(2x)}$.

Q13 Find $f'(x)$ if $f(x) = \sin(4x)\tan x^3$.

Q14 Find $\dfrac{dy}{dx}$ when $x = 1$ if $y = e^{x^2}\sqrt{x+1}$.

Q15 Differentiate the following with respect to x.

a) $\sqrt{(e^x + e^{2x})}$.

b) $3e^{2x+1} - \ln(1 - x^2) + 2x^3$.

Q16 A curve C has the equation $y = (x^2 - 1)^3$

a) Differentiate y with respect to x.

b) Hence find the equation of the normal to the curve C when $x = 2$ in the form $ax + by + c = 0$, where a, b, and c are integers.

Q17 Differentiate with respect to x:

a) $y = \cos x \ln x^2$

b) $y = \dfrac{e^{x^2 - x}}{(x + 2)^4}$

Q18 Find $\dfrac{dy}{dx}$ if $y = \dfrac{\sqrt{x^2 + 3}}{\cos 3x}$.

1   Find $\dfrac{dy}{dx}$ for each of the following functions. Simplify your answer where possible.

     a) $y = \ln(3x + 1)\sin(3x + 1)$.   *(4 marks)*

     b) $y = \sin^3(2x^2)$ *(3 marks)*

     c) $y = 2\operatorname{cosec}(3x)$ *(2 marks)*

2   Use the quotient rule to show that, for the function $f(x) = \sec x$:

$$f'(x) = \sec x \tan x.$$

                                                    (4 marks)

3   A sketch of the function $f(x) = 4\ln(3x)$ is shown in the diagram.

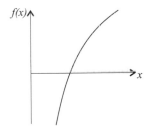

     a)   Find $f'(x)$ at the point where $x = 1$.   *(3 marks)*

     b)   Find the equation of the tangent to the curve at the point $x = 1$.   *(3 marks)*

4   A curve with equation $y = e^x \sin x$ has two turning points in the interval $\pi < x < \pi$

     a)   Find the value of x at each of these turning points.   *(6 marks)*

     b)   Determine the nature of each of the turning points.   *(5 marks)*

5   The curve shown below has the equation $x = \sqrt{y^2 + 3y}$.

a)   Find $\dfrac{dy}{dx}$ at the point (2, 1).

(5 marks)

b)   Hence find the equation of the tangent to the curve at (2, 1), in the form
$y = ax + b$, where a and b are constants.

(2 marks)

6   Differentiate the following with respect to x.

a) $\sqrt{(e^x + e^{2x})}$.

(3 marks)

b) $3e^{2x+1} - \ln(1 - x^2) + 2x^3$.

(3 marks)

7   Find the gradient of the tangent to the curve:

$$y = \sin^2 x - 2\cos(2x)$$

at the point where $x = \dfrac{\pi}{12}$ radians.

(4 marks)

8   Given that $y = \dfrac{e^x + x}{e^x - x}$, find $\dfrac{dy}{dx}$ when $x = 0$.

(3 marks)

9   Find the equation of the normal to the curve $x = \sin(4y)$ that passes through the point $\left(0, \dfrac{\pi}{4}\right)$.
Give your answer in the form $y = mx + c$, where m and c are constants to be found.

(6 marks)

1. Location of Roots

Sometimes finding the solutions of an equation algebraically is quite difficult. In these situations, it's often helpful to find roughly where the roots are (the points where f(x) = 0) by looking at the graph.

Learning Objectives:

- Be able to locate the roots of f(x) = 0 by finding changes in sign of f(x) between two values of *x*.
- Be able to choose upper and lower bounds to show that a root is accurate to a certain number of decimal places.
- Be able to sketch functions and use the sketches to find approximate locations of roots.

Locating roots by changes of sign

'Solving' or 'finding the roots of' an equation (where f(x) = 0) is the same as finding the values of *x* where the graph crosses the *x*-axis.

- The graph of the function gives you a rough idea of **how many** roots there are and **where** they are. E.g. the function $f(x) = 3x^2 - x^3 - 2$ (below) has 3 roots, since it crosses the *x*-axis three times (i.e. there are 3 solutions to the equation $3x^2 - x^3 - 2 = 0$). From the graph you can see there's a root at $x = 1$ and two others near $x = -1$ and $x = 3$.

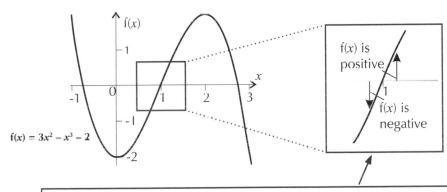

$f(x) = 3x^2 - x^3 - 2$

For each root in the graph above, f(x) goes from positive to negative or vice versa — **f(x) changes sign as it passes through a root.** So to find if there's a root between two values 'a' and 'b', work out f(a) and f(b). If the signs are different, there's a root somewhere between them.

- Be careful though — this only applies to **continuous functions** (where there is no break or jump in the line of the graph). In some graphs, like tan *x*, the line jumps from positive to negative without actually crossing the *x*-axis, so you might get fooled into thinking there's a root when there isn't.

Tip: The graph doesn't have to be continuous throughout — only in the bit where you're trying to find a root.

- Often you'll be given an **approximation** to a root and be asked to show that it's correct to a certain accuracy. To do this, choose the right **upper and lower bounds** and work out if there's a sign change between them.

The **lower bound** is the **lowest** value a number could have and still be **rounded up** to the correct answer. The **upper bound** is the **upper limit** of the values which will be **rounded down** to the correct answer.

Example

Show that one root of the equation $x^3 - x^2 - 9 = 0$ is $x = 2.472$ correct to 3 d.p.

Tip: Although 2.4725 would actually be rounded up to 2.473, everything below it would be rounded down to 2.472. It's just a limit.

- If $x = 2.472$ is a root rounded to 3 decimal places, the exact root must lie between the **upper and lower bounds** of this value — **2.4715** and **2.4725**. Any value in this interval would be rounded to 2.472 to 3 d.p.

$$2.471 \quad 2.4715 \quad 2.472 \quad 2.4725 \quad 2.473$$

- The function $f(x) = x^3 - x^2 - 9$ is **continuous**, so you know a root lies in the interval $2.4715 \leq x < 2.4725$ if $f(2.4715)$ and $f(2.4725)$ have **different signs**.

Tip: The function is continuous because it's just a cubic curve:

It has no breaks or jumps.

- $f(2.4715) = 2.4715^3 - 2.4715^2 - 9 = \boxed{-0.0116...}$

  $f(2.4725) = 2.4725^3 - 2.4725^2 - 9 = \boxed{0.0017...}$

- $f(2.4715)$ and $f(2.4725)$ have different signs, so a root must lie between them.
  Since any value between would be rounded to 2.472 to 3 d.p. this answer must be correct.

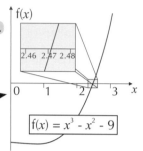

Exercise 1.1

Q1 $f(x) = x^3 - 5x + 1$

Show that there is a root of $f(x) = 0$ in the interval $2 < x < 3$.

Q2 $f(x) = \sin 2x - x$ (x is in radians).

Show that there is a root of $f(x) = 0$ in the interval $0.9 < x < 1.0$.

Q2 Hint: Remember to set your calculator to radians before doing this question.

Q3 $f(x) = x^3 + \ln x - 2$

Show that there is a root of $f(x) = 0$ in the interval $1.2 < x < 1.3$.

Q4 $f(x) = x^2 + \dfrac{1}{x} - 7$

Show that there is a root of $f(x)$ in the interval $2.5 < x < 2.6$.

Q5   Show that there is a root, α, of the equation $\cos x + x = 0$ which lies in the interval $-0.8 < \alpha < -0.7$ (α is in radians).

Q6   Show that there is a root, β, of the equation $e^x + x - 8 = 0$ which lies in the interval $1 < \beta < 2$.

Q7   Show that there are 2 solutions, α and β, to the equation $3x - x^4 + 3 = 0$, such that $1.6 < \alpha < 1.7$ and $-1 < \beta < 0$.

Q8   Show that there are 2 solutions, α and β, to the equation $e^{x-2} - \sqrt{x} = 0$, such that $0.01 < \alpha < 0.02$ and $2.4 < \beta < 2.5$.

Q9 Show that $x = 2.8$ is a solution to the equation $x^3 - 7x - 2 = 0$ to 1 d.p.

Q10 Show that $x = 0.7$ is a solution to the equation $2x - \frac{1}{x} = 0$ to 1 d.p.

Q11 $f(x) = e^x - x^3 - 5x$
Verify that a root of the equation $f(x) = 0$ is $x = 0.25$ correct to 2 d.p.

Q12 $f(x) = x^3 - 2x^2 - 3$
Verify that $x = 2.486$ is a root of the equation $f(x) = 0$ correct to 3 d.p.

Q13 Show that a solution to the equation $4x - 2x^3 = 15$ lies between -2.3 and -2.2.

Q13 Hint: Roots of $f(x)$ are given when $f(x) = 0$, so you might need to rearrange the equation before doing any calculations.

Q14 Show that a solution to the equation $\ln(x + 3) = 5x$ lies between 0.23 and 0.24.

Q15 Shows that a solution to the equation $e^{3x}\sin x = 5$ lies between $x = 0$ and $x = 1$ (x is in radians).

Sketching graphs to find approximate roots

Sometimes it's easier to find the number of roots and roughly where they are if you **sketch** the graphs first.

- In questions like this you'll often be given **2 equations** to **sketch** on the same set of axes. Sketching graphs was first covered in C1 if you need a reminder.

- At the points where they **cross** each other, the two equations are equal. So for $y = x + 3$ and $y = x^2$, at the points of intersection you know that $x + 3 = x^2$, which you can rearrange to get $x^2 - x - 3 = 0$.

Tip: Setting the equations equal to each other and then rearranging them to get $f(x) = 0$ gets you to where you were in the previous section.

> The **number of roots** of this 'combined' equation is the same as the number of **points of intersection** of the original two graphs. The sketch you made will also show roughly **where** the roots are (it's the same x-value for both), so locating them is a bit easier.

Examples

a) **On the same set of axes, sketch the graphs $y = \ln x$ and $y = (x - 3)^2$.**

- Just sketch the two graphs on a set of axes. You don't need to draw perfectly accurate graphs, but do try and make sure they're as neat as possible.
- The important things are that they're the correct shape and that they cross the axes in the right places.

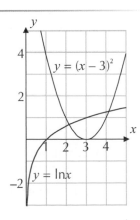

b) Hence work out the number of roots of the equation
$\ln x - (x - 3)^2 = 0$.

- This equation is a combination of the previous two, so what it's asking is 'how many times do the two graphs cross each other?'. The graphs cross twice, so the equation has two roots.

c) Show that there is a solution between 2 and 3, and find this solution 1 decimal place.

- You can see there's a solution there just by looking at the graph, but to make sure, work it out using the method from the previous topic — put 2 and 3 into the equation and check for a sign change.

$$\ln 2 - (2 - 3)^2 = -0.306...$$
$$\ln 3 - (3 - 3)^2 = 1.098...$$

Tip: This is basically the trial and improvement method that you'll have used at GCSE for approximating solutions.

- The sign has changed, so there is a root between 2 and 3.

- Looking at the picture, you can see that the root is very close to 2, so try again using $x = 2$ and $x = 2.2$.

$$\ln 2.2 - (2.2 - 3)^2 = 0.148...$$

- f(2.2) is positive, so the root is between 2 and 2.2. Now try again with $x = 2.1$, as it's halfway between the two and will tell you which it's closer to.

$$\ln 2.1 - (2.1 - 3)^2 = -0.068...$$ so the root is between 2.1 and 2.2.

- Now you just need to check if it rounds up to 2.2 or down to 2.1 — 2.15 is the upper bound for 2.1 and lower bound for 2.2, so try that.

$$\ln 2.15 - (2.15 - 3)^2 = 0.0429...$$ So the root is between 2.1 and 2.15.

- So the answer rounds down, and the value of the root to 1 d.p is 2.1.

Exercise 1.2

Sketch all graphs in this exercise for $-5 < x < 5$ unless otherwise stated.

Q1 Hint: Remember, roots are solutions of an equation in the form f(x) = 0, so you might need to do some rearranging.

Q1 a) On the same axes, sketch the graphs of $y = \frac{1}{x}$ and $y = x - 2$.

b) Using your graph from part a) write down the number of roots of the equation $\frac{1}{x} = x - 2$ in this interval.

c) Show that one root of the equation $\frac{1}{x} = x - 2$ lies in the interval $2.4 < x < 2.5$.

Q2 a) On the same axes, sketch the graphs of $y = 2x^3 - 7x$ and $y = x^2$.

b) Using your graph from part a) write down the number of roots of the equation $2x^3 - x^2 - 7x = 0$ in this interval.

c) Show that the equation $2x^3 - x^2 - 7x = 0$ has a root between $x = -2$ and $x = -1$.

Q3 a) On the same axes, sketch the graphs of $y = 2x^2 + 5$ and $y = x + 8$.

b) Write down the number of roots of the equation $2x^2 + 5 = x + 8$.

c) Show that the equation $2x^2 + 5 = x + 8$ has a root in the interval (1, 2).

Q3 Hint: 'In the interval (x, y)' means between x and y — it's just another way examiners write it to try and confuse you.

Q4 a) Sketch the graphs of $y = 2^x - 3$ and $y = \ln x$ on the same axes.

b) $f(x) = \ln x - 2^x + 3$. Using your graph write down the number of roots of the equation $f(x) = 0$.

c) Show that the equation $f(x) = 0$ has a root between 1.8 and 2.2 and find this root to 1 decimal place.

Q5 a) Sketch the graphs of $y = \sqrt{x+1}$ and $y = 2x$ on the same axes.

b) Write down the number of roots of the equation $\sqrt{x+1} = 2x$.

c) Show that the equation $\sqrt{x+1} = 2x$ has a root in the interval (0.6, 0.7).

d) By rearranging the equation $\sqrt{x+1} = 2x$, use the quadratic formula to find the root of the equation from part c) to 3 s.f.

Q6 a) On the same axes sketch the graphs of $y = \sqrt[3]{x}$ and $y = \cos x$, where x is in radians, for $-2\pi < x < 2\pi$.

b) $f(x) = \cos x - \sqrt[3]{x}$. Write down the number of roots of the equation $f(x) = 0$ in this interval.

c) Show that a root of the equation $f(x) = 0$ lies in the interval (0.5, 0.6).

d) Find the root from part c) to 2 significant figures.

Q7 a) Sketch the graphs of $y = e^{2x}$ and $y = 3 - x^2$ on the same axes.

b) Using your graph from part a), explain how you know that the equation $e^{2x} + x^2 = 3$ has two roots.

c) Show that the negative root of the equation $e^{2x} + x^2 = 3$ lies between $x = -2$ and $x = -1$, and find this root to 1 decimal place.

2. Iterative Methods

Learning Objectives

- Be able to use iteration formulas to find a solution of an equation to a given level of accuracy.
- Be able to find and rearrange iteration formulas and understand why some don't converge to a solution of an equation.

Another way of finding roots of an equation is with iteration formulas. They can seem fiddly to work with but are actually pretty simple to use.

Using iteration formulas

- Some equations are too difficult to solve algebraically, so you need to find **approximations** to the roots to a certain level of accuracy. In exam questions you'll usually be told the value of x that a root is close to, and then **iteration** does the rest.

- Iteration is a numerical method for **solving equations**, like **trial and improvement**. You put an approximate value of a root x into an iteration formula, and it gives you a **slightly more accurate** value. You then repeat as necessary until you have an answer that's to the **level of accuracy** that you want.

Example

Use the iteration formula $x_{n+1} = \sqrt[3]{x_n + 4}$ to solve $x^3 - 4 - x = 0$, to 2 d.p. Start with $x_0 = 2$.

- The notation x_n just means the approximation of x at the nth iteration. Putting x_0 in the formula for x_n gives you x_{n+1}, which is x_1 — the first iteration.

- $x_0 = 2$, so $x_1 = \sqrt[3]{x_0 + 4} = \sqrt[3]{2 + 4} = 1.8171...$

- This value now gets put back into the formula to find x_2:
  $x_1 = 1.8171...$, so $x_2 = \sqrt[3]{x_1 + 4} = \sqrt[3]{1.8171... + 4} = 1.7984...$

- Carry on until you get answers that are the same when rounded to 2 d.p:
  $x_2 = 1.7984...$, so $x_3 = \sqrt[3]{x_2 + 4} = \sqrt[3]{1.7984... + 4} = 1.7965...$

- x_2, x_3 and all further iterations are the same when rounded to 2 d.p., so the root is $x = 1.80$ to 2 d.p.

- Sometimes an iteration formula will just **not find a root**. In these cases, no matter how close to the root you have x_0, the iteration sequence **diverges** — the numbers get further and further apart.

- The iteration might also **stop working**, like if you have to take the square root of a negative number.

- However, you'll nearly always be given a formula that converges to a certain root, otherwise there's not much point in using it.

- If your formula diverges when it shouldn't, chances are you went wrong somewhere, so go back and double check every stage.

Tip: This doesn't mean you'll never see a diverging formula in an exam, but if you do it will usually be followed by a question like 'what do you notice about the iterations?' — usually a clue that it diverges, bounces up and down or does something else unexpected.

Example

The equation $x^3 - x^2 - 9 = 0$ has a root close to $x = 2.5$.
What is the result of using $x_{n+1} = \sqrt{x_n^3 - 9}$ with $x_0 = 2.5$ to find this root?

- Start with $x_1 = \sqrt{2.5^3 - 9} = 2.5739...$ (seems okay so far).

Tip: The list of results $x_1, x_2, x_3...$ is called the iteration sequence.

- Subsequent iterations give: $x_2 = 2.8376...$, $x_3 = 3.7214...$, $x_4 = 6.5221...$

- The results are getting further and further apart with each iteration.

- So the sequence diverges

Exercise 2.1

Q1 a) Show that the equation $x^3 + 3x^2 - 7 = 0$ has a root in the interval $(1, 2)$.

Q1-7 Hint: Leave the numbers from each iteration in your calculator so that you don't lose any accuracy with each step.

   b) Use the iterative formula $x_{n+1} = \sqrt{\dfrac{7 - x_n^3}{3}}$ with starting value $x_0 = 1$ to find values for x_1, x_2, x_3 and x_4 to 3 decimal places.

Q2 An intersection of the curves $y = \ln x$ and $y = x - 2$ is at the point $x = \alpha$, where α is 3.1 to 1 decimal place.

Q1-7 Hint: You can use the ANS button on your calculator to speed things up. Enter the starting value, and then type the iteration formula replacing x_n with 'ANS' — each time you press enter you'll get another iteration.

   a) Starting with $x_0 = 3.1$, use the iterative formula $x_{n+1} = 2 + \ln x_n$ to find the first 5 iterations, giving your answers to 4 decimal places.

   b) Write down an estimate of the value of α to 3 decimal places.

Q3 a) Show that the equation $x^4 - 5x + 3 = 0$ has a root between $x = 1.4$ and $x = 1.5$.

   b) Use the iterative formula $x_{n+1} = \sqrt[3]{5 - \dfrac{3}{x_n}}$ and $x_0 = 1.4$ to find iterations x_1 to x_6 to 3 decimal places.

   c) Hence write down an approximation of the root from part a) to 2 decimal places.

Q4 $f(x) = x^2 - 5x - 2$

    a) Show that a root of the equation $f(x) = 0$ lies between $x = 5$ and $x = 6$.

    b) The root in part a) can be estimated using the iterative formula $x_{n+1} = \frac{2}{x_n} + 5$. Using a starting value of $x_0 = 5$ find the values of x_1, x_2, x_3 and x_4, giving your answers to 4 significant figures.

Q5 Use the iterative formula $x_{n+1} = 2 - \ln x_n$ with $x_0 = 1.5$ to find the root of the equation $\ln x = 2 - x$ to 2 decimal places.

Q6 a) Show that the equation $e^x - 10x = 0$ has a root in the interval $(3, 4)$.

    b) Using the iterative formula $x_{n+1} = \ln(10x_n)$ with an appropriate starting value find values for x_1, x_2, x_3 and x_4 to 3 d.p.

    c) Verify that the value of the root from part a) is $x = 3.577$ to 3 d.p.

    d) Describe what happens when you use the alternative formula $x_{n+1} = \frac{e^{x_n}}{10}$ with $x_0 = 3$.

Q7 $f(x) = x^2 - 5x - 10$

The iterative formula $x_{n+1} = \frac{x_n^2 - 3x_n}{2} - 5$ can be used to find approximations to a root of the equation $f(x) = 0$.

    a) Find the values of x_1, x_2, x_3 and x_4, starting with $x_0 = -1$ and describe what is happening to the sequence $x_1, x_2, x_3, x_4...$

    b) Using the alternative iterative formula $x_{n+1} = \sqrt{5x_n + 10}$ with starting value $x_0 = 6$, find a root to the equation $f(x) = 0$ to 3 significant figures. Verify your answer is correct to this level of accuracy.

Finding iteration formulas

- The iteration formula is just a **rearrangement** of the equation, leaving a single 'x' on one side.

- There are often **lots of different ways** to rearrange the equation, so in the exam you'll usually be asked to '**show that**' it can be rearranged in a certain way, rather than starting from scratch.

- Sometimes a rearrangement of the equation leads to a **divergent iteration** when you come to working out the steps.

- This is the reason you won't be asked to both rearrange **and** use a formula to find a root without prompting.

Examples

Show that $x^3 - x^2 - 9 = 0$ can be rearranged into $x = \sqrt{\dfrac{9}{x-1}}$.
Use this to make an iteration formula and find the value of a root to 2 d.p. with starting value $x_0 = 2.5$.

- The '9' is on its own in the fraction so try:
$$x^3 - x^2 - 9 = 0 \Rightarrow x^3 - x^2 = 9$$

- The LHS can be factorised now: $x^2(x - 1) = 9$

- Get the x^2 on its own by dividing by $x - 1$: $x^2 = \dfrac{9}{x - 1}$

- Finally square root both sides: $x = \sqrt{\dfrac{9}{x - 1}}$

- You can now use the iteration formula $x_{n+1} = \sqrt{\dfrac{9}{x_n - 1}}$ to find approximations of the roots.

$$x_1 = \sqrt{\frac{9}{2.5 - 1}} = 2.449... \qquad x_2 = \sqrt{\frac{9}{2.449 - 1}} = 2.491...$$

and so on, until you find after 16 iterations that the value of the root, to 2 d.p., is:

$$x = 2.47.$$

Tip: Don't worry — you'll never have to carry out as many as 16 iterations in an exam.

Show that $x^3 - x^2 - 9 = 0$ can also be rearranged into $x = \sqrt{x^3 - 9}$ and use this to make an iteration formula

- Start by isolating the x^2 term: $x^2 = x^3 - 9$

- Now just square root both sides: $x = \sqrt{x^3 - 9}$

- Which makes the iteration formula: $x_{n+1} = \sqrt{x_n^3 - 9}$

- This is the iteration formula used in the example on page 139, so if you tried to use it to find a root you'd end up with a diverging sequence and it wouldn't find a root.

Tip: This shows why you'll never just be given an equation and told to find a root by first making an iteration formula.

Exercise 2.2

Q1 Show that the equation $x^2 - 5x + 1 = 0$ can be written in the form:

a) $x = \sqrt{5x - 1}$

b) $x = 5 - \dfrac{1}{x}$

c) $x = \dfrac{x^2 + 1}{5}$

Q2 Hint: Think about which parts you need to get on their own before starting to rearrange the equation. In part c), for example, turn $7x$ into $5x + 2x$ to get where you want.

Q2 Show that the equation $x^4 + 7x - 3 = 0$ can be written in the form:

a) $x = \sqrt[4]{3 - 7x}$

b) $x = \dfrac{3}{x^3} - \dfrac{7}{x^2}$

c) $x = \dfrac{3 - 5x - x^4}{2}$

d) $x = \dfrac{\sqrt{3 - 7x}}{x}$

Q3 a) Show that the equation $x^3 - 2x^2 - 5 = 0$ can be rewritten as $x = 2 + \dfrac{5}{x^2}$.

b) Use the iterative formula $x_{n+1} = 2 + \dfrac{5}{x_n^2}$ with starting value $x_0 = 2$ to find x_5 to 1 decimal place.

c) Verify that the value found in part b) is a root of the equation $x^3 - 2x^2 - 5 = 0$ to 1 decimal place.

Q4 a) Rearrange the equation $x^2 + 3x - 8 = 0$ into the form $x = \frac{a}{x} + b$ where a and b are values to be found.

b) Verify that a root of the equation $x^2 + 3x - 8 = 0$ lies in the interval $(-5, -4)$.

c) Use the iterative formula $x_{n+1} = \frac{a}{x_n} + b$ with $x_0 = -5$ to find the values for $x_1 - x_6$, giving your answers to 3 d.p. Hence find a value of the root of the equation $x^2 + 3x - 8 = 0$ to 2 d.p.

Q5 a) Show that the equation $2^{x-1} = 4\sqrt{x}$ can be written as $x = 2^{2x-6}$.

b) Use the iterative formula $x_{n+1} = 2^{2x_n - 6}$ starting with $x_0 = 1$ to find the values of x_1, x_2, x_3 and x_4, giving your answers to 4 d.p.

c) Verify that the value for x_4 is a correct approximation to 4 d.p. for the root of the equation $2^{x-1} = 4\sqrt{x}$.

Q5 Hint: Start by rewriting everything as powers of 2 or x if you're struggling. You're going to need the rules for multiplying powers for this question.

Q6 $f(x) = \ln 2x + x^3$

a) Show that $f(x) = 0$ has a solution in the interval $0.4 < x < 0.5$.

Q6 Hint: Remember that $\ln e^x = x$.

b) Show that $f(x) = 0$ can be rewritten in the form $x = \frac{e^{-x^3}}{2}$.

c) Using an iterative formula based on part b) and an appropriate value for x_0 find an approximation of the root of the equation $f(x) = 0$ to 3 decimal places.

Q7 $f(x) = x^2 - 9x - 20$

a) Find an iterative formula for $f(x) = 0$ in the form $x_{n+1} = \sqrt{px_n + q}$ where p and q are constants to be found.

b) By using the formula in part a) and a starting value of $x_0 = 10$, find an approximation to a root of the equation $f(x) = 0$. Give your answer to 3 significant figures.

c) Show that an alternative iterative formula is $x_{n+1} = \frac{x_n^2 - 4x_n}{5} - 4$.

d) By using the iterative formula in part c) with starting value $x_0 = 1$ find the value of $x_1, x_2 ... x_8$.

e) Describe the behaviour of this sequence.

Q1-7 Hint: You can generate hundreds of iterations really fast using a basic computer spreadsheet. It's quick to set up and can even round automatically to a certain number of decimal places. See what happens if you try it with a few of these examples.

Combining the methods

When it comes to the exam, they'll often set you questions that **combine** all (or at least most) of the methods covered in this chapter into one long question.

Here you can see an **exam-style question** worked from start to finish, just how they'd want you to do it in the real thing.

Tip: Remember to show **all** of your working. That way, even if you get your final answer wrong, you can still get 3 or 4 marks for showing that you understood what the question was asking.

Example

The graph below shows both roots of the continuous function $f(x) = 6x - x^2 + 13$.

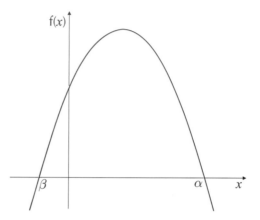

a) **Show that the positive root, α, lies in the interval $7 < x < 8$.**

b) **Show that $6x - x^2 + 13 = 0$ can be rearranged into the formula:**
$$x = \sqrt{6x + 13}$$

c) **Use the iteration formula $x_{n+1} = \sqrt{6x_n + 13}$ and $x_0 = 7$ to find α to 1 d.p.**

d) **Show that the negative root, β, is -1.690 to 3 d.p.**

a) $f(x)$ is a **continuous function**, so if $f(7)$ and $f(8)$ have **different signs** then there is a root in the interval $7 < x < 8$:

$$f(7) = (6 \times 7) - 7^2 + 13 = 6.$$

$$f(8) = (6 \times 8) - 8^2 + 13 = -3.$$

There is a **change of sign** so $7 < \alpha < 8$.

b) Get the x^2 **on its own** to make: $6x + 13 = x^2$

Now take the (positive) square root to leave: $x = \sqrt{6x + 13}$.

Tip: The key with the rearranging questions is being able to pick up hints that show how it needs to be rearranged. Here the $\sqrt{\ }$ sign shows you'll need to get the x^2 on its own and square root both sides.

c) Using $x_{n+1} = \sqrt{6x_n + 13}$ with $x_0 = 7$, gives $x_1 = \sqrt{6 \times 7 + 13}$
$$= 7.4161...$$

Continuing the iterations:

$$x_2 = \sqrt{6 \times 7.4161... + 13} = 7.5826...$$

$$x_3 = \sqrt{6 \times 7.5826... + 13} = 7.6482...$$

$$x_4 = \sqrt{6 \times 7.6482... + 13} = 7.6739...$$

$$x_5 = \sqrt{6 \times 7.6739... + 13} = 7.6839...$$

$$x_6 = \sqrt{6 \times 7.6839... + 13} = 7.6879...$$

$$x_7 = \sqrt{6 \times 7.6879... + 13} = 7.6894...$$

x_4 to x_7 all round to 7.7 to 1 d.p., so to 1 d.p. $\alpha = 7.7$.

d) If $\beta = -1.690$ to 3 d.p. the **upper and lower bounds** are -1.6895 and -1.6905. The root must lie **between** these values in order to be rounded to -1.690.

As the function is **continuous**, if $f(-1.6895)$ and $f(-1.6905)$ have **different signs** then $-1.6905 < \beta < -1.6895$:

$$f(-1.6895) = (6 \times -1.6895) - (-1.6895)^2 + 13 = 0.00858...$$

$$f(-1.6905) = (6 \times -1.6905) - (-1.6905)^2 + 13 = -0.00079...$$

There is a **change of sign**, so $-1.6905 < \beta < -1.6895$, and so

$$\beta = -1.690 \text{ to 3 d.p.}$$

Review Exercise — Chapter 5

Q1 The graph shows the function $f(x) = e^x - x^3$ for $0 \le x \le 5$. How many roots does the equation $e^x - x^3 = 0$ have in the interval $0 \le x \le 5$?

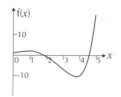

Q2 Show that there is a root in the interval:

    a) $3 < x < 4$ for $\sin(2x) = 0$ (where x is in radians).

    b) $2.1 < x < 2.2$ for $\ln(x - 2) + 2 = 0$.

    c) $4.3 < x < 4.5$ for $x^3 - 4x^2 = 7$.

Q3 By selecting an appropriate interval show that, to 1 d.p, $x = 1.2$ is a root of the equation $x^3 + x - 3 = 0$.

Q4 Use the formula $x_{n+1} = -\frac{1}{2}\cos x_n$, with $x_0 = -1$, to find a root of $\cos x + 2x = 0$ to 2 d.p.

Q5 Use the formula $x_{n+1} = \sqrt{\ln x_n + 4}$, with $x_0 = 2$, to find a root of $x^2 - \ln x - 4 = 0$ to 3 d.p.

Q6 a) Show that the equation $2x^2 - x^3 + 1 = 0$ can be written in the form:

    (i) $x = \sqrt{\dfrac{-1}{2 - x}}$ (ii) $x = \sqrt[3]{2x^2 + 1}$ (iii) $x = \sqrt{\dfrac{x^3 - 1}{2}}$

    b) Use iteration formulas based on each of the above rearrangements with $x_0 = 2.3$ to find a root of $2x^2 - x^3 + 1 = 0$ to 2 d.p. Which of the three formulas converge to a root?

Q7 a) On the same axes sketch the graphs of $y = \ln x$ and $y = \dfrac{2}{x}$. Hence find the number of roots of the equation $\ln x - \dfrac{2}{x} = 0$.

    b) Show that there is a root of the equation $\ln x - \dfrac{2}{x} = 0$ between $x = 2$ and $x = 3$.

Q8 a) Sketch the graphs of $y = \dfrac{1}{x + 1}$ and $y = x - 2$ on the same axes.

    b) $f(x) = \dfrac{1}{x + 1} - x + 2$

    Show that a root of the equation $f(x) = 0$ lies between $x = -1.4$ and $x = -1.3$.

    c) Show that the equation $f(x) = 0$ can be written in the form $x^2 - x - 3 = 0$.

> **Q9 Hint:** x^x looks scary but it's no harder than others — just put the numbers in as usual.

Q9 a) Show that the equation $x^x = 3$ has a root between $x = 1.5$ and $x = 2$

    b) Using the iterative formula $x_{n+1} = 3^{\frac{1}{x_n}}$, with an appropriate value for x_0, find an approximation for the root of the equation $x^x = 3$ to 1 decimal place.

    c) An alternative iterative formula is $x_{n+1} = 3x_n^{1 - x_n}$. Using a starting value of $x_0 = 1.5$, find x_n values up to and including x_5. What happens if you use this formula?

Q10 a) Show that a solution to the equation $2x - 5\cos x = 0$ (where x is in radians) lies in the interval $(1.1, 1.2)$.

    b) Show that the equation in part a) can be written as $x = p\cos x$, stating the value of p.

    c) Using an iterative formula based on part b) and a starting value of $x_0 = 1.1$, find the values up to and including x_8, giving your answers to 4 decimal places. Comment on your findings.

    d) Find an alternative iterative formula that will find an approximation to the root in part a) and give the value of that root to 3 significant figures. Verify your solution.

> **Q10 Hint:** You're going to need to take arccos ($\cos^{-1}$) of both sides here.

Exam-Style Questions — Chapter 5

1   The sketch below shows part of the graph of the function $f(x) = 2xe^x - 3$.
    The curve crosses the x-axis at the point $P(p, 0)$, as shown, so p is a root
    of the equation $f(x) = 0$.

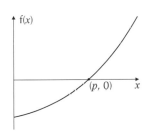

   a)   Show that $0.7 < p < 0.8$.   *(3 marks)*

   b)   Show that $f(x) = 0$ can be rewritten as $x = \dfrac{3}{2}e^{-x}$.   *(2 marks)*

   c)   Starting with $x_0 = 0.7$, use the iteration

   $$x_{n+1} = \frac{3}{2}e^{-x_n}$$

   to find x_1, x_2, x_3 and x_4 to 4 d.p.   *(3 marks)*

   d)   Show that $p = 0.726$ to 3 d.p.   *(3 marks)*

2   The graph of the function:
    $$y = \sin 3x + 3x, \quad 0 < x < \pi$$
    meets the line $y = 1$ when $x = a$.

   a)   Show that $0.1 < a < 0.2$.   *(4 marks)*

   b)   Show that the equation:
        $$\sin 3x + 3x = 1$$
        can be written as:
        $$x - \frac{1}{3}(1 - \sin 3x).$$ *(2 marks)*

   c)   Starting with $x_0 = 0.2$, use the iteration:
        $$x_{n+1} = \frac{1}{3}(1 - \sin 3x_n)$$
        to find x_4 to 3 d.p.   *(2 marks)*

3   The sequence given by:
$$x_{n+1} = \sqrt[3]{x_n^2 - 4}, \quad x_0 = -1$$
converges to a number 'b'.

   a)   Find the values of x_1, x_2, x_3 and x_4 correct to 4 decimal places.

   (3 marks)

   b)   Show that $x = b$ is a root of the equation:
   $$x^3 - x^2 + 4 = 0$$

   (2 marks)

   c)   Show that $b = -1.315$ to 3 decimal places, by choosing
        an appropriate interval.

   (3 marks)

4   The function:
$$f(x) = \ln (x + 3) - x + 2, \quad x > -3$$
has a root at $x = m$.

   a)   Show that m lies between 3 and 4.

   (3 marks)

   b)   Find, using iteration, the value of m correct to 2 decimal places.
        Use the iteration formula: $x_{n+1} = \ln (x_n + 3) + 2$
        with $x_0 = 3$.

   (3 marks)

   c)   Use a suitable interval to verify that your answer to part b) is correct
        to 2 decimal places.

   (3 marks)

5    $f(x) = \cot x + 3 \cos x - 1$, where x is in radians

   a)   Show that $f(x)$ has a root between $x = 1.3$ and $x = 1.4$

   (3 marks)

   b)   Show that $f(x) = 0$ can be rearranged to produce the iterative formula:

   $$x_{n+1} = \arccos \left(\frac{1 - \cot x_n}{3}\right)$$

   (3 marks)

   c)   Use the iterative formula in part b) to find x_n up to and including x_6,
        with starting value $x_0 = 1.4$. Give your answers to 4 decimal places.

   (3 marks)

   d)   Using your answer to part c), give a value of the root between 1.3 and 1.4
        to 2 decimal places.

   (1 mark)

1. Proof

Mathematical proofs are all about showing that a statement is true (or false). There are a number of different ways to do this, and you need to know how they work in case you have to prove something for yourself.

Different types of proof

Simple proofs — odd and even numbers

Before you get onto the trickier proofs, there are some nice simple proofs about **odd** and **even numbers** that are really useful. But first you need to know these 'proper' definitions for them:

> Any **even** number can be written as **2a**, where *a* is an integer.

> Any **odd** number can be written as **2b + 1**, where *b* is an integer.

In the proofs below, **2j + 1** and **2k + 1** represent any two **odd numbers**, and **2l** and **2m** represent any two **even numbers** (where *j*, *k*, *l* and *m* are integers).

Learning Objectives:

- Be able to show that sums and products of integers are odd or even (as required).
- Be able to use direct proof, proof by contradiction and proof by exhaustion to show that statements are true.
- Be able to use disproof by counter-example to show that statements are false.

Examples

a) **Prove that the sum of two odd numbers is even.**

   Proof: $(2j + 1) + (2k + 1) = 2j + 2k + 2 = 2(j + k + 1) = $ even

   so odd + odd = even

b) **Prove that the sum of an odd number and an even number is odd.**

   Proof: $(2j + 1) + (2l) = 2j + 2l + 1 = 2(j + l) + 1 = $ odd

   so odd + even = odd

c) **Prove that the sum of two even numbers is even.**

   Proof: $2l + 2m = 2(l + m) = $ even

   so even + even = even

d) **Prove that the product of two odd numbers is odd.**

   Proof: $(2j + 1)(2k + 1) = 4jk + 2j + 2k + 1 = 2(2jk + j + k) + 1 = $ odd

   so odd × odd = odd

Tip: You can prove that e.g. the product of two even numbers is even in a similar way.

Direct proof

A **direct proof** (or 'proof by direct argument') is when you use **known facts** to build up your argument and show a statement **must** be true.

Tip: Remember — a quotient is what you get when you divide one number by another.

Example

A definition of a rational number is 'a number that can be written as a quotient of two integers, where the denominator is non-zero'.

Use this definition to prove that the following statement is true:
    "The product of two rational numbers is always a rational number."

- Take **any two** rational numbers and call them *a* and *b*.
- By the **definition** of rational numbers you can write them in the form $a = \frac{p}{q}$ and $b = \frac{r}{s}$, where *p*, *q*, *r* and *s* are all integers, and *q* and *s* are non-zero.
- The **product** of *a* and *b* is $ab = \frac{p}{q} \times \frac{r}{s} = \frac{pr}{qs}$.
- *pr* and *qs* are the products of integers, so they must also be integers, and because *q* and *s* are non-zero, *qs* must also be non-zero.
- We've shown that *ab* is a quotient of two integers and has a non-zero denominator, so by definition, ***ab* is rational**.
- Hence the original statement is **true**.

Tip: Here, the "known facts" are the definition of a rational number, the fact that the products of integers are integers, and the fact that the products of non-zero integers are also non-zero.

Tip: Remember that an identity is true for all values of the unknown (e.g. *x* or θ) rather than just one particular value. An identity is shown by the symbol $\equiv$.

If you have to prove that an **identity** is true, it's enough to show that one side of the identity can be **rearranged** into the other — like for the proofs of the **trig identities** in Chapter 2, and in the example below.

Example

Prove that: $\dfrac{\sin 2\theta}{1 - \cos 2\theta} \equiv \cot \theta$

Expand the left-hand side using the **double angle formulas** for sin and cos (see p.68)...

$$\frac{\sin 2\theta}{1 - \cos 2\theta} \equiv \frac{2 \sin \theta \cos \theta}{1 - (1 - 2\sin^2\theta)}$$

$$\equiv \frac{2 \sin \theta \cos \theta}{2 \sin^2 \theta}$$ ...then **rearrange** and **simplify** until you get the right-hand side.

$$\equiv \frac{\cos \theta}{\sin \theta}$$

$$\equiv \boxed{\cot \theta}$$

Tip: Here, the "known facts" are the double angle formulas.

Tip: Remember that $\tan \theta \equiv \dfrac{\sin \theta}{\cos \theta}$ and $\cot \theta \equiv \dfrac{1}{\tan \theta}$.

Proof by contradiction

To prove a statement by **contradiction**, you say 'suppose the statement **isn't true**...', then prove that something **impossible** would have to be true for that to be the case.

Example

Prove the following statement: *"If x^2 is even, then x must be even."*

- You can prove the statement by contradiction. Suppose the statement is **not true**. Then there must be an **odd number** x for which x^2 is **even**.

- If x is odd, then you can write x as $2k + 1$, where k is an integer.

- Now, $x^2 = (2k + 1)^2 = 4k^2 + 4k + 1$
  $4k^2 + 4k = 2(2k^2 + 2k)$ is **even** because it is $2 \times$ an integer
  $\Rightarrow 4k^2 + 4k + 1$ is **odd**.

- But this **isn't possible** if the statement that x^2 is even is true.
  You've **contradicted** the statement that there is an odd number x for which x^2 is even.

- So if x^2 is **even**, then x must be **even**, hence the original statement is **true**.

Tip: This proof uses the definitions of odd and even numbers from page 149.

Proof by exhaustion

In **proof by exhaustion** you break things down into two or more **cases**. You have to make sure that your cases cover **all possible situations**, then prove separately that the statement is true for **each case**.

Example

Prove the following statement:
"For any integer x, the value of $f(x) = x^3 + x + 1$ is an odd integer."

- To prove the statement, split the situation into **two cases**:
    (i) x is an **even number**, and (ii) x is an **odd number**.

- (i)   If x is an **even integer**, then it can be written as $x = 2n$,
    for some integer n. Substitute $x = 2n$ into the function:
    $f(2n) = (2n)^3 + 2n + 1 = 8n^3 + 2n + 1 = 2(4n^3 + n) + 1$
    n is an integer $\Rightarrow (4n^3 + n)$ is an integer
    $\qquad\qquad\qquad \Rightarrow 2(4n^3 + n)$ is an even integer
    $\qquad\qquad\qquad \Rightarrow 2(4n^3 + n) + 1$ is an **odd integer**
    So $f(x)$ is **odd** when x is **even**.

- (ii)   If x is an **odd integer**, then it can be written as $x = 2m + 1$,
    for some integer m. Substitute $x = 2m + 1$ into the function:
    $f(2m + 1) = (2m + 1)^3 + 2m + 1 + 1$
    $\qquad\qquad = (8m^3 + 12m^2 + 6m + 1) + 2m + 1 + 1$
    $\qquad\qquad = 8m^3 + 12m^2 + 8m + 3 = 2(4m^3 + 6m^2 + 4m) + 3$
    m is an integer $\Rightarrow (4m^3 + 6m^2 + 4m)$ is an integer
    $\qquad\qquad\qquad \Rightarrow 2(4m^3 + 6m^2 + 4m)$ is an even integer
    $\qquad\qquad\qquad \Rightarrow 2(4m^3 + 6m^2 + 4m) + 3$ is an **odd integer**
    So $f(x)$ is **odd** when x is **odd**.

- You have shown that $f(x)$ is **odd** when x is even **and** when x is odd.
  As any integer x **must** be either odd or even, you have therefore shown that $f(x)$ is **odd** for **any** integer x, so the statement is **true**.

Tip: These two cases cover all possible situations, because an integer is always either odd or even.

Tip: Again, you need to use the definitions of odd and even numbers — and the fact that sums and products of integers are also integers.

Disproof by counter-example

Disproof by **counter-example** is the easiest way to show a mathematical statement is **false**. All you have to do is find **one case** where the statement doesn't hold.

Example

Disprove the following statement:
"*For any pair of real numbers x and y, if $x > y$, then $x^2 + x > y^2 + y$.*"

- To **disprove** the statement, it's enough to find just **one example** of x and y where $x > y$, but $x^2 + x \leq y^2 + y$.

- Let $x = 2$ and $y = -4$.
  Then $2 > -4 \Rightarrow x > y$
  but $x^2 + x = 2^2 + 2 = 6$
  and $y^2 + y = (-4)^2 + (-4) = 12$,
  so $x^2 + x < y^2 + y$

- So when $x = 2$ and $y = -4$, the first part of the statement holds, but the second part of the statement **doesn't**.

- So the statement is **not true**.

Tip: You might have to try a few different numbers before you come up with an example that doesn't work.

Exercise 1.1

Q1 Hint: These proofs are similar to the ones on p.149.

Q1   a) Prove that the product of two even numbers is even.
       b) Prove that the product of an odd number and an even number is even.

Q2   Prove by exhaustion that the product of any three consecutive integers is even.

Q3   Disprove the following statement:
       "$n^2 - n - 1$ is a prime number for any integer $n > 2$."

Q4   "The graph of $y = \ln x$ has no turning points."
       Use proof by contradiction to prove the statement above.

Q5   Disprove the following: $\sqrt{x^2 + y^2} < x + y$.

Q6   Prove that $\cos^2 \theta(1 - \tan^2 \theta) \equiv \cos 2\theta$.

Q7   a) Prove the statement below:
           "For any integer n, $n^2 - n - 1$ is always odd."
       b) Hence prove that $(n^2 - n - 2)^3$ is always even.

Glossary

A

Absolute value
Another name for the **modulus**.

Arccos
The **inverse** of the cosine function, also written as arccosine or $\cos^{-1}$.

Arcsin
The **inverse** of the sine function, also written as arcsine or $\sin^{-1}$.

Arctan
The **inverse** of the tangent function, also written as arctangent or $\tan^{-1}$.

Asymptote
A straight line that a graph approaches (but never touches).

C

Chain rule
A method for **differentiating** a function of a function.

Coefficient
The constant multiplying the variable(s) in an algebraic term.

Composite function
A combination of two or more functions acting on a value or set of values.

Continuous
A function is continuous if its graph contains no breaks or jumps.

Convergence
A sequence converges if the terms get closer and closer to a single value.

Cosec
The **reciprocal** of the sine function, sometimes written as cosecant.

Cot
The **reciprocal** of the tangent function, sometimes written as cotangent.

D

Degree
The highest power of x in a polynomial.

Derivative
The result after **differentiating** a function.

Differentiation
A method of finding the rate of change of a function with respect to a variable.

Direct proof
Using known facts to build up an argument to prove that a statement is true or false.

Disproof by counter-example
Finding one example of where a statement doesn't hold, hence showing that it is false.

Divergence
A sequence diverges if the terms get further and further apart.

Divisor
The number or expression that you're dividing by in a division.

Domain
The set of values that can be input into a **mapping** or **function**. Usually given as the set of values that x can take.

E

e
An **irrational number** for which the gradient of $y = e^x$ is equal to e^x.

Equating coefficients
Making the coefficients of equivalent terms on each side of an identity equal in order to calculate the value of unknowns in the identity.

Exponential function
A function of the form $y = a^x$. $y = e^x$ is known as 'the' exponential function.

F

Function
A type of **mapping** which maps every number in the **domain** to only one number in the **range**.

G

Gradient
The gradient of a curve at a given point is how steep the curve is at that point.

I

Identity
An equation that is true for all values of a variable, usually denoted by the '$\equiv$' sign.

Integer
A whole number, including 0 and negative numbers. The set of integers has the notation $\mathbb{Z}$.

Inverse function
An inverse function, e.g. $f^{-1}(x)$, reverses the effect of the function $f(x)$.

Irrational number
A number that can't be written as a fraction of two integers.

Iteration
A numerical method for solving equations that allows you to find the approximate value of a **root** by repeatedly using an iteration formula.

Iteration sequence
The list of results x_1, x_2... etc. found with an iteration formula.

Logarithm
The logarithm to the base a of a number x (written $\log_a x$) is the power to which a must be raised to give that number.

Lower bound
The lowest value a number could take and still be rounded up to the correct answer.

Many-to-one function
A function where some values in the **range** correspond to more than one value in the **domain**.

Mapping
An operation that takes one number and transforms it into another.

Modulus
The modulus of a number is its positive numerical value.
The modulus of a function, f(x), makes every value of f(x) positive by removing any minus signs.

Natural logarithm
The **inverse function** of e^x, written as $\ln x$ or $\log_e x$.

Natural number
A positive integer, not including 0. The set of natural numbers has the notation $\mathbb{N}$.

Normal
A straight line that crosses a curve at a given point and is perpendicular to the curve at that point.

One-to-one function
A function where each value in the **range** corresponds to one and only one value in the **domain**.

Polynomial
An algebraic expression made up of the sum of constant terms and variables raised to positive **integer** powers.

Product rule
A method for **differentiating** a product of two functions.

Proof
Using mathematical arguments to show that a statement is true or false.

Proof by contradiction
Assuming that a statement is false, then showing that this assumption is impossible, to prove that the statement is true.

Proof by direct argument
See **direct proof**.

Proof by exhaustion
Splitting a situation into separate cases that cover all possible scenarios, then showing that the statement is true for each case, hence true overall.

Quotient
The result when you divide one thing by another, not including the **remainder**.

Quotient rule
A method of **differentiating** one function divided by another.

Range
The set of values output by a **mapping** or **function**. Usually given as a set of values that y or f(x) can take.

Rational expression
A function that can be written as a fraction where the numerator and denominator are both polynomials.

Rational number
A number that can be written as a fraction of two integers, where the denominator is non-zero.

Real number
Any positive or negative number (or 0) including all **rational** and **irrational** **numbers**, e.g. fractions, decimals, integers and surds. The set of real numbers has the notation $\mathbb{R}$.

Reciprocal
The reciprocal of a number or function is 1 divided by the number or function.

Remainder (algebraic division)
The expression left over following an algebraic division that has a **degree** lower than the **divisor**.

Root
A value of x at which a function is equal to 0.

Sec
The **reciprocal** of the cosine function, sometimes written as secant.

Second order derivative
The result of **differentiating** a function twice.

Stationary point
A point on a curve where the gradient is 0.

Tangent
A straight line which just touches the curve at a point, without going through it and that has the same **gradient** as the curve at that point.

Turning point
A **stationary point** that is a (local) maximum or minimum point of a curve.

Upper bound
The upper limit of the values that a number could take and still be rounded down to the correct answer.

Answers

Chapter 1: Algebra and Functions

1. Simplifying Expressions

Exercise 1.1 — Simplifying algebraic fractions

Q1 $\dfrac{4}{2x+10} = \dfrac{4}{2(x+5)} = \dfrac{2}{x+5}$

Q2 $\dfrac{5x}{x^2+2x} = \dfrac{5x}{x(x+2)} = \dfrac{5}{x+2}$

Q3 $\dfrac{6x^2-3x}{3x^2} = \dfrac{3x(2x-1)}{3x^2} = \dfrac{2x-1}{x}$

Q4 $\dfrac{4x^3}{x^3+3x^2} = \dfrac{4x^3}{x^2(x+3)} = \dfrac{4x}{x+3}$

Q5 $\dfrac{3x+6}{x^2+3x+2} = \dfrac{3(x+2)}{(x+1)(x+2)} = \dfrac{3}{x+1}$

Q6 $\dfrac{x^2+3x}{x^2+x-6}$ $\dfrac{x(x+3)}{(x-2)(x+3)} = \dfrac{x}{x-2}$

Q7 $\dfrac{2x-6}{x^2-9} = \dfrac{2(x-3)}{(x-3)(x+3)} = \dfrac{2}{x+3}$

Q8 $\dfrac{5x^2-20x}{2x^2-5x-12} = \dfrac{5x(x-4)}{(2x+3)(x-4)} = \dfrac{5x}{2x+3}$

Q9 $\dfrac{3x^2-7x-6}{2x^2-x-15} = \dfrac{(3x+2)(x-3)}{(2x+5)(x-3)} = \dfrac{3x+2}{2x+5}$

Q10 $\dfrac{x^3-4x^2-19x-14}{x^2-6x-7}$

$\qquad \dfrac{(x+1)(x+2)(x-7)}{(x+1)(x-7)} = x+2$

To factorise the cubic, try a few different values for x — once you've spotted that f(−1) = 0 (and so (x + 1) is a factor) you can take that out and see what's left to factorise.

Q11 $\dfrac{x^3-2x^2}{x^3-4x} = \dfrac{x^2(x-2)}{x(x^2-4)} = \dfrac{x^2(x-2)}{x(x-2)(x+2)} = \dfrac{x}{x+2}$

Q12 $\dfrac{1+\frac{1}{x}}{x+1} = \dfrac{\left(1+\frac{1}{x}\right)x}{(x+1)x} = \dfrac{x+1}{x(x+1)} = \dfrac{1}{x}$

Q13 $\dfrac{3+\frac{1}{x}}{2+\frac{1}{x}} = \dfrac{\left(3+\frac{1}{x}\right)x}{\left(2+\frac{1}{x}\right)x} = \dfrac{3x+1}{2x+1}$

Q14 $\dfrac{1+\frac{1}{2x}}{2+\frac{1}{x}} = \dfrac{\left(1+\frac{1}{2x}\right)2x}{\left(2+\frac{1}{x}\right)2x} = \dfrac{2x+1}{4x+2} = \dfrac{2x+1}{2(2x+1)} = \dfrac{1}{2}$

Q15 $\dfrac{\frac{1}{3x}-1}{3x^2-x} = \dfrac{\left(\frac{1}{3x}-1\right)3x}{(3x^2-x)3x} = \dfrac{-(3x-1)}{3x^2(3x-1)} = -\dfrac{1}{3x^2}$

Q16 $\dfrac{2+\frac{1}{x}}{6x^2+3x} = \dfrac{\left(2+\frac{1}{x}\right)x}{(6x^2+3x)x} = \dfrac{2x+1}{3x^2(2x+1)} = \dfrac{1}{3x^2}$

Q17 $\dfrac{\frac{3x}{x+2}}{\frac{x}{x+2}+\frac{1}{x+2}} = \dfrac{\left(\frac{3x}{x+2}\right)(x+2)}{\left(\frac{x}{x+2}+\frac{1}{x+2}\right)(x+2)} = \dfrac{3x}{x+1}$

Q18 $\dfrac{2+\frac{1}{x+1}}{3+\frac{1}{x+1}} = \dfrac{\left(2+\frac{1}{x+1}\right)(x+1)}{\left(3+\frac{1}{x+1}\right)(x+1)} = \dfrac{2(x+1)+1}{3(x+1)+1}$

$\qquad = \dfrac{2x+3}{3x+4}$

Q19 $\dfrac{1-\frac{2}{x+3}}{x+2} = \dfrac{\left(1-\frac{2}{x+3}\right)(x+3)}{(x+2)(x+3)} = \dfrac{x+3-2}{(x+2)(x+3)}$

$\qquad = \dfrac{x+1}{(x+2)(x+3)}$

Q20 $\dfrac{4-\frac{1}{x^2}}{2-\frac{1}{x}-\frac{1}{x^2}} = \dfrac{\left(4-\frac{1}{x^2}\right)x^2}{\left(2-\frac{1}{x}-\frac{1}{x^2}\right)x^2} = \dfrac{4x^2-1}{2x^2-x-1}$

$\qquad = \dfrac{(2x+1)(2x-1)}{(x-1)(2x+1)} = \dfrac{2x-1}{x-1}$

Exercise 1.2 — Adding and subtracting algebraic fractions

Q1 $\dfrac{2x}{3}+\dfrac{x}{5} = \dfrac{10x}{15}+\dfrac{3x}{15} = \dfrac{13x}{15}$

Q2 $\dfrac{2}{3x}-\dfrac{1}{5x} = \dfrac{10}{15x}-\dfrac{3}{15x} = \dfrac{7}{15x}$

Q3 $\dfrac{3}{x^2}+\dfrac{2}{x} = \dfrac{3}{x^2}+\dfrac{2x}{x^2} = \dfrac{3+2x}{x^2}$

Q4 $\dfrac{x+1}{3}+\dfrac{x+2}{4} = \dfrac{4(x+1)}{12}+\dfrac{3(x+2)}{12}$

$\qquad = \dfrac{4x+4+3x+6}{12} = \dfrac{7x+10}{12}$

Q5 $\dfrac{2x}{3}+\dfrac{x-1}{7x} = \dfrac{14x^2}{21x}+\dfrac{3(x-1)}{21x}$

$\qquad = \dfrac{14x^2+3x-3}{21x}$

Q6 $\dfrac{3x}{4}-\dfrac{2x-1}{5x} = \dfrac{15x^2}{20x}-\dfrac{4(2x-1)}{20x}$

$\qquad = \dfrac{15x^2-8x+4}{20x}$

Q7 $\dfrac{2}{x-1}+\dfrac{3}{x} = \dfrac{2x}{x(x-1)}+\dfrac{3(x-1)}{x(x-1)}$

$\qquad = \dfrac{2x+3x-3}{x(x-1)} = \dfrac{5x-3}{x(x-1)}$

Q8 $\dfrac{3}{x+1}+\dfrac{2}{x+2} = \dfrac{3(x+2)}{(x+1)(x+2)}+\dfrac{2(x+1)}{(x+1)(x+2)}$

$\qquad = \dfrac{3x+6+2x+2}{(x+1)(x+2)} = \dfrac{5x+8}{(x+1)(x+2)}$

Q9 $\dfrac{4}{x-3}-\dfrac{1}{x+4} = \dfrac{4(x+4)}{(x-3)(x+4)}-\dfrac{x-3}{(x-3)(x+4)}$

$\qquad = \dfrac{4x+16-x+3}{(x-3)(x+4)} = \dfrac{3x+19}{(x-3)(x+4)}$

Q10 $\dfrac{6}{x+2} + \dfrac{6}{x-2} = \dfrac{6(x-2)}{(x+2)(x-2)} + \dfrac{6(x+2)}{(x+2)(x-2)}$

$= \dfrac{6x-12+6x+12}{(x+2)(x-2)} = \dfrac{12x}{(x+2)(x-2)}$

Q11 $\dfrac{3}{x-2} - \dfrac{5}{2x+3} = \dfrac{3(2x+3)}{(x-2)(2x+3)} - \dfrac{5(x-2)}{(x-2)(2x+3)}$

$= \dfrac{6x+9-5x+10}{(x-2)(2x+3)} = \dfrac{x+19}{(x-2)(2x+3)}$

Q12 $\dfrac{3}{x+2} + \dfrac{x}{x+1} = \dfrac{3(x+1)}{(x+2)(x+1)} + \dfrac{x(x+2)}{(x+2)(x+1)}$

$- \dfrac{3x+3+x^2+2x}{(x+2)(x+1)} - \dfrac{x^2+5x+3}{(x+2)(x+1)}$

Q13 $\dfrac{5x}{(x+1)^2} - \dfrac{3}{x+1} = \dfrac{5x}{(x+1)^2} - \dfrac{3(x+1)}{(x+1)^2}$

$= \dfrac{5x-3x-3}{(x+1)^2} = \dfrac{2x-3}{(x+1)^2}$

Q14 $\dfrac{5}{x(x+3)} + \dfrac{3}{x+2}$

$= \dfrac{5(x+2)}{x(x+3)(x+2)} + \dfrac{3x(x+3)}{x(x+3)(x+2)}$

$= \dfrac{5x+10+3x^2+9x}{x(x+3)(x+2)} = \dfrac{3x^2+14x+10}{x(x+3)(x+2)}$

Q15 $\dfrac{x}{x^2-4} - \dfrac{1}{x+2} = \dfrac{x}{(x+2)(x-2)} - \dfrac{1}{x+2}$

$= \dfrac{x}{(x+2)(x-2)} - \dfrac{x-2}{(x+2)(x-2)}$

$= \dfrac{x-x+2}{(x+2)(x-2)} = \dfrac{2}{(x+2)(x-2)}$

Q16 $\dfrac{3}{x+1} + \dfrac{6}{2x^2+x-1} = \dfrac{3}{x+1} + \dfrac{6}{(x+1)(2x-1)}$

$= \dfrac{3(2x-1)}{(x+1)(2x-1)} + \dfrac{6}{(x+1)(2x-1)}$

$= \dfrac{6x-3+6}{(x+1)(2x-1)} = \dfrac{3(2x+1)}{(x+1)(2x-1)}$

Q17 $\dfrac{2}{x} + \dfrac{3}{x+1} + \dfrac{4}{x+2}$

$= \dfrac{2(x+1)(x+2)}{x(x+1)(x+2)} + \dfrac{3x(x+2)}{x(x+1)(x+2)}$

$+ \dfrac{4x(x+1)}{x(x+1)(x+2)}$

$= \dfrac{2x^2+6x+4+3x^2+6x+4x^2+4x}{x(x+1)(x+2)}$

$= \dfrac{9x^2+16x+4}{x(x+1)(x+2)}$

Q18 $\dfrac{3}{x+4} - \dfrac{2}{x+1} + \dfrac{1}{x-2}$

$= \dfrac{3(x+1)(x-2)}{(x+4)(x+1)(x-2)} - \dfrac{2(x+4)(x-2)}{(x+4)(x+1)(x-2)}$

$+ \dfrac{(x+4)(x+1)}{(x+4)(x+1)(x-2)}$

$= \dfrac{3x^2-3x-6-2x^2-4x+16+x^2+5x+4}{(x+4)(x+1)(x-2)}$

$= \dfrac{2(x^2-x+7)}{(x+4)(x+1)(x-2)}$

Q19 $2 - \dfrac{3}{x+1} + \dfrac{4}{(x+1)^2}$

$= \dfrac{2(x+1)^2}{(x+1)^2} - \dfrac{3(x+1)}{(x+1)^2} + \dfrac{4}{(x+1)^2}$

$= \dfrac{2x^2+4x+2-3x-3+4}{(x+1)^2} = \dfrac{2x^2+x+3}{(x+1)^2}$

Q20 $\dfrac{2x^2-x-3}{x^2-1} + \dfrac{1}{x(x-1)}$

$= \dfrac{(x+1)(2x-3)}{(x+1)(x-1)} + \dfrac{1}{x(x-1)}$

$= \dfrac{2x-3}{x-1} + \dfrac{1}{x(x-1)}$

$= \dfrac{x(2x-3)}{x(x-1)} + \dfrac{1}{x(x-1)}$

$= \dfrac{2x^2-3x+1}{x(x-1)} = \dfrac{(x-1)(2x-1)}{x(x-1)} = \dfrac{2x-1}{x}$

Exercise 1.3 — Multiplying and dividing algebraic fractions

Q1 a) $\dfrac{2x}{3} \times \dfrac{5x}{4} = \dfrac{x}{3} \times \dfrac{5x}{2} = \dfrac{x \times 5x}{3 \times 2} = \dfrac{5x^2}{6}$

b) $\dfrac{6x^3}{7} \times \dfrac{2}{x^2} = \dfrac{6x}{7} \times \dfrac{2}{1} = \dfrac{6x \times 2}{7 \times 1} = \dfrac{12x}{7}$

c) $\dfrac{8x^2}{3y^2} \times \dfrac{x^3}{4y} = \dfrac{2x^2}{3y^2} \times \dfrac{x^3}{y} = \dfrac{2x^2 \times x^3}{3y^2 \times y} = \dfrac{2x^5}{3y^3}$

d) $\dfrac{8x^4}{3y} \times \dfrac{6y^2}{5x} = \dfrac{8x^3}{1} \times \dfrac{2y}{5} = \dfrac{8x^3 \times 2y}{1 \times 5} = \dfrac{16x^3y}{5}$

Q2 a) $\dfrac{x}{3} \div \dfrac{3}{x} = \dfrac{x}{3} \times \dfrac{x}{3} = \dfrac{x \times x}{3 \times 3} = \dfrac{x^2}{9}$

b) $\dfrac{4x^3}{3} \div \dfrac{x}{2} = \dfrac{4x^3}{3} \times \dfrac{2}{x} = \dfrac{4x^2}{3} \times \dfrac{2}{1} = \dfrac{4x^2 \times 2}{3 \times 1} = \dfrac{8x^2}{3}$

c) $\dfrac{3}{2x} \div \dfrac{6}{x^3} = \dfrac{3}{2x} \times \dfrac{x^3}{6} = \dfrac{1}{2} \times \dfrac{x^2}{2} = \dfrac{1 \times x^2}{2 \times 2} = \dfrac{x^2}{4}$

d) $\dfrac{2x^3}{3y} \div \dfrac{4x}{y^2} = \dfrac{2x^3}{3y} \times \dfrac{y^2}{4x} = \dfrac{x^2}{3} \times \dfrac{y}{2} = \dfrac{x^2 \times y}{3 \times 2} = \dfrac{x^2y}{6}$

Q3 $\dfrac{x+2}{4} \times \dfrac{x}{3x+6} = \dfrac{x+2}{4} \times \dfrac{x}{3(x+2)}$

$= \dfrac{1}{4} \times \dfrac{x}{3} = \dfrac{1 \times x}{4 \times 3} = \dfrac{x}{12}$

Q4 $\dfrac{4x}{5} \div \dfrac{4x^2+8x}{15} = \dfrac{4x}{5} \times \dfrac{15}{4x(x+2)}$

$= \dfrac{1}{1} \times \dfrac{3}{(x+2)} = \dfrac{3}{(x+2)}$

Q5 $\dfrac{2x^2-2}{x} \times \dfrac{5x}{3x-3} = \dfrac{2(x-1)(x+1)}{x} \times \dfrac{5x}{3(x-1)}$

$= \dfrac{2(x+1)}{1} \times \dfrac{5}{3} = \dfrac{2(x+1) \times 5}{1 \times 3} = \dfrac{10(x+1)}{3}$

Q6 $\dfrac{2x^2+8x}{x^2-2x} \times \dfrac{x-1}{x+4} = \dfrac{2x(x+4)}{x(x-2)} \times \dfrac{x-1}{x+4}$

$= \dfrac{2}{x-2} \times \dfrac{x-1}{1} = \dfrac{2(x-1)}{x-2}$

Q7 $\dfrac{x^2-4}{9} \div \dfrac{x-2}{3} = \dfrac{(x+2)(x-2)}{9} \times \dfrac{3}{x-2}$

$= \dfrac{x+2}{3} \times \dfrac{1}{1} = \dfrac{x+2}{3}$

Q8 $\dfrac{2}{x^2+4x} \div \dfrac{1}{x+4} = \dfrac{2}{x(x+4)} \times \dfrac{x+4}{1} = \dfrac{2}{x} \times \dfrac{1}{1} = \dfrac{2}{x}$

Q9 $\dfrac{x^2+4x+3}{x^2+5x+6} \times \dfrac{x^2+2x}{x+1} = \dfrac{(x+1)(x+3)}{(x+2)(x+3)} \times \dfrac{x(x+2)}{x+1}$

$= \dfrac{1}{1} \times \dfrac{x}{1} = x$

Q10 $\dfrac{x^2+5x+6}{x^2-2x-3} \times \dfrac{3x+3}{x^2+2x} = \dfrac{(x+2)(x+3)}{(x-3)(x+1)} \times \dfrac{3(x+1)}{x(x+2)}$

$= \dfrac{x+3}{x-3} \times \dfrac{3}{x} = \dfrac{3(x+3)}{x(x-3)}$

Q11 $\dfrac{x^2 - 4}{6x - 3} \times \dfrac{2x^2 + 5x - 3}{x^2 + 2x}$

$= \dfrac{(x + 2)(x - 2)}{3(2x - 1)} \times \dfrac{(2x - 1)(x + 3)}{x(x + 2)}$

$= \dfrac{x - 2}{3} \times \dfrac{x + 3}{x} = \dfrac{(x - 2)(x + 3)}{3x}$

Q12 $\dfrac{x^2 + 7x + 6}{4x - 4} \div \dfrac{x^2 + 8x + 12}{x^2 - x}$

$= \dfrac{(x + 1)(x + 6)}{4(x - 1)} \times \dfrac{x(x - 1)}{(x + 2)(x + 6)}$

$= \dfrac{x + 1}{4} \times \dfrac{x}{x + 2} = \dfrac{x(x + 1)}{4(x + 2)}$

Q13 $\dfrac{x^2 + 4x + 4}{x^2 - 4x + 3} \times \dfrac{x^2 - 2x - 3}{2x^2 - 2x} \times \dfrac{4x - 4}{x^2 + 2x}$

$= \dfrac{(x + 2)^2}{(x - 3)(x - 1)} \times \dfrac{(x - 3)(x + 1)}{2x(x - 1)} \times \dfrac{4(x - 1)}{x(x + 2)}$

$= \dfrac{x + 2}{x - 1} \times \dfrac{x + 1}{x} \times \dfrac{2}{x} = \dfrac{2(x + 2)(x + 1)}{x^2(x - 1)}$

Q14 $\dfrac{x}{6x + 12} \div \dfrac{x^2 - x}{x + 2} \times \dfrac{3x - 3}{x + 1}$

$= \dfrac{x}{6(x + 2)} \times \dfrac{x + 2}{x(x - 1)} \times \dfrac{3(x - 1)}{x + 1}$

$= \dfrac{1}{2} \times \dfrac{1}{1} \times \dfrac{1}{x + 1} = \dfrac{1}{2(x + 1)}$

Q15 $\dfrac{x^2 + 5x}{2x^2 + 7x + 3} \times \dfrac{2x + 1}{x^3 - x^2} \div \dfrac{x + 5}{x^2 + x - 6}$

$= \dfrac{x(x + 5)}{(2x + 1)(x + 3)} \times \dfrac{2x + 1}{x^2(x - 1)} \times \dfrac{(x + 3)(x - 2)}{x + 5}$

$= \dfrac{1}{1} \times \dfrac{1}{x(x - 1)} \times \dfrac{x - 2}{1} = \dfrac{x - 2}{x(x - 1)}$

2. Algebraic Division

Exercise 2.1 — Algebraic division

Q1 a) $x^3 - 14x^2 + 6x + 11 \equiv (Ax^2 + Bx + C)(x + 1) + D$

The degree of the quotient is the difference between the degrees of the polynomial and the divisor, in this case $3 - 1 = 2$. The degree of the remainder must be less than the degree of the divisor (1) so it must be 0.

Set $x = -1$: $-1 - 14 - 6 + 11 = D$, so $D = -10$.

Set $x = 0$: $11 = C + D$, so $C = 21$.

Equating the coefficients of x^3 gives $1 = A$.

Equating the coefficients of x^2 gives:
$-14 = A + B$, so $B = -15$.

So $x^3 - 14x^2 + 6x + 11 \equiv (x^2 - 15x + 21)(x + 1) - 10$.

Quotient: $x^2 - 15x + 21$
Remainder: -10

b) $2x^3 + 5x^2 - 8x - 17 \equiv (Ax^2 + Bx + C)(x - 2) + D$

Set $x = 2$: $16 + 20 - 16 - 17 = D$, so $D = 3$.

Set $x = 0$: $-17 = -2C + D$, so $C = 10$.

Equating the coefficients of x^3 gives $2 = A$.

Equating the coefficients of x^2 gives:
$5 = -2A + B$, so $B = 9$.

So $2x^3 + 5x^2 - 8x - 17 \equiv (2x^2 + 9x + 10)(x - 2) + 3$.

Quotient: $2x^2 + 9x + 10$
Remainder: 3

c) $2x^3 + 4x^2 - 5x + 2 \equiv (Ax + B)(x^2 - 2x + 1) + Cx + D$

$\equiv (Ax + B)(x - 1)^2 + Cx + D$

Equating the coefficients of x^3 gives $2 = A$.

Equating the coefficients of x^2 gives $4 = B - 2A$, so $B = 8$.

Set $x = 0$: $2 = B + D$, so $D = -6$.

Set $x = 1$: $2 + 4 - 5 + 2 = C + D$, so $C = 9$.

So $2x^3 + 4x^2 - 5x + 2 \equiv (2x + 8)(x^2 - 2x + 1) + 9x - 6$.

Quotient: $2x + 8$
Remainder: $9x - 6$

Q2 $6x^4 + 11x^3 + 9x^2 + 15x - 2$
$\equiv (Ax^2 + Bx + C)(2x^2 + x + 3) + Dx + E$

Equating the coefficients of x^4 gives $6 = 2A$, so $A = 3$.

Equating the coefficients of x^3 gives $11 = A + 2B$,
so $B = 4$.

Equating the coefficients of x^2 gives $9 = 3A + B + 2C$,
so $C = -2$.

Set $x = 0$: $-2 = 3C + E$, so $E = 4$.

Set $x = 1$: $6 + 11 + 9 + 15 - 2 = 34 + D$, so $D = 5$.

So $6x^4 + 11x^3 + 9x^2 + 15x - 2$
$\equiv (3x^2 + 4x - 2)(2x^2 + x + 3) + 5x + 4$

Quotient: $3x^2 + 4x - 2$
Remainder: $5x + 4$

Q3 a)

$$
\begin{array}{r}
x^2 - 15x + 21 \text{ r } -10 \\
x + 1 \overline{) x^3 - 14x^2 + 6x + 11} \\
-\underline{x^3 + x^2} \\
-15x^2 + 6x \\
-\underline{15x^2 - 15x} \\
21x + 11 \\
-\underline{21x + 21} \\
-10
\end{array}
$$

Quotient: $x^2 - 15x + 21$
Remainder: -10

b)

$$
\begin{array}{r}
x^2 + 7x - 6 \text{ r } 5 \\
x + 3 \overline{) x^3 + 10x^2 + 15x - 13} \\
-\underline{x^3 + 3x^2} \\
7x^2 + 15x \\
-\underline{7x^2 + 21x} \\
-6x - 13 \\
-\underline{-6x - 18} \\
5
\end{array}
$$

Quotient: $x^2 + 7x - 6$
Remainder: 5

c)

$$
\begin{array}{r}
2x^2 + 9x + 10 \text{ r } 3 \\
x - 2 \overline{) 2x^3 + 5x^2 - 8x - 17} \\
-\underline{2x^3 - 4x^2} \\
9x^2 - 8x \\
-\underline{9x^2 - 18x} \\
10x - 17 \\
-\underline{10x - 20} \\
3
\end{array}
$$

Quotient: $2x^2 + 9x + 10$
Remainder: 3

d)

$$x + 5 \overline{)\begin{array}{l} 3x^2 - 15x - 3 \quad \text{r } 24 \\ 3x^3 + 0x^2 - 78x + 9 \end{array}}$$

$$\begin{array}{l} - \ \underline{3x^3 + 15x^2} \\ \quad -15x^2 - 78x \\ \quad - \ \underline{-15x^2 - 75x} \\ \qquad\qquad -3x + 9 \\ \qquad\qquad - \ \underline{-3x - 15} \\ \qquad\qquad\qquad\quad 24 \end{array}$$

Quotient: $3x^2 - 15x - 3$
Remainder: 24

e)

$$x - 1 \overline{)\begin{array}{l} x^3 + x^2 + x + 1 \\ x^4 + 0x^3 + 0x^2 + 0x - 1 \end{array}}$$

$$\begin{array}{l} - \ \underline{x^4 - x^3} \\ \quad x^3 + 0x^2 \\ \quad - \ \underline{x^3 - x^2} \\ \qquad x^2 + 0x \\ \qquad - \ \underline{x^2 - x} \\ \qquad\qquad x - 1 \\ \qquad\qquad - \ \underline{x - 1} \\ \qquad\qquad\qquad 0 \end{array}$$

Quotient: $x^3 + x^2 + x + 1$
Remainder: 0

f)

$$2x - 3 \overline{)\begin{array}{l} 4x^2 + 3x + 5 \quad \text{r } 25 \\ 8x^3 - 6x^2 + x + 10 \end{array}}$$

$$\begin{array}{l} - \ \underline{8x^3 - 12x^2} \\ \quad 6x^2 + x \\ \quad - \ \underline{6x^2 - 9x} \\ \qquad 10x + 10 \\ \qquad - \ \underline{10x - 15} \\ \qquad\qquad 25 \end{array}$$

Quotient: $4x^2 + 3x + 5$
Remainder: 25

g)

$$x^2 - 2x + 1 \overline{)\begin{array}{l} 2x + 8 \quad \text{r } 9x - 6 \\ 2x^3 + 4x^2 - 5x + 2 \end{array}}$$

$$\begin{array}{l} - \ \underline{2x^3 - 4x^2 + 2x} \\ \quad 8x^2 - 7x + 2 \\ \quad - \ \underline{8x^2 - 16x + 8} \\ \qquad\qquad 9x - 6 \end{array}$$

Quotient: $2x + 8$
Remainder: $9x - 6$

h)

$$2x^2 + x + 3 \overline{)\begin{array}{l} 3x^2 + 4x - 2 \quad \text{r } 5x + 4 \\ 6x^4 + 11x^3 + 9x^2 + 15x - 2 \end{array}}$$

$$\begin{array}{l} - \ \underline{6x^4 + 3x^3 + 9x^2} \\ \quad 8x^3 + 0x^2 + 15x \\ \quad - \ \underline{8x^3 + 4x^2 + 12x} \\ \qquad -4x^2 + 3x - 2 \\ \qquad - \ \underline{-4x^2 - 2x - 6} \\ \qquad\qquad 5x + 4 \end{array}$$

Quotient: $3x^2 + 4x - 2$
Remainder: $5x + 4$

Q4 Quotient: $5x^2 + x - 3$
Remainder: 24

Q5 Quotient: $3x - 11$
Remainder: $32x - 34$

Q6 Quotient: $3x^2 + 1$
Remainder: 0

3. Functions and Mappings

Exercise 3.1 — Mappings and functions

Q1
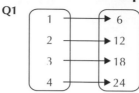

Q2
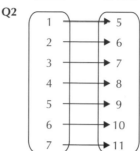

Q3
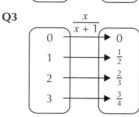

Range: $\left\{0, \frac{1}{2}, \frac{2}{3}, \frac{3}{4}\right\}$

Q4
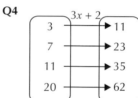

Domain: {3, 7, 11, 20}

Q5 $f(2) = 3(2) + 1 = 7$, $f(-1) = 3(-1) + 1 = -2$

Q6 $g(0) = \dfrac{1}{2(0) + 1} = 1$, $g(2) = \dfrac{1}{2(2) + 1} = \dfrac{1}{5}$

Q7 $h\left(\dfrac{\pi}{2}\right) = \sin\left(\dfrac{\pi}{2}\right) = 1$, $h\left(\dfrac{5\pi}{6}\right) = \sin\left(\dfrac{5\pi}{6}\right) = \dfrac{1}{2}$

Q8 $f(1) = \dfrac{1}{2 + \log_{10}1} = \dfrac{1}{2 + 0} = \dfrac{1}{2}$

$f(100) = \dfrac{1}{2 + \log_{10}100} = \dfrac{1}{2 + 2} = \dfrac{1}{4}$

Q9 **a)** Yes, it is a function.

b) No, because the map is not defined for elements 4 and 5 of the domain.

c) No, because a value in the domain can map to more than one value in the range.

Exercise 3.2 — Graphs of functions

Q1 **a)** Yes, it is a function.

b) No, because a value of x can map to more than one value of f(x).

Q2 a)

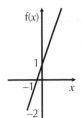

Range: f(x) ≥ –2

b)

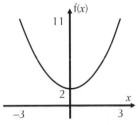

Range: 2 ≤ f(x) ≤ 11

c)

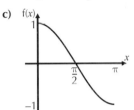

Range: –1 ≤ f(x) ≤ 1

d)

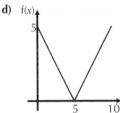

Range: 0 ≤ f(x) ≤ 5

Q3 a) The range shown is $3 \le f(x) \le 11$, so the domain is: $\frac{3-1}{2} < x < \frac{11-1}{2}$, which is $1 < x < 5$.

b) The domain shown is $-1 \le x \le 4$.
The range is between f(2) and f(–1):
$((2)^2 - 4(2) + 5) \le f(x) \le ((-1)^2 - 4(-1) + 5)$, which is $1 \le f(x) \le 10$.

Q4 When $x = 0$, $f(x) = 2$.
For large x, $x + 2 \approx x + 1$ so as $x \to \infty$,
$\frac{x+2}{x+1} \to 1$. So f(x) = 1 is an asymptote.
So the range is $1 < f(x) \le 2$.

Q5 The function $f(x) = \frac{1}{x-2}$ is undefined when $x = 2$,
so $a = 2$.

Q6 The function $f(x) = +\sqrt{9 - x^2}$ is only defined when $x^2 \le 9$, i.e. when $-3 < x < 3$. So $a = -3$ and $b = 3$.

Q7 The graph of $h(x) = +\sqrt{x + 1}$ is shown below.

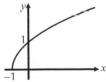

h(x) is undefined when x is less than –1.
Restricting the domain to $x \ge -1$ would make h(x) a function.

Q8 The graph of k : $x \to \tan x$ is shown below.

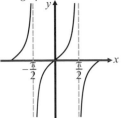

$\tan x$ is undefined at e.g. $-\frac{\pi}{2}$ and $\frac{\pi}{2}$
(it is also undefined periodically either side).
Restricting the domain to e.g. $-\frac{\pi}{2} < x < \frac{\pi}{2}$ would make this a function.

Q9 The function $m(x) = \frac{1}{x^2 - 4}$ is undefined when $x = 2$ and when $x = -2$.
So the largest continuous domain that makes it a function would be either $x > 2$ or $x < -2$.

Q10 a) It is not a function because it is not defined for all values of x in the domain (it's not defined at $x = 0$ or $x = 4$).

b) $x \in \mathbb{R}, x \neq 0$

Exercise 3.3 — Types of function

It helps to sketch the graph of each function to identify its type.

Q1 a) One-to-one:

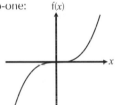

b) Many-to-one:

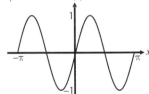

c) One-to-one:

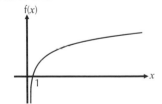

d) Many-to-one:

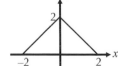

e) Many-to-one: $f(x)$

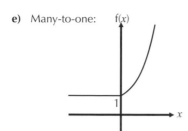

4. Composite Functions

Exercise 4.1 — Composite functions

Q1 a) Do $g(3) = 2(3) + 1 = 7$
then $f(7) = 7^2 = 49$, so $fg(3) = 49$.

b) $gf(3) = g(3^2) = g(9) = 2(9) + 1 = 19$

c) $f^2(5) = f(5^2) = f(25) = 25^2 = 625$

d) $g^2(2) = g(2(2) + 1) = g(5) = 2(5) + 1 = 11$

Q2 $fg\left(\frac{\pi}{2}\right) = f\left(2\left(\frac{\pi}{2}\right)\right) = f(\pi) = \sin \pi = 0$
$gf\left(\frac{\pi}{2}\right) = g\left(\sin\left(\frac{\pi}{2}\right)\right) = g(1) = 2(1) = 2$

Q3 a) $gf(1) = g\left(\frac{3}{1+2}\right) = g(1) = 2(1) = 2.$
$fg(1) = f(2(1)) = f(2) = \frac{3}{2+2} = \frac{3}{4}.$
$f^2(4) = f\left(\frac{3}{4+2}\right) = f\left(\frac{1}{2}\right) = \frac{3}{\frac{1}{2}+2} = \frac{6}{1+4} = 1\frac{1}{5}$

b) $g(-1) = -2$, and $f(-2)$ has a denominator of 0 which is undefined.

Q4 a) $fg(x) = f(x^2) = 2x^2 - 1$

b) $gf(x) = g(2x - 1) = (2x - 1)^2$

c) $f^2(x) = f(2x - 1) = 2(2x - 1) - 1 = 4x - 3$

Q5 a) $fg(x) = f(2x) = \cos 2x$

b) $gf(x) = 2\cos x$

Q6 $fg(x) = f(x + 4) = \frac{2}{x + 4 - 1} = \frac{2}{x + 3}$
$gf(x) = g\left(\frac{2}{x-1}\right) = \frac{2}{x-1} + 4$
$= \frac{2}{x-1} + \frac{4x-4}{x-1} = \frac{4x-2}{x-1} = \frac{2(2x-1)}{x-1}$

Q7 $f^2(x) = f\left(\frac{x}{1-x}\right) = \frac{\frac{x}{1-x}}{1 - \frac{x}{1-x}} = \frac{x}{(1-x) - x} = \frac{x}{1-2x}$

$gfg(x) = gf(x^2) = g\left(\frac{x^2}{1-x^2}\right) = \left(\frac{x^2}{1-x^2}\right)^2 = \frac{x^4}{(1-x^2)^2}$

Q8 a) $fg(x) = f(2x - 3) = (2x - 3)^2$, range: $fg(x) \geq 0$.

b) $gf(x) = g(x^2) = 2x^2 - 3$, range: $gf(x) \geq -3$.

Q9 a) $fg(x) = f(5x) = \frac{1}{5x}$, domain $x > 0$, range: $fg(x) > 0$.

b) $gf(x) = g\left(\frac{1}{x}\right) = \frac{5}{x}$, domain $x > 0$, range: $gf(x) > 0$.

Q10 $fgh(x) = fg(x^2 + 1) = f(5(x^2 + 1) - 1)$
$= f(5x^2 + 4) = 3(5x^2 + 4) + 2 = 15x^2 + 14$

Exercise 4.2 — Solving composite function equations

Q1 $fg(x) = f(3x - 4) = 2(3x - 4) + 1 = 6x - 7$
$6x - 7 = 23$
$x = 5$

Q2 $gf(x) = g\left(\frac{1}{x}\right) = \frac{2}{x} + 5$
$\frac{2}{x} + 5 = 6 \Rightarrow x = 2$

Q3 $gf(x) = g(x^2) = \frac{x^2}{x^2 - 3}$
$\frac{x^2}{x^2 - 3} = 4 \Rightarrow x^2 = 4x^2 - 12 \Rightarrow x^2 = 4$
$x = 2$ or $x = -2$

Q4 $gf(x) = g(x + 3) = (x + 3)^2 - 1$
$(x + 3)^2 - 1 = 3 \Rightarrow x = \pm\sqrt{4} - 3$
$x = -1$ or $x = -5$

Q5 $fg(x) = f(3x - 2) = (3x - 2)^2 + 1$
$(3x - 2)^2 + 1 = 50 \Rightarrow x = \frac{\pm\sqrt{49} + 2}{3}$
$x = 3$ or $x = -\frac{5}{3}$

Q6 $fg(x) = f(2x + 1) = 2^{(2x + 1)}$
$2^{(2x + 1)} = 32 \Rightarrow 2x + 1 = 5$
$x = 2$

Q7 $fg(x) = f(3 - x) = \log_{10}(3 - x)$
$\log_{10}(3 - x) = 0 \Rightarrow 3 - x = 1$
$x = 2$

Q8 $fg(x) = f(x^2 + 2x) = 2^{(x^2 + 2x)}$
$2^{(x^2 + 2x)} = 8 \Rightarrow x^2 + 2x = 3 \Rightarrow (x - 1)(x + 3) = 0$
$x = 1$ or $x = -3$

Q9 $fg(x) = f(2x - 1) = \frac{2x - 1}{2x - 1 + 1} = \frac{2x - 1}{2x} = 1 - \frac{1}{2x}$
$gf(x) = g\left(\frac{x}{x + 1}\right) = 2\left(\frac{x}{x + 1}\right) - 1 = \frac{x - 1}{x + 1}$
$1 - \frac{1}{2x} = \frac{x - 1}{x + 1} \Rightarrow 2x(x + 1) - (x + 1) = 2x(x - 1)$
$x = \frac{1}{3}$

Q10 $fg(x) = f(x + 1) = 2^{(x + 1)}$
$gf(x) = g(2^x) = 2^x + 1$
$2^{(x + 1)} = 2^x + 1$
$2 = 1 + \frac{1}{2^x} \Rightarrow 2^x = 1 \Rightarrow \log_2 1 = x$
$x = 0$

5. Inverse Functions

Exercise 5.1 — Inverse functions and their graphs

Q1 Yes, as the graph shows a one-to-one function.

Q2 No, as it is a many-to-one map, and many-to-one functions do not have inverse functions.

Q3 No, as $\sin x$ is a many-to-one function over the domain $x \in \mathbb{R}$.

Q4 No, as it is a many-to-one function over the domain $x \in \mathbb{R}$.

Q5 Yes, as it is a one-to-one function over the domain $x \geq 4$.

Q6 a) $f(x) = 3x + 4$ with domain $x \in \mathbb{R}$ has a range $f(x) \in \mathbb{R}$.

Replace f(x) with y: $y = 3x + 4$

Rearrange: $x = \dfrac{y - 4}{3}$

Replace with $f^{-1}(x)$ and x: $f^{-1}(x) = \dfrac{x - 4}{3}$.

The domain of $f^{-1}(x)$ is $x \in \mathbb{R}$
and the range is $f^{-1}(x) \in \mathbb{R}$.

b) $f(x) = 5(x - 2)$ with domain $x \in \mathbb{R}$ has a range $f(x) \in \mathbb{R}$.
Replace f(x) with y: $y = 5(x - 2)$

Rearrange: $x = \dfrac{y}{5} + 2$

Replace with $f^{-1}(x)$ and x: $f^{-1}(x) = \dfrac{x}{5} + 2$.

The domain of $f^{-1}(x)$ is $x \in \mathbb{R}$
and the range is $f^{-1}(x) \in \mathbb{R}$.

c) $f(x) = \dfrac{1}{x + 2}$ with domain $x > -2$ has a range $f(x) > 0$.

Replace f(x) with y: $y = \dfrac{1}{x + 2}$

Rearrange: $x = \dfrac{1}{y} - 2$

Replace with $f^{-1}(x)$ and x: $f^{-1}(x) = \dfrac{1}{x} - 2$.

The domain of $f^{-1}(x)$ is the range of f(x): $x > 0$.
The range of $f^{-1}(x)$ is the domain of f(x): $f^{-1}(x) > -2$.

d) $f(x) = x^2 + 3$ with domain $x > 0$ has a range $f(x) > 3$.
Replace f(x) with y: $y = x^2 + 3$
Rearrange: $x = \sqrt{y - 3}$
Replace with $f^{-1}(x)$ and x: $f^{-1}(x) = \sqrt{x - 3}$.

The domain of $f^{-1}(x)$ is the range of f(x): $x > 3$.
The range of $f^{-1}(x)$ is the domain of f(x): $f^{-1}(x) > 0$.

Q7 a) $f(x) = \dfrac{3x}{x + 1}$ with domain $x > -1$ has a range $f(x) < 3$ — you can work this out by sketching the graph. If you consider what happens as $x \to \infty$ you'll see that f(x) approaches 3.

Replace f(x) with y: $y = \dfrac{3x}{x + 1}$
Rearrange: $y(x + 1) = 3x \Rightarrow yx + y = 3x$

$\Rightarrow (3 - y)x = y \Rightarrow x = \dfrac{y}{3 - y}$

Replace with $f^{-1}(x)$ and x: $f^{-1}(x) = \dfrac{x}{3 - x}$.
The domain of $f^{-1}(x)$ is the range of f(x): $x < 3$.
The range of $f^{-1}(x)$ is the domain of f(x): $f^{-1}(x) > -1$.

b) $f^{-1}(2) = \dfrac{2}{3 - 2} = 2$

c) $f^{-1}\left(\dfrac{1}{2}\right) = \dfrac{\frac{1}{2}}{3 - \frac{1}{2}} = \dfrac{1}{6 - 1} = \dfrac{1}{5}$

Q8 a) $f(x) = \dfrac{x - 4}{x + 3}$ with domain $x > -3$ has a range $f(x) < 1$ — again, sketching the graph will help. If you consider what happens as $x \to \infty$ you'll see that f(x) approaches 1.

Replace f(x) with y: $y = \dfrac{x - 4}{x + 3}$
Rearrange: $y(x + 3) = x - 4 \Rightarrow yx + 3y = x - 4$

$x(1 - y) = 3y + 4 \Rightarrow x = \dfrac{3y + 4}{1 - y}$

Replace with $f^{-1}(x)$ and x: $f^{-1}(x) = \dfrac{3x + 4}{1 - x}$.
The domain of $f^{-1}(x)$ is the range of f(x): $x < 1$.
The range of $f^{-1}(x)$ is the domain of f(x): $f^{-1}(x) > -3$.

b) $f^{-1}(0) = \dfrac{3(0) + 4}{1 - 0} = 4$

c) $f^{-1}\left(-\dfrac{2}{5}\right) = \dfrac{3\left(-\frac{2}{5}\right) + 4}{1 + \frac{2}{5}} = \dfrac{-6 + 20}{5 + 2} = \dfrac{14}{7} = 2$

Q9 f(x) has a domain of $x > 3$, and a range of $f(x) \in \mathbb{R}$.
So $f^{-1}(x)$ has a domain $x \in \mathbb{R}$ and range $f^{-1}(x) > 3$.

Q10 f(x) has a domain of $1 \le x \le 7$, which will give a range of $(4(1) - 2) \le f(x) \le (4(7) - 2)$, $2 \le f(x) \le 26$.
So $f^{-1}(x)$ has a domain $2 \le x \le 26$ and range $1 \le f^{-1}(x) \le 7$.

Q11 f(x) has a domain of $x < 2$, and a range of $f(x) < 1$.
So $f^{-1}(x)$ has a domain $x < 1$ and range $f^{-1}(x) < 2$.

Q12

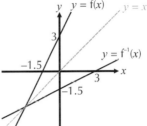

Q13 a)

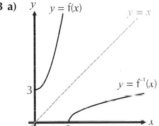

b) f(x) has a domain of $x > 0$, which will give a range of $f(x) > 3$.
So $f^{-1}(x)$ has a domain $x > 3$ and range $f^{-1}(x) > 0$.

Q14 a)

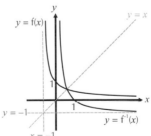

b) There is one point where the graphs intersect.

Q15 a) $f(x) = \dfrac{1}{x - 3}$ with domain $x > 3$ has a range $f(x) > 0$.

Replace f(x) with y: $y = \dfrac{1}{x - 3}$

Rearrange: $x = \dfrac{1}{y} + 3$

Replace with $f^{-1}(x)$ and x: $f^{-1}(x) = \dfrac{1}{x} + 3$.
The domain of $f^{-1}(x)$ is the range of f(x): $x > 0$.
The range of $f^{-1}(x)$ is the domain of f(x): $f^{-1}(x) > 3$.

b)

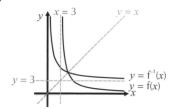

c) There is one solution as the graphs intersect once.

d) $\dfrac{1}{x-3} - \dfrac{1}{x} + 3$

$x^2 - 3x - 1 = 0$

So using the quadratic formula gives:

$x = \dfrac{3 + \sqrt{13}}{2}$

We ignore the negative solutions to the quadratic equation because we're only considering the domain $x > 3$.

6. Modulus

Exercise 6.1 — The graphs of $|f(x)|$ and $f(|x|)$

Q1 a)

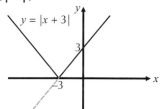

b)

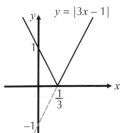

c)

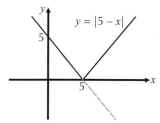

d)

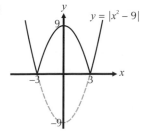

e)

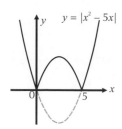

Q2

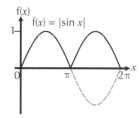

Q3

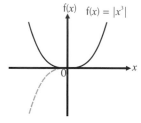

Q4

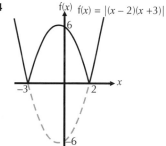

Q5 a) $y = f(|x|)$

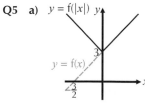

b)

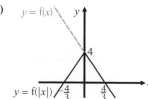

c) $y = f(|x|)$

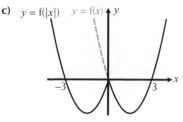

d) $y = f(|x|)$ $y = f(x)$
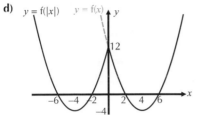

e) $y = f(|x|)$
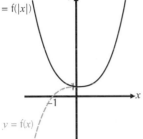

f) $y = f(|x|)$
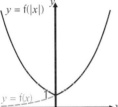

g)
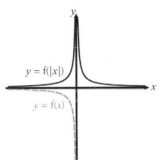

h) $y = f(|x|)$ $y = f(x)$
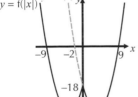

i) $y = f(|x|)$
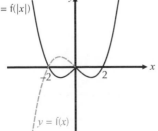

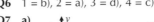
Q6   1 = b), 2 = a), 3 = d), 4 = c)

Q7 a)
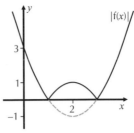

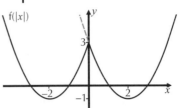

b)
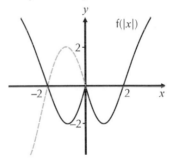

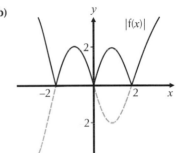

Q8 a)
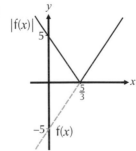

b)
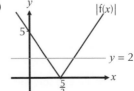

The line $y = 2$ intersects with the line $|3x - 5|$ in two places so there are 2 solutions to $|3x - 5| = 2$.

Q9

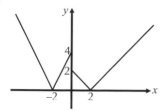

Q10 a)

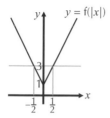

b) There are two solutions to $4|x| + 1 = 3$.
Reading off the graph, these are:
$x = \frac{1}{2}$ and $x = -\frac{1}{2}$.

Q11 1 = d), 2 = b), 3 = a), 4 = c)

Exercise 6.2 — Solving modulus equations

Q1 a) Draw the line $y = 2$ to show how many times it intersects with the curve:

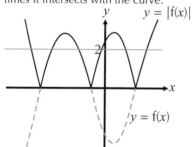

There are 6 points of intersection, so there are 6 solutions to the equation $|f(x)| = 2$.

b) The graph shows that 3 of the points of intersection occur where $y = |f(x)|$ is the same as $y = f(x)$, so 3 solutions could be found by solving $f(x) = 2$.

c) The other 3 solutions can be found by solving $-f(x) = 2$.

Q2

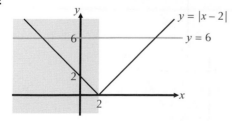

The graph shows that there are two solutions to $|x - 2| = 6$. $x - 2 \geq 0$ for $x \geq 2$
$x - 2 < 0$ for $x < 2$ (shaded)

So there are two equations to solve:
(1) $x - 2 = 6 \Rightarrow x = 8$
(this is valid as it's in the range $x \geq 2$)
(2) $-(x - 2) = 6 \Rightarrow x = -4$
(this is also valid as it's in the range $x < 2$)
So the two solutions are $x = 8$ and $x = -4$.

Q3

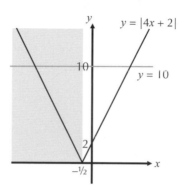

The graph shows that there are two solutions to $|4x + 2| = 10$.

$4x + 2 \geq 0$ for $x \geq -\frac{1}{2}$

$4x + 2 < 0$ for $x < -\frac{1}{2}$ (shaded)

So there are two equations to solve:
(1) $4x + 2 = 10 \Rightarrow x = 2$

(this is valid as it's in the range $x \geq -\frac{1}{2}$)
(2) $-(4x + 2) = 10 \Rightarrow x = -3$

(this is also valid as it's in the range $x < -\frac{1}{2}$)
So the two solutions are $x = 2$ and $x = -3$.

Q4 Rearranging the equation gives $|3x - 4| = 1$.

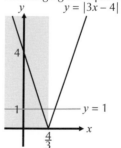

The graph shows that there are two solutions to $|3x - 4| = 1$.

$3x - 4 \geq 0$ for $x \geq \frac{4}{3}$

$3x - 4 < 0$ for $x < \frac{4}{3}$ (shaded)

So there are two equations to solve:
(1) $3x - 4 = 1 \Rightarrow x = \frac{5}{3}$
(this is valid as it's in the range $x \geq \frac{4}{3}$)
(2) $-(3x - 4) = 1 \Rightarrow x = 1$

(this is also valid as it's in the range $x < \frac{4}{3}$)
So the two solutions are $x = \frac{5}{3}$ and $x = 1$.

Q5

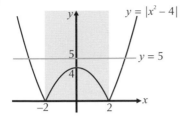

The graph shows that there are two solutions, both in the positive area of the graph where $x \le -2$ or $x \ge 2$.

So there is just one equation to solve:

$x^2 - 4 = 5 \Rightarrow x = \pm 3$ (both of these solutions are valid as they are in the range $x \le -2$ or $x \ge 2$).

Q6

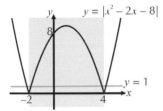

The graph shows that there are four solutions to $|x^2 - 2x - 8| = 1$.

$x^2 - 2x - 8 \ge 0$ for $x \le -2$ and $x \ge 4$

$x^2 - 2x - 8 < 0$ for $-2 < x < 4$ (shaded)

So there are two equations to solve:

(1) $x^2 - 2x - 8 = 1 \Rightarrow x^2 - 2x - 9 = 0$
Using the quadratic formula $x = 1 \pm \sqrt{10}$
(both of these solutions are valid as they are in the range $x \le -2$ or $x \ge 4$)

(2) $-(x^2 - 2x - 8) = 1 \Rightarrow x^2 - 2x - 7 = 0$
Using the quadratic formula $x = 1 \pm \sqrt{8}$
(both of these solutions are valid as they are in the range $-2 < x < 4$)

So the four solutions are $x = 1 + \sqrt{10}$, $x = 1 - \sqrt{10}$, $x = 1 + 2\sqrt{2}$ and $x = 1 - 2\sqrt{2}$.

Q7

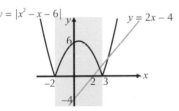

The graph shows that there are two solutions to $|x^2 - x - 6| = 2x - 4$.

$x^2 - x - 6 \ge 0$ for $x \le -2$ and $x \ge 3$

$x^2 - x - 6 < 0$ for $-2 < x < 3$ (shaded)

So there are two equations to solve:

(1) $x^2 - x - 6 = 2x - 4 \Rightarrow x^2 - 3x - 2 = 0$

Using the quadratic formula $x = \dfrac{3 \pm \sqrt{17}}{2}$, but the only valid solution (in the range $x \ge 3$) is $\dfrac{3 + \sqrt{17}}{2}$.

(2) $-(x^2 - x - 6) = 2x - 4 \Rightarrow x^2 + x - 10 = 0$

Using the quadratic formula $x = \dfrac{-1 \pm \sqrt{41}}{2}$,

but the only valid solution (in the range $-2 < x < 3$) is $\dfrac{-1 + \sqrt{41}}{2}$.

So the solutions are $x = \dfrac{3 + \sqrt{17}}{2}$ and $x = \dfrac{-1 + \sqrt{41}}{2}$.

Q8 a)

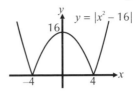

b)

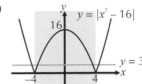

The graph shows that there are four solutions to $|x^2 - 16| = 3$.

$x^2 - 16 \ge 0$ for $x \le -4$ and $x \ge 4$

$x^2 - 16 < 0$ for $-4 < x < 4$ (shaded)

So there are two equations to solve:

(1) $x^2 - 16 = 3 \Rightarrow x = \pm\sqrt{19}$
(both of these solutions are valid as they are in the range $x \le -4$ or $x \ge 4$)

(2) $-(x^2 - 16) = 3 \Rightarrow x = \pm\sqrt{13}$
(both of these solutions are valid as they are in the range $-4 < x < 4$)

So the four solutions are $x = \sqrt{19}$, $x = -\sqrt{19}$, $x = \sqrt{13}$ and $x = -\sqrt{13}$.

Q9 a)

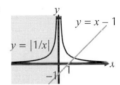

b) The graph shows that there is just one solution, in the positive area of the graph where $x > 0$.

So there is just one equation to solve:

$\dfrac{1}{x} = x - 1 \Rightarrow x^2 - x - 1 = 0 \Rightarrow x = \dfrac{1 \pm \sqrt{5}}{2}$.

But only $\dfrac{1 + \sqrt{5}}{2}$ is valid (i.e. in the range $x > 0$).

Q10 a)

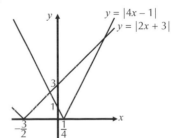

b) The graph shows that there are two solutions, one where both $2x + 3$ and $4x - 1$ are positive, and one where $2x + 3$ is positive but $4x - 1$ is negative.

So there are two equations to solve:

(1) $4x - 1 = 2x + 3 \Rightarrow x = 2$

(2) $-(4x - 1) = 2x + 3 \Rightarrow x = -\dfrac{1}{3}$

So the two solutions are $x = 2$ and $x = -\dfrac{1}{3}$.

Or using the algebraic method, solve:

$(2x + 3)^2 = (4x - 1)^2$

$4x^2 + 12x + 9 = 16x^2 - 8x + 1$

$3x^2 - 5x - 2 = 0$

$(3x + 1)(x - 2) = 0$

So $x = 2$ and $x = -\dfrac{1}{3}$.

Q11 a)

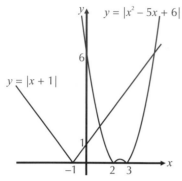

$y = |x^2 - 5x + 6|$

$y = |x + 1|$

b) The graph shows that there are two solutions, both of which where both f(x) and g(x) are positive.

So there is one equation to solve:

$x^2 - 5x + 6 = x + 1 \Rightarrow x^2 - 6x + 5 = 0$

$\Rightarrow (x - 5)(x - 1) = 0$

So the two solutions are $x = 5$ and $x = 1$.

7. Transformations of graphs

Exercise 7.1 — Transformations of graphs

Q1

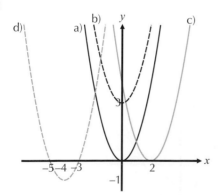

The coordinates of the turning points are:

a) (0, 0)   **b)** (0, 3)

c) (2, 0)   **d)** (−4, −1)

Q2 a)

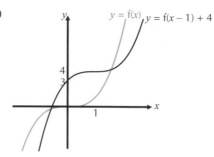

$y = f(x)$, $y = f(x - 1) + 4$

b) $y = (x - 1)^3 + 4$

Q3

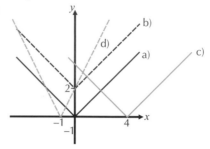

The transformations can be described as follows:

b) A translation of 2 up.

c) A translation of 4 right.

d) A translation of 1 left and a stretch vertically by a scale factor of 2.

Q4

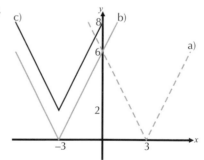

Q5

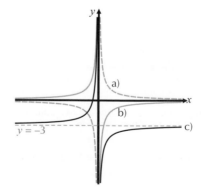

$y = -3$

Q6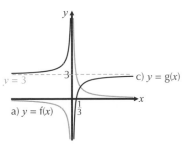

d) The minimum points on graph c) are at (90, 0) and (270, 0).

Q7 The maximum value of sin x is 1, and the minimum value is -1, so:

Transformed Function	New equation	Max value	Min value
f(x) + 2	sin x + 2	3	1
f(x – 90°)	sin(x – 90°)	1	–1
f(3x)	sin 3x	1	–1
4f(x)	4 sin x	4	–4

Q8 The point of inflection of x^3 is at (0, 0), so:

Transformed Function	New equation	Coordinates of point of inflection
f(x) + 1	$x^3 + 1$	(0, 1)
f(x – 2)	$(x – 2)^3$	(2, 0)
–f(x) – 3	$-x^3 – 3$	(0, –3)
f(–x) + 4	$-x^3 + 4$	(0, 4)

Q9 a)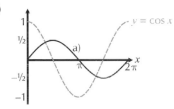

b) $y = \frac{1}{2}\cos\left(x - \frac{\pi}{2}\right)$

Q10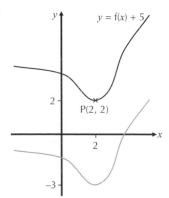

b) Reflect in the y-axis (or x-axis) and translate 3 up.

Q11

Original graph	New graph	Sequence of transformations
$y = x^3$	$y = (x – 4)^3 + 5$	Translate 4 right and 5 up.
$y = 4^x$	$y = 4^{3x} – 1$	Stretch horizontally by a factor of $\frac{1}{3}$ and translate 1 down.
$y = |x + 1|$	$y = 1 – |2x + 1|$	Stretch horizontally by a factor of $\frac{1}{2}$, reflect in the x-axis and translate 1 up.
$y = \sin x$	$y = -3 \sin 2x + 1$	Stretch horizontally by a factor of $\frac{1}{2}$, stretch vertically by a factor of 3, reflect in the x-axis and translate 1 up.

Q12 a) $y = 2x^2 – 4x + 6 = 2[x^2 – 2x + 3] = 2[(x – 1)^2 + 2]$

b) Translate 1 right, then translate 2 up, then stretch vertically by a factor of 2.

c)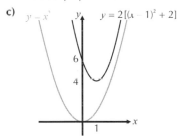

d) The minimum point is at (1, 4).
You can work out the minimum point by performing the transformations on the minimum point of the graph $y = x^2$ (which is (0, 0)).

Q13 a) Stretch horizontally, scale factor $\frac{1}{3}$, then stretch vertically, scale factor 4.

b) Stretch horizontally, scale factor $\frac{1}{2}$, then reflect in the x-axis, then translate 4 up.

c) Translate $\frac{\pi}{3}$ right, then stretch vertically, scale factor 2.

Q14 a)

b)

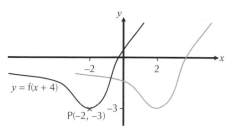

c)

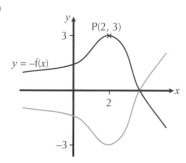

Q15 a)

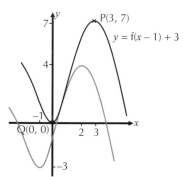

b)

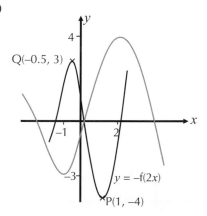

c)

Q(-3, 3) ... y = |f(x + 2)| ... P(0, 4)

Review Exercise — Chapter 1

Q1 a) $\dfrac{4x^2 - 25}{6x - 15} = \dfrac{(2x + 5)(2x - 5)}{3(2x - 5)} = \dfrac{2x + 5}{3}$

b) $\dfrac{2x + 3}{x - 2} \times \dfrac{4x - 8}{2x^2 - 3x - 9}$

$= \dfrac{2x + 3}{x - 2} \times \dfrac{4(x - 2)}{(2x + 3)(x - 3)}$

$= \dfrac{4}{x - 3}$

c) $\dfrac{x^2 - 3x}{x + 1} \div \dfrac{x}{2} = \dfrac{x(x - 3)}{x + 1} \times \dfrac{2}{x}$

$= \dfrac{x - 3}{x + 1} \times 2 = \dfrac{2(x - 3)}{x + 1}$

Q2 a) $\dfrac{x}{2x + 1} + \dfrac{3}{x^2} + \dfrac{1}{x}$

$= \dfrac{x^2(x)}{x^2(2x + 1)} + \dfrac{3(2x + 1)}{x^2(2x + 1)} + \dfrac{x(2x + 1)}{x^2(2x + 1)}$

$= \dfrac{x^3 + 6x + 3 + 2x^2 + x}{x^2(2x + 1)}$

$= \dfrac{x^3 + 2x^2 + 7x + 3}{x^2(2x + 1)}$

b) $\dfrac{2}{x^2 - 1} - \dfrac{3x}{x - 1} + \dfrac{x}{x + 1}$

$= \dfrac{2}{(x + 1)(x - 1)} - \dfrac{3x(x + 1)}{(x + 1)(x - 1)}$

$\qquad + \dfrac{x(x - 1)}{(x + 1)(x - 1)}$

$= \dfrac{2 - 3x^2 - 3x + x^2 - x}{(x + 1)(x - 1)} = \dfrac{2 - 2x^2 - 4x}{(x + 1)(x - 1)}$

$= \dfrac{2(1 - x^2 - 2x)}{(x + 1)(x - 1)}$

Q3
$$\begin{array}{r} x^2 - 2x + 7 \text{ r } -9 \\ x + 4 \overline{)\, x^3 + 2x^2 - x + 19} \\ -\ \underline{x^3 + 4x^2} \\ -2x^2 - x \\ -\ \underline{-2x^2 - 8x} \\ 7x + 19 \\ -\ \underline{7x + 28} \\ -9 \end{array}$$

so $(x^3 + 2x^2 - x + 19) \div (x + 4)$
$= x^2 - 2x + 7$ remainder -9.

Q4 $2x^3 + 8x^2 + 7x + 8 \equiv (Ax^2 + Bx + C)(x + 3) + D$.
Set $x = -3$: $2(-3)^3 + 8(-3)^2 + 7(-3) + 8 = 0 + D$
$\Rightarrow D = 5$.
Set $x = 0$: $0 + 8 = C(0 + 3) + D \Rightarrow C = 1$.
Equating the coefficients of x^3 gives $2 = A$.
Finally, equating the coefficients of x^2 gives
$8 = 3A + B \Rightarrow 8 = (3 \times 2) + B$, so $B = 2$.
So $2x^3 + 8x^2 + 7x + 8 = (2x^2 + 2x + 1)(x + 3) + 5$. The
result when $2x^3 + 8x^2 + 7x + 8$ is divided by $(x + 3)$ is
$2x^2 + 2x + 1$ remainder 5.

Q5 a) Range $f(x) \geq -16$. This is a function, and it's one-
to-one (the domain is restricted so every x-value
is mapped to only one value of $f(x)$).

b) To find the range of this function, you need to
find the minimum point of $x^2 - 7x + 10$ — do this
by completing the square:
$x^2 - 7x + 10 = (x - 3.5)^2 - 12.25 + 10$
$= (x - 3.5)^2 - 2.25$.

As $(x - 3.5)^2 \geq 0$ the minimum value of
$x^2 - 7x + 10$ is -2.25, so the range is $f(x) \geq -2.25$.
This is a function, and it's many-to-one (as more than
one x-value is mapped to the same value of $f(x)$).
You could also have found the minimum point by
differentiating, setting the derivative equal to O and
solving for x.

c) Range $f(x) \geq 0$. This is not a function as $f(x)$
doesn't exist for $x < 0$.

d) Sketch the graph for this one:

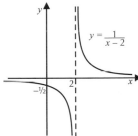

$y = \dfrac{1}{x-2}$

From the graph, the range is $f(x) \in \mathbb{R}$, $f(x) \neq 0$.
This is not a function as it's not defined for $x = 2$.
If you're not sure about any of the domains or ranges
for the other parts, draw the graphs and see if that helps
you figure it out.

Q6 a) $f(0) = \dfrac{5}{(2 \times 0) + 1} = 5$

$f\left(\dfrac{1}{2}\right) = \dfrac{5}{\left(2 \times \frac{1}{2}\right) + 1} = 2\frac{1}{2}$

b)

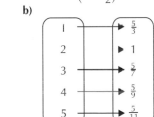

$1 \to \frac{5}{3}$
$2 \to 1$
$3 \to \frac{5}{7}$
$4 \to \frac{5}{9}$
$5 \to \frac{5}{11}$

Range $\{\frac{5}{3}, 1, \frac{5}{7}, \frac{5}{9}, \frac{5}{11}\}$

c) Yes.

d) No — the map is not defined for $x = -\dfrac{1}{2}$.

Q7 a)

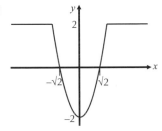

b) $-2 < f(x) \leq 2$

Q8 a) $fg(2) = f(2(2) + 3) = f(7) = \dfrac{3}{7}$.
$gf(1) = g(3/1) = g(3) = 2(3) + 3 = 9$.
$fg(x) = f(2x + 3) = \dfrac{3}{2x + 3}$.

b) $fg(2) = f(2 + 4) = f(6) = 3(6^2) = 3 \times 36 = 108$.

$gf(1) = g(3(1^2)) = g(3) = 3 + 4 = 7$.
$fg(x) = f(x + 4) = 3(x + 4)^2$.

Q9 a) $fg(1) = f(10^{1+1}) = \log_{10}(10^2) = 2$
$gf(1) = g(\log_{10}1) = g(0) = 10^{0+1} = 10$
$f^2(10) = f(\log_{10}10) = f(1) = \log_{10}1 = 0$
$g^2(-1) = g(10^{-1+1}) = g(1) = 10^{1+1} = 100$

b) Because $f(1) = \log_{10}1 = 0$, and $f(0) = \log_{10}0$,
which is undefined.

Q10 $fg(x) = f(x + 7) = 3(x + 7) = 3x + 21$
$gf(x) = g(3x) = 3x + 7$
$g^2(x) = g(x + 7) = (x + 7) + 7 = x + 14$

Q11 a) The domain of $fg(x)$ must be $x \leq 12$ since this is
the domain of $g(x)$. But $x + 3$ (the input into $f(x)$)
must also be ≥ 2, so $x + 3 \geq 2 \Rightarrow x \geq -1$. So the
complete domain for $fg(x)$ is $-1 \leq x \leq 12$.
The range can be found by putting the limits of
the domain into $fg(x)$:
$(4(-1) + 12) \leq fg(x) \leq (4(12) + 12)$
$8 \leq fg(x) \leq 60$

b) $fg(x) = f(x + 3) = 4(x + 3) = 4x + 12$

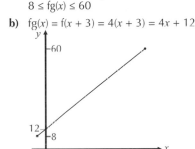

c) The domain of $gf(x)$ must be $x \geq 2$ since this is
the domain of $f(x)$. But $4x$ (the input into $g(x)$)
must also be ≤ 12, so $4x \leq 12 \Rightarrow x \leq 3$. So the
complete domain for $gf(x)$ is $2 \leq x \leq 3$.
The range can be found by putting the limits of
the domain into $gf(x)$:
$(4(2) + 3) \leq gf(x) \leq (4(3) + 3)$
$11 \leq gf(x) \leq 15$

d) $gf(x) = g(4x) = 4x + 3$

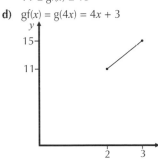

Q12 f is a one-to-one function so it has an inverse.
The domain of the inverse is the range of the function
and vice versa, so the domain of $f^{-1}(x)$ is $x \geq 3$ and the
range is $f^{-1}(x) \in \mathbb{R}$.

Q13 First replace $f(x)$ with y to get an equation for y in
terms of x, then rearrange to make x the subject:
$$y = \sqrt{2x - 4}$$
$$y^2 = 2x - 4$$
$$y^2 + 4 = 2x$$
$$x = \frac{y^2 + 4}{2} = \frac{y^2}{2} + 2$$

Finally replace x with $f^{-1}(x)$ and y with x:

$f^{-1}(x) = \frac{x^2}{2} + 2$, which has domain $x \geq 0$
(as the range of f is $f(x) \geq 0$) and range $f^{-1}(x) \geq 2$ (as the domain of f is $x \geq 2$).

Q14 In the domain $0 \leq x \leq \frac{\pi}{2}$, $\cos x$ is a one-to-one function, as shown:

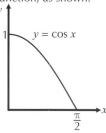

One-to-one functions have inverses,
so $f^{-1}(x)$ does exist.

Q15 First replace $f(x)$ with y to get an equation for y in terms of x: $y = \log_{10}(x + 4)$.
Then rearrange the equation to make x the subject.
First do 10 to the power of each side to get rid of the log, then rearrange:
$10^y = x + 4 \Rightarrow x = 10^y - 4$.
Finally replace x with $f^{-1}(x)$ and y with x:
$f^{-1}(x) = 10^x - 4$.
The question doesn't ask for the domain and range but the range is the domain of f(x): $f^{-1}(x) > -4$ and the domain is the range of f(x): $x \in \mathbb{R}$.

Q16 a) $f^{-1}(x) = x - 4$.

b) $g(x) = \frac{3}{x + 1}$
Replace with y: $y = \frac{3}{x + 1}$
Rearrange: $x = \frac{3}{y} - 1$
Replace with $g^{-1}(x)$ and x: $g^{-1}(x) = \frac{3}{x} - 1$.

c) $f^{-1}g^{-1}(x) = f^{-1}(\frac{3}{x} - 1) = \frac{3}{x} - 1 - 4 = \frac{3}{x} - 5$

d) $gf(x) = g(x + 4) = \frac{3}{(x + 4) + 1} = \frac{3}{x + 5}$.

e) Let $h(x)$ be the inverse of $gf(x)$.
Replace with y: $y = \frac{3}{x + 5}$
Rearrange: $x = \frac{3}{y} - 5$
Replace with $h(x)$ and x: $h(x) = \frac{3}{x} - 5$.
This is the same as $f^{-1}g^{-1}(x)$.

Q17 a)

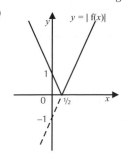

b)

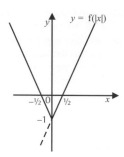

Q18 Using the algebraic (squaring) method:
$(3x - 1)^2 = (4 - x)^2$
$9x^2 - 6x + 1 = 16 - 8x + x^2$
$8x^2 + 2x - 15 = 0$
$(4x - 5)(2x + 3) = 0$

So the two solutions are: $x = \frac{5}{4}$ and $x = -\frac{3}{2}$.
You could also solve this by sketching the graphs of $f(x) = |3x - 1|$ and $g(x) = |4 - x|$ and solving $f(x) = g(x)$ or $-f(x) = g(x)$ depending on where the roots lie.

Q19 a) $f(x) = x^2 - 2x - 8 = (x + 2)(x - 4)$
So the graph of $f(x)$ touches the x-axis at -2 and 4, crosses the y-axis at -8 ($f(0) = -8$), and has a minimum point at $(1, -9)$.
You could use calculus to find the coordinates of the turning point.

For $y = |f(x)|$ reflect the negative part in the x-axis, and for $y = f(|x|)$ reflect the $x > 0$ part in the y-axis:

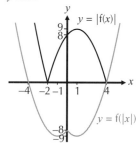

b) The graph below shows there are 2 solutions, one for $f(x) = -5$ (in the region $x \geq 0$) and one for $f(-x) = -5$ (in the region $x < 0$).

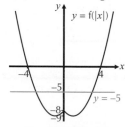

Since the graph is symmetrical about the y-axis we can find the positive solution and then use this to find the negative solution:
$x^2 - 2x - 8 = -5 \Rightarrow x^2 - 2x - 3 = 0$
$\Rightarrow (x + 1)(x - 3) = 0$
$\Rightarrow x = -1$ (not valid as x must be positive)
and $x = 3$ (valid).
So the valid solutions are $x = 3$ and $x = -3$ (for the negative part of the graph).

Solving algebraically: For $x < 0$, $f(-x) = -5 \Rightarrow$
$(-x)^2 - 2(-x) - 8 = -5 \Rightarrow x^2 + 2x - 8 = -5$
$\Rightarrow (x-1)(x+3) = 0 \Rightarrow x = 1$(not valid for $x < 0$)
or $x = -3$ (valid)

Q20 a)

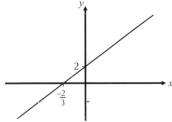

b)

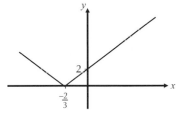

c)

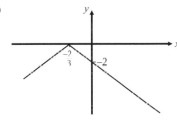

Q21

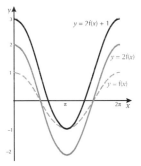

Exam-Style Questions — Chapter 1

1 $\dfrac{2x^2 - 9x - 35}{x^2 - 49} = \dfrac{(2x+5)(x-7)}{(x+7)(x-7)} = \dfrac{2x+5}{x+7}$

[3 marks available — 1 mark for factorising the numerator, 1 mark for factorising the denominator and 1 mark for correct answer (after cancelling)]

2 **a)** $\dfrac{x^2 - x - 20}{2x+4} \div \dfrac{x^2 - 16}{x+2}$

$= \dfrac{(x+4)(x-5)}{2(x+2)} \times \dfrac{x+2}{(x+4)(x-4)}$

$= \dfrac{x-5}{2} \times \dfrac{1}{x-4} = \dfrac{x-5}{2(x-4)}$

[3 marks available — 1 mark for turning the second fraction upside down, 1 mark for correct factorisations and 1 mark for correct answer (after cancelling)]

b) $\dfrac{x^2 - x - 20}{2x+4} - \dfrac{x^2 - 16}{x+2}$

$= \dfrac{x^2 - x - 20}{2(x+2)} - \dfrac{2x^2 - 32}{2(x+2)}$

$= \dfrac{x^2 - x - 20 - 2x^2 + 32}{2(x+2)}$

$= \dfrac{-x^2 - x + 12}{2(x+2)} = \dfrac{-(x^2 + x - 12)}{2(x+2)}$

$= \dfrac{-(x-3)(x+4)}{2(x+2)}$

[3 marks available — 1 mark correctly writing the fractions over a common denominator, 1 mark for correct subtraction of the numerators and 1 mark for correct answer (allow unfactorised answer)]

3 To transform the curve $y = x^3$ into $y = (x-1)^3$, translate it 1 unit horizontally to the right *[1 mark]*.
To transform this into the curve $y = 2(x-1)^3$, stretch it vertically by a scale factor of 2 *[1 mark]*. Finally, to transform into the curve $y = 2(x-1)^3 + 4$, the whole curve is translated 4 units upwards *[1 mark]*.

4 **a)** $gf(x) = g(x^2 - 3)$ *[1 mark]* $= \dfrac{1}{x^2 - 3}$ *[1 mark]*

b) $\dfrac{1}{x^2 - 3} = \dfrac{1}{6} \Rightarrow x^2 - 3 = 6 \Rightarrow x^2 = 9$

$\Rightarrow x = 3, x = -3$

[3 marks available — 1 mark for rearranging to solve equation, 1 mark for each correct solution]

c) **(i)** $f(x)$ is a many-to-one function, so the inverse would be one-to-many, which is not a function, so $f^{-1}(x)$ does not exist *[1 mark]*.

(ii) $f(x)$ is a one-to-one function over the domain $x \geq 0$ *[1 mark]*, so $f^{-1}(x)$ would exist if $f(x)$ had this restricted domain.
There are other restricted domains which would work so you could have another answer here.

5 First put $x = -6$ into the identity
$x^3 + 15x^2 + 43x - 30 \equiv (Ax^2 + Bx + C)(x+6) + D$:
$(-6)^3 + 15(-6)^2 + 43(-6) - 30 = D \Rightarrow 36 = D$ *[1 mark]*
Now set $x = 0 : -30 = 6C + D$, so $C = -11$ *[1 mark]*.
Equating the coefficients of x^3 gives $1 = A$. Equating the coefficients of x^2 gives $15 = 6A + B$, so $B = 9$ *[1 mark]*.
So:
$x^3 + 15x^2 + 43x - 30 = (x^2 + 9x - 11)(x+6) + 36$.
You could also do this question by algebraic long division — you just have to use your answer to work out A, B, C and D.

6 **a)** $fg(6) = f(\sqrt{(3 \times 6) - 2}) = f(\sqrt{16})$ *[1 mark]*
$= f(4) = 2^4 = 16$ *[1 mark]*

b) $gf(2) = g(2^2) = g(4)$ *[1 mark]*
$= \sqrt{(3 \times 4) - 2} = \sqrt{10}$ *[1 mark]*

c) **(i)** First, write $y = g(x)$ and rearrange to make x the subject:
$y = \sqrt{3x - 2}$
$\Rightarrow y^2 = 3x - 2$
$\Rightarrow y^2 + 2 = 3x$
$\Rightarrow \dfrac{y^2 + 2}{3} = x$ *[1 mark]*

Then replace x with $g^{-1}(x)$ and y with x:
$g^{-1}(x) = \frac{x^2 + 2}{3}$ *[1 mark]*.

(ii) $fg^{-1}(x) = f\left(\frac{x^2 + 2}{3}\right)$ *[1 mark]*

$= 2^{\frac{x^2+2}{3}}$ *[1 mark]*

7 **a)**

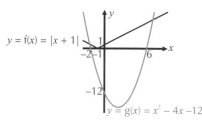

[2 marks available — 1 mark for each graph sketched with the intercepts]
$x^2 - 4x - 12 = (x + 2)(x - 6)$, so the x-intercepts are −2 and 6. To draw $|x + 1|$, just reflect the negative part of the graph of $y = x + 1$ in the x-axis.

b) The two graphs intersect twice, so there are two valid solutions to $x^2 - 4x - 12 = |x + 1|$. Looking at where $f(x) \geq 0$ and where $f(x) < 0$ gives:
(1) $x^2 - 4x - 12 = x + 1$ for $x \geq -1$ *[1 mark]*.
$\Rightarrow x^2 - 5x - 13 = 0$
(2) $x^2 - 4x - 12 = -x - 1$ for $x < -1$ *[1 mark]*.
$\Rightarrow x^2 - 3x - 11 = 0$

Solving (1) using the quadratic formula gives:
$x = \frac{5 \pm \sqrt{77}}{2}$.
Since $x \geq -1$, the only valid solution is
$x = \frac{5 + \sqrt{77}}{2}$ *[1 mark]*.

Solving (2) using the quadratic formula gives:
$x = \frac{3 \pm \sqrt{53}}{2}$.
Since $x < -1$, the only valid solution is
$x = \frac{3 - \sqrt{53}}{2}$ *[1 mark]*.

8 **a)** A reflection in the y-axis is a transformation of the form $f(-x)$ *[1 mark]*. A translation of 3 up becomes $f(-x) + 3$ *[1 mark]*, then a translation of 2 right becomes $f(-(x - 2)) + 3$ *[1 mark]*.
So $g(x) = f(2 - x) + 3$.
Make sure you do $f(-(x - 2))$ instead of $f(-x - 2)$ here.

b) Original coordinates of P: (1, 2).
After reflection in the y-axis: (−1, 2).
After translation of 3 up and 2 right: (1, 5) *[1 mark]*.
Original coordinates of Q: (3, 6).
After reflection in the y-axis: (−3, 6).
After translation of 3 up and 2 right: (−1, 9) *[1 mark]*.
Do a quick sketch of the graph if you need to.

9 **a)** The range of f is $f(x) > 0$ *[1 mark]*.

b) (i) Let $y = f(x)$. Then $y = \frac{1}{x + 5}$.
Rearrange this to make x the subject:
$y(x + 5) = 1 \Rightarrow x + 5 = \frac{1}{y}$
$\Rightarrow x = \frac{1}{y} - 5$ *[1 mark]*

Finally, write out in terms of x and $f^{-1}(x)$:
$f^{-1}(x) = \frac{1}{x} - 5$ *[1 mark]*.

(ii) The domain of the inverse is the same as the range of the function, so $x > 0$ *[1 mark]*. The range of the inverse is the same as the domain of the function, so $f^{-1}(x) > -5$ *[1 mark]*.

c)

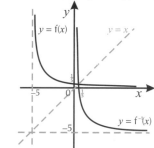

[2 marks available — 1 mark for each correct curve, each with correct intersections and asymptotes as shown]

10 **a)**

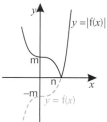

[2 marks available — 1 mark for reflecting in x-axis at $x = n$, 1 mark for crossing y-axis at $y = m$]

b)

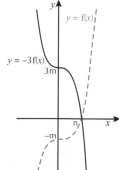

[2 marks available — 1 mark for reflecting in x-axis and 1 mark for crossing y-axis at $y = 3m$ (due to stretch by scale factor 3)]

c)

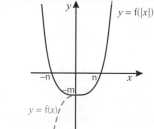

[2 marks available — 1 mark for reflecting in y-axis and 1 mark for crossing the x-axis at $-n$]

Chapter 2: Trigonometry

1. Inverse Trig Functions

Exercise 1.1 — Arcsin, arccos and arctan

Q1 **a)** If $x = \arccos 1$, then $1 = \cos x$ so $x = 0$.

b) If $x = \arcsin \frac{\sqrt{3}}{2}$ then $\frac{\sqrt{3}}{2} = \sin x$ so $x = \frac{\pi}{3}$.

c) If $x = \arctan \sqrt{3}$ then $\sqrt{3} = \tan x$ so $x = \frac{\pi}{3}$.

Q2 **a)**

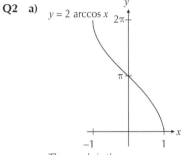

$y = 2 \arccos x$

The graph is the same as $y = \arccos x$ but stretched vertically by a factor of 2, so the y-coordinates of the endpoints and y-intercept are doubled.

b)

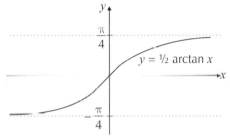

$y = \frac{1}{2} \arctan x$

The range is $-\frac{\pi}{4} < \frac{1}{2}\arctan x < \frac{\pi}{4}$.

The graph is the same as $y = \arctan x$ but stretched vertically by a factor of ½, so the y-coordinates of the asymptotes are halved.

Q3

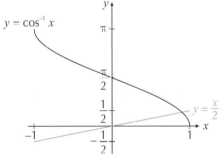

$y = \cos^{-1} x$

$y = \frac{x}{2}$

The graphs intersect once, so there is one real root of the equation $\cos^{-1} x = \frac{x}{2}$.

Q4 **a)** $\sin^{-1}(-1) = -\frac{\pi}{2}$.

This is one of the endpoints of the arcsin x graph.

b) To find $\cos^{-1}\left(-\frac{\sqrt{3}}{2}\right)$, first find the angle a for which $\cos a = \frac{\sqrt{3}}{2}$:

So $\cos \frac{\pi}{6} = \frac{\sqrt{3}}{2}$:

Now use the CAST diagram to find the negative solutions that lie in the domain $0 \le x \le \pi$:

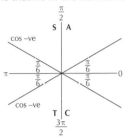

The only negative solution in that domain is $\pi - \frac{\pi}{6} = \frac{5\pi}{6}$.

So $\cos^{-1}\left(-\frac{\sqrt{3}}{2}\right) = \frac{5\pi}{6}$.

Q5 **a)** $\arcsin \frac{1}{2} = \frac{\pi}{6}$, so $\tan(\arcsin \frac{1}{2}) = \tan \frac{\pi}{6} = \frac{1}{\sqrt{3}}$.

b) This is just the cos function followed by its inverse function so the answer is $\frac{2\pi}{3}$.

c) $\arcsin \frac{1}{2} = \frac{\pi}{6}$, so $\cos(\arcsin \frac{1}{2}) = \cos \frac{\pi}{6} = \frac{\sqrt{3}}{2}$.

Q6 To find the inverse of the function, first write as $y = 1 + \sin 2x$, then rearrange to make x the subject:

$\sin 2x = y - 1 \Rightarrow 2x = \sin^{-1}(y - 1) \Rightarrow x = \frac{1}{2}\sin^{-1}(y - 1)$.

Now replace x with $f^{-1}(x)$ and y with x:

$f^{-1}(x) = \frac{1}{2}\sin^{-1}(x - 1) = \frac{1}{2}\arcsin(x - 1)$

2. Cosec, Sec and Cot

Exercise 2.1 — Graphs of cosec, sec and cot

Q1 **a)**

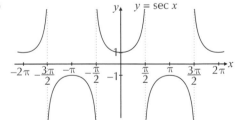

$y = \sec x$

b) The minimum points are at $(-2\pi, 1)$, $(0, 1)$ and $(2\pi, 1)$.

c) The maximum points are at $(-\pi, -1)$ and $(\pi, -1)$.

d) The range is $y \in \mathbb{R}$, $y \ge 1$ or $y \le -1$.
You could also say that y is undefined for $-1 < y < 1$.

Q2 a)

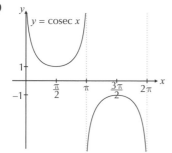

b) There is a maximum at $(\frac{3\pi}{2}, -1)$ and a minimum at $(\frac{\pi}{2}, 1)$.

c) The domain is $x \in \mathbb{R}$, $x \neq n\pi$ (where n is an integer). The range is $y \in \mathbb{R}$, $y \geq 1$ or $y \leq -1$.
The domain is all real numbers except those for which cosec x is undefined (i.e. at the asymptotes).

Q3 A horizontal translation right by $\frac{\pi}{2}$ (or 90°) or a horizontal translation left by $\frac{3\pi}{2}$ (or 270°).

Q4 a) If $f(x) = \cot x$, then $y = \cot \frac{x}{4} = f(\frac{x}{4})$.
This is a horizontal stretch scale factor 4.

b) The period of $y = \cot x$ is 180°, so the period of $y = \cot \frac{x}{4}$ is 180° × 4 = 720°.

c)

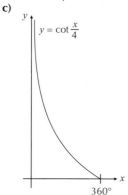

Q5 a) $y = 2 + \sec x$ is the graph of $y = \sec x$ translated vertically up by 2:

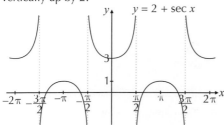

b) The minimum points are at $(-2\pi, 3)$, $(0, 3)$ and $(2\pi, 3)$. The maximum points are at $(-\pi, 1)$ and $(\pi, 1)$.
The maximum and minimum points have the same x-coordinates as on the graph of y = sec x, but the y-coordinates have all been increased by 2.

c) The domain is $x \in \mathbb{R}$, $x \neq \left(n\pi + \frac{\pi}{2}\right)$ (where n is an integer).
The range is $y \in \mathbb{R}$, $y \geq 3$ or $y \leq 1$.

Q6 a) $y = 2\,\text{cosec}\,2x$ is the graph of $y = \text{cosec}\,x$ stretched horizontally by a factor of $\frac{1}{2}$ and stretched vertically by a factor of 2.

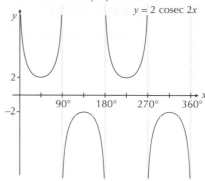

b) The minimum points are at (45°, 2) and (225°, 2).

c) The maximum points are at (135°, −2) and (315°, −2).

d) $y = 2\,\text{cosec}\,2x$ is undefined when $x = 0°$, 90°, 180°, 270° and 360°.

Q7 a) If $f(x) = \text{cosec}\,x$, then $y = 2 + 3\,\text{cosec}\,x = 3f(x) + 2$, which is a vertical stretch scale factor 3, followed by a vertical translation of 2 up. Vertical transformations do not affect the position of the asymptotes, so they are in the same position as for the graph of $y = \text{cosec}\,x$, i.e. at $n\pi$ or $180n°$, where n is an integer.

b) The period of the graph will be the same as for the graph of $y = \text{cosec}\,x$, i.e. 360°.
Vertical transformations will not affect how often the graph repeats itself.

c)

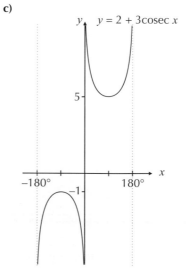

d) The range is $y \in \mathbb{R}$, $y \geq 5$ or $y \leq -1$.

Exercise 2.2 — Evaluating cosec, sec and cot

Q1 **a)** $\operatorname{cosec} 80° = \dfrac{1}{\sin 80°} = 1.02$

b) $\sec 75° = \dfrac{1}{\cos 75°} = 3.86$

c) $\cot 30° = \dfrac{1}{\tan 30°} = 1.73$

d) $\sec(-70)° = \dfrac{1}{\cos(-70°)} = 2.92$

e) $3 - \cot 250° = 3 - \dfrac{1}{\tan 250°} = 2.64$

f) $2 \operatorname{cosec} 25° = \dfrac{2}{\sin 25°} = 4.73$

Q2 **a)** $\sec 3 = \dfrac{1}{\cos 3} = -1.01$

b) $\cot 0.6 = \dfrac{1}{\tan 0.6} = 1.46$

c) $\operatorname{cosec} 1.8 = \dfrac{1}{\sin 1.8} = 1.03$

d) $\sec(-1) = \dfrac{1}{\cos(-1)} = 1.85$

e) $\operatorname{cosec} \dfrac{\pi}{8} = \dfrac{1}{\sin \frac{\pi}{8}} = 2.61$

f) $8 + \cot \dfrac{\pi}{8} = 8 + \dfrac{1}{\tan \frac{\pi}{8}} = 10.4$

g) $\dfrac{1}{1 + \sec \frac{\pi}{10}} = \dfrac{1}{1 + \frac{1}{\cos \frac{\pi}{10}}} = 0.487$

h) $\dfrac{1}{6 + \cot \frac{\pi}{5}} = \dfrac{1}{6 + \frac{1}{\tan \frac{\pi}{5}}} = 0.136$

Q3 **a)** $\sec 60° = \dfrac{1}{\cos 60°} = \dfrac{1}{\left(\frac{1}{2}\right)} = 2$

b) $\operatorname{cosec} 30° = \dfrac{1}{\sin 30°} = \dfrac{1}{\left(\frac{1}{2}\right)} = 2$

c) $\cot 45° = \dfrac{1}{\tan 45°} = \dfrac{1}{1} = 1$

d) $\operatorname{cosec} \dfrac{\pi}{3} = \dfrac{1}{\sin\left(\frac{\pi}{3}\right)} = \dfrac{1}{\left(\frac{\sqrt{3}}{2}\right)} = \dfrac{2}{\sqrt{3}}$

e) $\sec(-180°) = \dfrac{1}{\cos(-180°)} = \dfrac{1}{\cos 180°} = -1$

The graph of y = cos x is symmetrical about the y-axis, so cos (−x) = cos x.

f) $\operatorname{cosec} 135° = \operatorname{cosec}(180° - 45°)$

$= \dfrac{1}{\sin(180° - 45°)}$

The CAST diagram below shows that sin 135° is the same size as sin 45°, and also lies in a positive quadrant for sin:

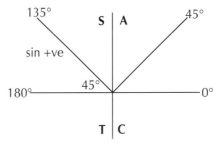

So $\operatorname{cosec} 135° = \dfrac{1}{\sin 45°} = \dfrac{1}{\left(\frac{1}{\sqrt{2}}\right)} = \sqrt{2}$.

g) $\cot 330° = \cot(360° - 30°) = \dfrac{1}{\tan(360° - 30°)}$

The CAST diagram below shows that tan 330° is the same size as tan 30°, but lies in a negative quadrant for tan:

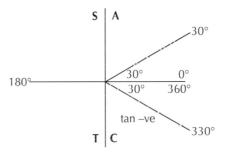

So $\cot 330° = \dfrac{1}{-\tan 30°} = \dfrac{1}{\left(-\frac{1}{\sqrt{3}}\right)} = -\sqrt{3}$.

h) $\sec \dfrac{5\pi}{4} = \sec\left(\pi + \dfrac{\pi}{4}\right) = \dfrac{1}{\cos\left(\pi + \frac{\pi}{4}\right)}$

The CAST diagram below shows that $\cos\left(\pi + \dfrac{\pi}{4}\right)$ is the same size as $\cos \dfrac{\pi}{4}$, but lies in a negative quadrant for cos:

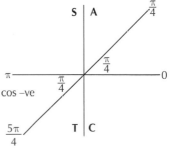

So $\sec \dfrac{5\pi}{4} = \dfrac{1}{-\cos \frac{\pi}{4}} = \dfrac{1}{\left(-\frac{1}{\sqrt{2}}\right)} = -\sqrt{2}$.

i) $\operatorname{cosec} \frac{5\pi}{3} = \operatorname{cosec}\left(2\pi - \frac{\pi}{3}\right) = \dfrac{1}{\sin\left(2\pi - \frac{\pi}{3}\right)}$

The CAST diagram shows that
$\sin\left(2\pi - \frac{\pi}{3}\right) = -\sin\frac{\pi}{3}$, so:

$$\frac{1}{\sin\left(2\pi - \frac{\pi}{3}\right)} = \frac{1}{-\sin\frac{\pi}{3}} = \frac{1}{-\left(\frac{\sqrt{3}}{2}\right)} = -\frac{2}{\sqrt{3}}$$

j) $\operatorname{cosec} \frac{2\pi}{3} = \operatorname{cosec}\left(\pi - \frac{\pi}{3}\right) = \dfrac{1}{\sin\left(\pi - \frac{\pi}{3}\right)}$

The CAST diagram shows that
$\sin\left(\pi - \frac{\pi}{3}\right) = \sin\frac{\pi}{3}$, so:

$$\frac{1}{\sin\left(\pi - \frac{\pi}{3}\right)} = \frac{1}{\sin\frac{\pi}{3}} = \frac{1}{\left(\frac{\sqrt{3}}{2}\right)} = \frac{2}{\sqrt{3}}$$

k) $3 - \cot\frac{3\pi}{4} = 3 - \cot\left(\pi - \frac{\pi}{4}\right) = 3 - \dfrac{1}{\tan\left(\pi - \frac{\pi}{4}\right)}$

$= 3 - \dfrac{1}{-\tan\frac{\pi}{4}} = 3 - \left(\dfrac{1}{-1}\right) = 4$

l) $\dfrac{\sqrt{3}}{\cot\frac{\pi}{6}} = \dfrac{\sqrt{3}}{\left(\frac{1}{\tan\frac{\pi}{6}}\right)} = \sqrt{3}\left(\tan\frac{\pi}{6}\right)$

$= \sqrt{3} \times \dfrac{1}{\sqrt{3}} = 1$

Q4 a) $\dfrac{1}{1 + \sec 60°} = \dfrac{1}{1 + \left(\frac{1}{\cos 60°}\right)}$

$= \dfrac{1}{1 + \frac{1}{\left(\frac{1}{2}\right)}} = \dfrac{1}{3}$

b) $\cot 315° = \cot(360° - 45°) = \dfrac{1}{\tan(360° - 45°)}$

$= \dfrac{1}{-\tan 45°} = -1$, so:

$\dfrac{2}{6 + \cot 315°} = \dfrac{2}{6 + (-1)} = \dfrac{2}{5}$

c) $\dfrac{1}{\sqrt{3} - \sec 30°} = \dfrac{1}{\sqrt{3} - \left(\frac{1}{\cos 30°}\right)}$

$= \dfrac{\cos 30°}{\sqrt{3}(\cos 30°) - 1} = \dfrac{\left(\frac{\sqrt{3}}{2}\right)}{\sqrt{3}\left(\frac{\sqrt{3}}{2}\right) - 1}$

$= \dfrac{\frac{\sqrt{3}}{2}}{3 - 2} = \sqrt{3}$

d) $1 + \cot 420° = 1 + \cot(360° + 60°) = 1 + \cot 60°$

$= 1 + \dfrac{1}{\tan 60°} = 1 + \dfrac{1}{\sqrt{3}} = \dfrac{3 + \sqrt{3}}{3}$

e) $\cot 150° = \cot(180° - 30°) = \dfrac{1}{\tan(180° - 30°)}$

$= \dfrac{1}{-\tan 30°} = \dfrac{1}{-\left(\frac{1}{\sqrt{3}}\right)} = -\sqrt{3}$

So:

$\dfrac{2}{7 + \sqrt{3}\cot 150°} = \dfrac{2}{7 + \sqrt{3}(-\sqrt{3})} = \dfrac{2}{7 - 3} = \dfrac{1}{2}$

Exercise 2.3 — Simplifying expressions and solving equations

Q1 a) $\dfrac{1}{\cos x} = \sec x$, so $\sec x + \sec x = 2\sec x$

b) $(\operatorname{cosec}^2 x)(\sin^2 x) = \dfrac{1}{\sin^2 x}(\sin^2 x) = 1$

c) $\dfrac{1}{\tan x} = \cot x$, so $2\cot x + \cot x = 3\cot x$

d) $\dfrac{\sec x}{\operatorname{cosec} x} = \dfrac{\left(\frac{1}{\cos x}\right)}{\left(\frac{1}{\sin x}\right)} = \dfrac{\sin x}{\cos x} = \tan x$

e) $(\cos x)(\operatorname{cosec} x) = \dfrac{\cos x}{\sin x} = \dfrac{1}{\left(\frac{\sin x}{\cos x}\right)}$

$= \dfrac{1}{\tan x} = \cot x$

f) $\dfrac{\operatorname{cosec}^2 x}{\cot x} = \dfrac{\left(\frac{1}{\sin^2 x}\right)}{\left(\frac{1}{\tan x}\right)} = \dfrac{\tan x}{\sin^2 x}$

$= \dfrac{\left(\frac{\sin x}{\cos x}\right)}{\sin^2 x} = \dfrac{\sin x}{\cos x \sin^2 x}$

$= \dfrac{1}{\cos x \sin x} = \sec x \operatorname{cosec} x$

Q2 a) $\sin x \cot x = \sin x \left(\dfrac{1}{\tan x}\right)$

$= \sin x \left(\dfrac{\cos x}{\sin x}\right)$

$= \cos x$

b) $\sec x - \cos x = \dfrac{1}{\cos x} - \cos x$

$= \dfrac{1 - \cos^2 x}{\cos x}$

Use the identity $\sin^2 x + \cos^2 x \equiv 1$:

$= \dfrac{\sin^2 x}{\cos x} = \left(\dfrac{\sin x}{\cos x}\right)\sin x = \tan x \sin x$

c) $\tan x \operatorname{cosec} x = \left(\dfrac{\sin x}{\cos x}\right)\left(\dfrac{1}{\sin x}\right)$

$= \dfrac{1}{\cos x} = \sec x$

d) $\dfrac{(\tan^2 x)(\operatorname{cosec} x)}{\sin x} = \dfrac{\left(\frac{\sin^2 x}{\cos^2 x}\right)\left(\frac{1}{\sin x}\right)}{\sin x}$

$= \dfrac{\left(\frac{\sin x}{\cos^2 x}\right)}{\sin x} = \dfrac{1}{\cos^2 x} = \sec^2 x$

Q3 a) $\sec x = 1.9 \Rightarrow \cos x = \dfrac{1}{1.9} = 0.52631...$

$x = \cos^{-1}(0.52631...) = 58.2°$ to 1 d.p.

There is another positive solution in the interval
$0 \le x \le 360°$ at $(360° - 58.2°)$,
so $x = 301.8°$ to 1 d.p.
Remember, you can use the graphs or the CAST diagram to find other solutions in the interval.

b) $\cot x = 2.4 \Rightarrow \tan x = 0.41666...$

$x = 22.6°$ to 1 d.p.

There is another positive solution in the interval
$0 \le x \le 360°$ at $(180° + 22.6°)$,
so $x = 202.6°$ to 1 d.p.

c) $\operatorname{cosec} x = -2 \Rightarrow \sin x = -0.5$

$\sin^{-1}(-0.5) = -30°$ which is not in the interval
$0° \le x \le 360°$

There are two negative solutions in the interval

$0 \leq x \leq 360°$ at $(180° + 30°)$ and $(360° - 30°)$, so $x = 210°$ and $330°$

d) $\sec x = -1.3 \Rightarrow \cos x = -0.76923...$

$\cos^{-1}(-0.76923...) = 140.3°$ to 1 d.p.

There are two negative solutions in the interval $0 \leq x \leq 360°$ at $140.3°$ and $(360° - 140.3°)$, so $x = 140.3°$ and $219.7°$

e) $\cot x = -2.4 \Rightarrow \tan x = -0.41666...$

$\tan^{-1}(-0.41666...) = -22.6°$ to 1 d.p.

There are two negative solutions in the interval $0 \leq x \leq 360°$ at $(-22.6° + 180°)$ and $(-22.6° + 360°)$, so $x = 157.4°$ and $337.4°$

f) $4 \sec 2x = -7 \Rightarrow \cos 2x = -0.57142...$

$\cos^{-1}(-0.57142...) = 124.84990...$

You need to find all solutions for x in the interval $0 \leq x \leq 360°$ so $0 \leq 2x \leq 2 \times 360°$ so you'll need to look for solutions for 2x in the interval $0 \leq 2x \leq 720°$.

There are four negative solutions for $2x$ in the interval $0 \leq x \leq 720°$ at $124.849...$, $(360° - 124.849...°)$, $(360° + 124.849...°)$ and $(720° - 124.849...°)$ and each of these needs to be divided by 2 to give x.

So $x = 62.4°, 117.6°, 242.4°$ and $297.6°$.

Q4 a) $\sec x - 2 \rightarrow \cos x - 0.5 \rightarrow x - \cos^{-1}(0.5) - \frac{\pi}{3}$

There is another positive solution in the interval $0 \leq x \leq 2\pi$ at $(2\pi - \frac{\pi}{3})$, so $x = \frac{5\pi}{3}$

b) $\csc x = -2 \Rightarrow \sin x = -0.5 \Rightarrow \sin^{-1}(-0.5) = -\frac{\pi}{6}$

There are two negative solutions in the interval $0 \leq x \leq 2\pi$ at $(\pi + \frac{\pi}{6})$ and $(2\pi - \frac{\pi}{6})$, so $x - \frac{7\pi}{6}$ and $\frac{11\pi}{6}$

c) $\cot 2x - 1 \rightarrow \tan 2x - 1 \rightarrow 2x - \tan^{-1}(1) - \frac{\pi}{4}$

Don't forget to double the interval for the next bit because you're looking for solutions for 2x instead of x...

There are 3 other positive solutions for $2x$ in the interval $0 \leq 2x \leq 4\pi$, at $(\pi + \frac{\pi}{4})$, $(2\pi + \frac{\pi}{4})$ and $(3\pi + \frac{\pi}{4})$, so $x = \frac{\pi}{8}, \frac{5\pi}{8}, \frac{9\pi}{8}$ and $\frac{13\pi}{8}$

d) $\sec 5x = -1 \Rightarrow \cos 5x = -1$

$5x = \cos^{-1}(-1) = \pi$

In this case you're looking for solutions for 5x — the interval you'll need to look in is $0 \leq 5x \leq 10\pi$ since $0 \leq x \leq 2\pi$. And use the fact that the cos graph repeats itself every 2π. $(\pi, -1)$ is a minimum point on the graph, so this will be repeated every 2π.

There are 4 other solutions for $5x$ in the interval $0 \leq 5x \leq 10\pi$, at $3\pi, 5\pi, 7\pi$, and 9π, so

$x = \frac{\pi}{5}, \frac{3\pi}{5}, \pi, \frac{7\pi}{5}$ and $\frac{9\pi}{5}$

Q5 $\cot 2x - 4 = -5 \Rightarrow \tan 2x = -1$

$\tan^{-1}(1) = \frac{\pi}{4}$

There are 4 negative solutions for $2x$ in the interval $0 \leq 2x \leq 4\pi$, at $(\pi - \frac{\pi}{4})$, $(2\pi - \frac{\pi}{4})$, $(3\pi - \frac{\pi}{4})$

and $(4\pi - \frac{\pi}{4})$, so

$x = \frac{3\pi}{8}, \frac{7\pi}{8}, \frac{11\pi}{8}$ and $\frac{15\pi}{8}$

Q6 $2 \csc 2x = 3 \Rightarrow \sin 2x = \frac{2}{3}$

$2x = \sin^{-1}\left(\frac{2}{3}\right) = 41.81031...°$

There are three other positive solutions for $2x$ in the interval $0 \leq 2x \leq 720°$ at $(180° - 41.81...°)$, $(360° + 41.81...°)$ and $(540° - 41.81...°)$,

so $x = 20.9°, 69.1°, 200.9°$ and $249.1°$ to 1 d.p.

Q7 $-2 \sec x = 4 \Rightarrow \cos x = -0.5$

$\cos^{-1}(-0.5) = \frac{2\pi}{3}$

There are 2 negative solutions in the interval $0 \leq x \leq 2\pi$ at $\frac{2\pi}{3}$ and $(2\pi - \frac{2\pi}{3})$, so

$x = \frac{2\pi}{3}$ and $\frac{4\pi}{3}$.

Q8 $\sqrt{3} \csc 3x = 2 \Rightarrow \sin 3x = \frac{\sqrt{3}}{2}$

$3x = \sin^{-1}\left(\frac{\sqrt{3}}{2}\right) = \frac{\pi}{3}$

There are 5 other positive solutions in the interval $0 \leq 3x \leq 6\pi$, at $(\pi - \frac{\pi}{3})$, $(2\pi + \frac{\pi}{3})$, $(3\pi - \frac{\pi}{3})$, $(4\pi + \frac{\pi}{3})$ and $(5\pi - \frac{\pi}{3})$, so

$x = \frac{\pi}{9}, \frac{2\pi}{9}, \frac{7\pi}{9}, \frac{8\pi}{9}, \frac{13\pi}{9}$ and $\frac{14\pi}{9}$

Q9 a) $\sec^2 x - 2\sqrt{2} \sec x + 2$ factorises to $(\sec x - \sqrt{2})^2$.

$(\sec x - \sqrt{2})^2 = 0$

$\sec x = \sqrt{2}$

$\cos x = \frac{1}{\sqrt{2}}$

$x = 45°$

b) $\cot^2 x - \frac{4}{\sqrt{3}} \cot x + 1$ factorises to

$(\cot x - \sqrt{3})(\cot x - \frac{1}{\sqrt{3}})$

So $(\cot x - \sqrt{3})(\cot x - \frac{1}{\sqrt{3}}) = 0$

$\Rightarrow \cot x = \sqrt{3}$ and $\cot x = \frac{1}{\sqrt{3}}$

$\Rightarrow \tan x = \frac{1}{\sqrt{3}}$ and $\tan x = \sqrt{3}$

So $x = 30°$ and $60°$

Q10 $(\csc x - 3)(2 \tan x + 1) = 0$ means that either $\csc x = 3$ (and so $\sin x = \frac{1}{3}$) or $\tan x = -\frac{1}{2}$.

The solutions for $\sin x = \frac{1}{3}$ are $x = 19.5°$ or $x = 180° - 19.5° = 160.5°$.

The solutions for $\tan x = -\frac{1}{2}$ are

$x = -26.6° + 180° = 153.4°$ or

$x = -26.6° + 360° = 333.4°$.

So $x = 19.5°, 160.5°, 153.4°, 333.4°$ are all solutions.

3. Identities Involving Cosec, Sec and Cot

Exercise 3.1 — Using the identities

Q1 $\cosec^2 x + 2 \cot^2 x$
$= \cosec^2 x + 2 (\cosec^2 x - 1)$
$= 3 \cosec^2 x - 2$

Q2 $\tan^2 x - \dfrac{1}{\cos^2 x} = \tan^2 x - \sec^2 x$
$= \tan^2 x - (1 + \tan^2 x) = -1$

Q3 $x + \dfrac{1}{x} = \sec\theta + \tan\theta + \dfrac{1}{\sec\theta + \tan\theta}$
$= \dfrac{(\sec\theta + \tan\theta)^2 + 1}{\sec\theta + \tan\theta}$
$= \dfrac{\sec^2\theta + 2\sec\theta\tan\theta + \tan^2\theta + 1}{\sec\theta + \tan\theta}$

But since $\sec^2\theta = \tan^2\theta + 1$:

$x + \dfrac{1}{x} = \dfrac{\sec^2\theta + 2\sec\theta\tan\theta + \sec^2\theta}{\sec\theta + \tan\theta}$
$= \dfrac{2\sec\theta(\sec\theta + \tan\theta)}{\sec\theta + \tan\theta} = 2\sec\theta$

Q4 **a)** $\tan^2 x = 2\sec x + 2$
$\Rightarrow \sec^2 x - 1 = 2\sec x + 2$
$\Rightarrow \sec^2 x - 2\sec x - 3 = 0$

b) Solve $\sec^2 x - 2\sec x - 3 = 0$

This factorises to give: $(\sec x - 3)(\sec x + 1) = 0$
So $\sec x = 3 \Rightarrow \cos x = \dfrac{1}{3}$
and $\sec x = -1 \Rightarrow \cos x = -1$

Solving these over the interval $0° \leq x \leq 360°$ gives:
$x = 70.5°, 180°$ and $289.5°$ (to 1 d.p.)
Just use the graph of cos x or the CAST diagram as usual to find all the solutions in the interval.

Q5 **a)** $2\cosec^2 x = 5 - 5\cot x$
$\Rightarrow 2(1 + \cot^2 x) = 5 - 5\cot x$
$\Rightarrow 2\cot^2 x + 5\cot x - 3 = 0$

b) Solve $2\cot^2 x + 5\cot x - 3 = 0$

This factorises to give: $(2\cot x - 1)(\cot x + 3) = 0$

So $\cot x = \dfrac{1}{2} \Rightarrow \tan x = 2$
and $\cot x = -3 \Rightarrow \tan x = -\dfrac{1}{3}$
Solving these over the interval $-\pi \leq x \leq \pi$ gives:
$x = -2.03, -0.32, 1.11, 2.82$ (to 2 d.p.)

Q6 **a)** $2\cot^2 A + 5\cosec A = 10$
$\Rightarrow 2(\cosec^2 A - 1) + 5\cosec A = 10$
$\Rightarrow 2\cosec^2 A - 2 + 5\cosec A = 10$
$\Rightarrow 2\cosec^2 A + 5\cosec A - 12 = 0$

b) Solve $2\cosec^2 A + 5\cosec A - 12 = 0$
This factorises to give:
$(\cosec A + 4)(2\cosec A - 3) = 0$

So $\cosec A = -4 \Rightarrow \sin A = -\dfrac{1}{4}$
Or $\cosec x = \dfrac{3}{2} \Rightarrow \sin A = \dfrac{2}{3}$
The solutions (to 1 d.p.) are
$A = 194.5°, 345.5°, 41.8°, 138.2°$.

Q7 $\sec^2 x + \tan x = 1$
$\Rightarrow 1 + \tan^2 x + \tan x = 1$
$\Rightarrow \tan^2 x + \tan x = 0$
$\Rightarrow \tan x(\tan x + 1) = 0$
So $\tan x = 0 \Rightarrow x = 0, \pi, 2\pi$.

And $\tan x = -1 \Rightarrow x = \dfrac{3\pi}{4}, \dfrac{7\pi}{4}$.

Q8 **a)** $\cosec^2\theta + 2\cot^2\theta = 2$
$\Rightarrow \cosec^2\theta + 2(\cosec^2\theta - 1) = 2$
$\Rightarrow 3\cosec^2\theta - 2 = 2$
$\Rightarrow 3\cosec^2\theta = 4$
$\Rightarrow \cosec^2\theta = \dfrac{4}{3}$
$\Rightarrow \cosec\theta = \pm\dfrac{2}{\sqrt{3}} \Rightarrow \sin\theta = \pm\dfrac{\sqrt{3}}{2}$

b) Solving $\sin\theta = \pm\dfrac{\sqrt{3}}{2}$ over the interval
$0° \leq x \leq 180°$ gives: $\theta = 60°, 120°$.

Q9 $\sec^2 x = 3 + \tan x$
$\Rightarrow (1 + \tan^2 x) = 3 + \tan x$
$\Rightarrow \tan^2 x - \tan x - 2 = 0$
$\Rightarrow (\tan x - 2)(\tan x + 1) = 0$
So $\tan x = 2$ or $\tan x = -1$.
Solving over the interval $0° \leq x \leq 360°$ gives:
$x = 63.4°, 135°, 243.4°$ and $315°$ (to 1 d.p.)

Q10 $\cot^2 x + \cosec^2 x = 7$
$\Rightarrow \cot^2 x + (1 + \cot^2 x) = 7$
$\Rightarrow 2\cot^2 x + 1 = 7$
$\Rightarrow \cot^2 x = 3 \Rightarrow \cot x = \pm\sqrt{3} \Rightarrow \tan x = \pm\dfrac{1}{\sqrt{3}}$
Solving over the interval $0 \leq x \leq 2\pi$ gives:
$x = \dfrac{\pi}{6}$ and $\dfrac{7\pi}{6}$ when $\tan x = +\dfrac{1}{\sqrt{3}}$
and $x = \dfrac{5\pi}{6}$ and $\dfrac{11\pi}{6}$ when $\tan x = -\dfrac{1}{\sqrt{3}}$.

Q11 $\tan^2 x + 5\sec x + 7 = 0$
$\Rightarrow (\sec^2 x - 1) + 5\sec x + 7 = 0$
$\Rightarrow \sec^2 x + 5\sec x + 6 = 0$
$\Rightarrow (\sec x + 2)(\sec x + 3) = 0$

So $\sec x = -2 \Rightarrow \cos x = -\dfrac{1}{2}$
and $\sec x = -3 \Rightarrow \cos x = -\dfrac{1}{3}$
Solving over the interval $0 \leq x \leq 2\pi$ gives:
$x = 1.91, 2.09, 4.19$ and 4.37 (to 2 d.p.)

Q12 Drawing a right angled triangle will help to solve this question:

$\tan\theta = \dfrac{60}{11}$

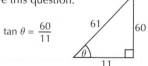

Notice that $180° \leq \theta \leq 270°$ — this puts us in the 3rd quadrant of the CAST diagram so sin will be −ve, cos will be −ve and tan will be +ve.

a) From the triangle, $\sin\theta = -\dfrac{\text{opp}}{\text{hyp}} = -\dfrac{60}{61}$.

b) $\cos\theta = -\dfrac{\text{adj}}{\text{hyp}} = -\dfrac{11}{61} \Rightarrow \sec\theta = \dfrac{1}{\left(-\dfrac{11}{61}\right)} = -\dfrac{61}{11}$.

c) $\cosec\theta = \dfrac{1}{\sin\theta} = \dfrac{1}{\left(-\dfrac{60}{61}\right)} = -\dfrac{61}{60}$.

Q13 Drawing a right angled triangle will help to solve this question:

$\csc \theta = -\dfrac{17}{15}$

$\sin \theta = -\dfrac{15}{17}$

Notice that $180° \leq \theta \leq 270°$ — this puts us in the 3rd quadrant of the CAST diagram so sin will be –ve, cos will be –ve and tan will be +ve.

a) $\cos \theta = -\dfrac{\text{adj}}{\text{hyp}} = -\dfrac{8}{17}$.

b) $\sec \theta = \dfrac{1}{\cos \theta} = -\dfrac{17}{8}$.

c) $\tan \theta = \dfrac{\text{opp}}{\text{adj}} = \dfrac{15}{8}$ so $\cot \theta = \dfrac{1}{\tan \theta} = \dfrac{8}{15}$.

Q14 $\cos x = \dfrac{1}{6} \Rightarrow \sec x = 6$

So $\sec^2 x = 36$

$\Rightarrow 1 + \tan^2 x = 36$

$\Rightarrow \tan^2 x = 35$

$\Rightarrow \tan x = \pm\sqrt{35}$

Exercise 3.2 — Proving other identities

Q1 a) $\sec^2 \theta - \csc^2 \theta \equiv (1 + \tan^2 \theta) - (1 + \cot^2 \theta)$

$\equiv \tan^2 \theta - \cot^2 \theta$

b) $\tan^2 \theta - \cot^2 \theta$ is the difference between two squares, and so can be written as:

$(\tan \theta + \cot \theta)(\tan \theta - \cot \theta)$.

So is $\sec^2 \theta - \csc^2 \theta$, so it can be written $(\sec \theta + \csc \theta)(\sec \theta - \csc \theta)$.

So using the result from part a),

$(\sec \theta + \csc \theta)(\sec \theta - \csc \theta) \equiv (\tan \theta + \cot \theta)(\tan \theta - \cot \theta)$.

Q2 First expand the bracket:

$(\tan x + \cot x)^2 \equiv \tan^2 x + \cot^2 x + 2 \tan x \cot x$

$\equiv \tan^2 x + \cot^2 x + \dfrac{2 \tan x}{\tan x}$

$\equiv \tan^2 x + \cot^2 x + 2$

Split up that '+2' into two lots of '+1' so it starts to resemble the identities...

$\equiv (1 + \tan^2 x) + (1 + \cot^2 x)$

$\equiv \sec^2 x + \csc^2 x$

Q3 $\cot^2 x + \sin^2 x \equiv (\csc^2 x - 1) + (1 - \cos^2 x)$

$\equiv \csc^2 x - \cos^2 x$

This is the difference of two squares...

$\equiv (\csc x + \cos x)(\csc x - \cos x)$

Q4 $\dfrac{(\sec x - \tan x)(\tan x + \sec x)}{\csc x - \cot x}$

$\equiv \dfrac{\sec^2 x - \tan^2 x}{\csc x - \cot x}$

$\equiv \dfrac{(1 + \tan^2 x) - \tan^2 x}{\csc x - \cot x}$

$\equiv \dfrac{1}{\csc x - \cot x}$

Multiply top and bottom by (cosec x + cot x)...

$\equiv \dfrac{\csc x + \cot x}{(\csc x - \cot x)(\csc x + \cot x)}$

$\equiv \dfrac{\csc x + \cot x}{\csc^2 x - \cot^2 x}$

$\equiv \dfrac{\csc x + \cot x}{(1 + \cot^2 x) - \cot^2 x}$

$\equiv \cot x + \csc x$

Q5 $\dfrac{\cot x}{1 + \csc x} + \dfrac{1 + \csc x}{\cot x}$

$\equiv \dfrac{\cot^2 x + (1 + \csc x)^2}{\cot x (1 + \csc x)}$

$\equiv \dfrac{(\csc^2 x - 1) + (1 + 2 \csc x + \csc^2 x)}{\cot x (1 + \csc x)}$

$\equiv \dfrac{2 \csc x (1 + \csc x)}{\cot x (1 + \csc x)}$

$\equiv \dfrac{2 \csc x}{\cot x} \equiv \dfrac{2 \tan x}{\sin x} \equiv \dfrac{2 \sin x}{\sin x \cos x} \equiv \dfrac{2}{\cos x} \equiv 2 \sec x$

Q6 $\dfrac{\csc x + 1}{\csc x - 1} = \dfrac{(\csc x + 1)(\csc x + 1)}{(\csc x - 1)(\csc x + 1)}$

$\equiv \dfrac{\csc^2 x + 2 \csc x + 1}{\csc^2 x - 1}$

$\equiv \dfrac{\csc^2 x + 2 \csc x + 1}{(1 + \cot^2 x) - 1}$

$\equiv \dfrac{\csc^2 x + 2 \csc x + 1}{\cot^2 x}$

$\equiv \dfrac{\csc^2 x}{\cot^2 x} + \dfrac{2 \csc x}{\cot^2 x} + \dfrac{1}{\cot^2 x}$

$\equiv \dfrac{\tan^2 x}{\sin^2 x} + \dfrac{2 \tan^2 x}{\sin x} + \tan^2 x$

$\equiv \dfrac{\sin^2 x}{\cos^2 x \sin^2 x} + \dfrac{2 \sin^2 x}{\cos^2 x \sin x} + \tan^2 x$

$\equiv \dfrac{1}{\cos^2 x} + \dfrac{2 \sin x}{\cos x \cos x} + \tan^2 x$

$\equiv \dfrac{1}{\cos^2 x} + \dfrac{2 \tan x}{\cos x} + \tan^2 x$

$\equiv \sec^2 x + 2 \tan x \sec x + (\sec^2 x - 1)$

$\equiv 2 \sec^2 x + 2 \tan x \sec x - 1$

4. The Addition Formulas

Exercise 4.1 — Finding exact values

Q1 a) $\cos 72° \cos 12° + \sin 72° \sin 12°$

$= \cos (72° - 12°) = \cos 60° = \dfrac{1}{2}$

b) $\cos 13° \cos 17° - \sin 13° \sin 17°$

$= \cos (13° + 17°) = \cos 30° = \dfrac{\sqrt{3}}{2}$

c) $\dfrac{\tan 12° + \tan 18°}{1 - \tan 12° \tan 18°} = \tan (12° + 18°)$

$= \tan 30° = \dfrac{1}{\sqrt{3}}$

d) $\dfrac{\tan 500° - \tan 140°}{1 + \tan 500° \tan 140°} = \tan (500° - 140°)$

$= \tan 360° = 0$

Answers **179**

e) $\sin 35° \cos 10° + \cos 35° \sin 10°$

$= \sin(35° + 10°) = \sin 45° = \dfrac{1}{\sqrt{2}}$

f) $\sin 69° \cos 9° - \cos 69° \sin 9°$

$= \sin(69° - 9°) = \sin 60° = \dfrac{\sqrt{3}}{2}$

Q2 a) $\sin \dfrac{2\pi}{3} \cos \dfrac{\pi}{2} - \cos \dfrac{2\pi}{3} \sin \dfrac{\pi}{2} = \sin\left(\dfrac{2\pi}{3} - \dfrac{\pi}{2}\right)$

$= \sin \dfrac{\pi}{6} = \dfrac{1}{2}$

b) $\cos 4\pi \cos 3\pi + \sin 4\pi \sin 3\pi$

$= \cos(4\pi - 3\pi) = \cos \pi = -1$

c) $\dfrac{\tan\dfrac{5\pi}{12} + \tan\dfrac{5\pi}{4}}{1 - \tan\dfrac{5\pi}{12}\tan\dfrac{5\pi}{4}} = \tan\left(\dfrac{5\pi}{12} + \dfrac{5\pi}{4}\right)$

$= \tan \dfrac{5\pi}{3} = \tan\left(2\pi - \dfrac{\pi}{3}\right) = -\tan \dfrac{\pi}{3} = -\sqrt{3}$

Q3 a) $\sin(5x - 2x) = \sin 3x$

b) $\cos(4x + 6x) = \cos 10x$

c) $\tan(7x + 3x) = \tan 10x$

d) $5 \sin(2x + 3x) = 5 \sin 5x$

e) $8 \cos(7x - 5x) = 8 \cos 2x$

Q4 Before answering a)-d), calculate $\cos x$ and $\sin y$:

$\sin x = \dfrac{3}{4} \Rightarrow \sin^2 x = \dfrac{9}{16} \Rightarrow \cos^2 x = 1 - \dfrac{9}{16} = \dfrac{7}{16}$

$\Rightarrow \cos x = \dfrac{\sqrt{7}}{4}$

x is acute, so cos x must be positive, therefore take the positive square root.

$\cos y = \dfrac{3}{\sqrt{10}} \Rightarrow \cos^2 y = \dfrac{9}{10}$

$\Rightarrow \sin^2 y = 1 - \dfrac{9}{10} = \dfrac{1}{10} \Rightarrow \sin y = \dfrac{1}{\sqrt{10}}$

Again, y is acute, so sin y must be positive, so you can take the positive square root. If you don't like using this method, you can use the triangle method to work out sin y and cos x.

a) $\sin(x + y) = \sin x \cos y + \cos x \sin y$

$= \left(\dfrac{3}{4} \times \dfrac{3}{\sqrt{10}}\right) + \left(\dfrac{\sqrt{7}}{4} \times \dfrac{1}{\sqrt{10}}\right)$

$= \dfrac{9 + \sqrt{7}}{4\sqrt{10}} = \dfrac{9\sqrt{10} + \sqrt{70}}{40}$

b) $\cos(x - y) = \cos x \cos y + \sin x \sin y$

$= \left(\dfrac{\sqrt{7}}{4} \times \dfrac{3}{\sqrt{10}}\right) + \left(\dfrac{3}{4} \times \dfrac{1}{\sqrt{10}}\right)$

$= \dfrac{3\sqrt{7} + 3}{4\sqrt{10}} = \dfrac{3\sqrt{70} + 3\sqrt{10}}{40}$

c) $\mathrm{cosec}(x + y) = \dfrac{1}{\sin(x + y)} = \dfrac{40}{9\sqrt{10} + \sqrt{70}}$

$= \dfrac{18\sqrt{10} - 2\sqrt{70}}{37}$

d) $\sec(x - y) = \dfrac{1}{\cos(x - y)} = \dfrac{40}{3\sqrt{70} + 3\sqrt{10}}$

$= \dfrac{2\sqrt{70} - 2\sqrt{10}}{9}$

Q5 $\cos \dfrac{\pi}{12} = \cos\left(\dfrac{\pi}{4} - \dfrac{\pi}{6}\right) = \cos \dfrac{\pi}{4} \cos \dfrac{\pi}{6} + \sin \dfrac{\pi}{4} \sin \dfrac{\pi}{6}$

$= \left(\dfrac{1}{\sqrt{2}} \times \dfrac{\sqrt{3}}{2}\right) + \left(\dfrac{1}{\sqrt{2}} \times \dfrac{1}{2}\right) = \dfrac{\sqrt{3} + 1}{2\sqrt{2}}$

Now rationalise the denominator...

$= \dfrac{(\sqrt{3} + 1) \times \sqrt{2}}{(2\sqrt{2}) \times \sqrt{2}} = \dfrac{\sqrt{6} + \sqrt{2}}{4}$

Q6 $\sin 75° = \sin(30° + 45°)$

$= \sin 30° \cos 45° + \cos 30° \sin 45°$

$= \left(\dfrac{1}{2} \times \dfrac{1}{\sqrt{2}}\right) + \left(\dfrac{\sqrt{3}}{2} \times \dfrac{1}{\sqrt{2}}\right)$

$= \dfrac{1 + \sqrt{3}}{2\sqrt{2}} = \dfrac{(1 + \sqrt{3}) \times \sqrt{2}}{(2\sqrt{2}) \times \sqrt{2}} = \dfrac{\sqrt{6} + \sqrt{2}}{4}$

Q7 $\tan 75° = \tan(45° + 30°) = \dfrac{\tan 45° + \tan 30°}{1 - \tan 45° \tan 30°} =$

$\dfrac{1 + \dfrac{1}{\sqrt{3}}}{1 - 1 \times \dfrac{1}{\sqrt{3}}} = \dfrac{\left(\dfrac{\sqrt{3} + 1}{\sqrt{3}}\right)}{\left(\dfrac{\sqrt{3} - 1}{\sqrt{3}}\right)} = \dfrac{\sqrt{3} + 1}{\sqrt{3} - 1}.$

Exercise 4.2 — Simplifying, solving equations and proving identities

Q1 $\tan(A - B) \equiv \dfrac{\sin(A - B)}{\cos(A - B)}$

$\equiv \dfrac{\sin A \cos B - \cos A \sin B}{\cos A \cos B + \sin A \sin B}$

Divide through by cos A cos B...

$\equiv \dfrac{\left(\dfrac{\sin A \cos B}{\cos A \cos B}\right) - \left(\dfrac{\cos A \sin B}{\cos A \cos B}\right)}{\left(\dfrac{\cos A \cos B}{\cos A \cos B}\right) + \left(\dfrac{\sin A \sin B}{\cos A \cos B}\right)}$

$\equiv \dfrac{\left(\dfrac{\sin A}{\cos A}\right) - \left(\dfrac{\sin B}{\cos B}\right)}{1 + \left(\dfrac{\sin A}{\cos A}\right)\left(\dfrac{\sin B}{\cos B}\right)}$

Now use tan = sin / cos...

$\equiv \dfrac{\tan A - \tan B}{1 + \tan A \tan B}$

Q2 a) $\dfrac{\cos(A - B) - \cos(A + B)}{\cos A \sin B}$

$\equiv \dfrac{(\cos A \cos B + \sin A \sin B) - (\cos A \cos B - \sin A \sin B)}{\cos A \sin B}$

$\equiv \dfrac{2 \sin A \sin B}{\cos A \sin B} \equiv \dfrac{2 \sin A}{\cos A} \equiv 2 \tan A$

b) $\dfrac{1}{2}[\cos(A - B) - \cos(A + B)]$

$\equiv \dfrac{1}{2}[(\cos A \cos B + \sin A \sin B)$

$\qquad - (\cos A \cos B - \sin A \sin B)]$

$\equiv \dfrac{1}{2}(2 \sin A \sin B) \equiv \sin A \sin B$

c) $\sin(x + 90°)$

$\equiv \sin x \cos 90° + \cos x \sin 90°$

$\equiv \sin x (0) + \cos x (1) \equiv \cos x$

Q3 $4 \sin x \cos \dfrac{\pi}{3} - 4 \cos x \sin \dfrac{\pi}{3} = \cos x$

$\Rightarrow 2 \sin x - 2\sqrt{3} \cos x = \cos x$

$\Rightarrow 2 \sin x = (1 + 2\sqrt{3}) \cos x$

$\Rightarrow \dfrac{\sin x}{\cos x} = \dfrac{1 + 2\sqrt{3}}{2} = \tan x$

$\Rightarrow x = -1.99$ and 1.15 to 2 d.p.

Q4 a) $\tan\left(-\frac{\pi}{12}\right) = \tan\left(\frac{\pi}{6} - \frac{\pi}{4}\right) \equiv \dfrac{\tan\frac{\pi}{6} - \tan\frac{\pi}{4}}{1 + \tan\frac{\pi}{6}\tan\frac{\pi}{4}}$

$$\equiv \dfrac{\frac{1}{\sqrt{3}} - 1}{1 + \frac{1}{\sqrt{3}}}$$

$$\equiv \dfrac{1 - \sqrt{3}}{\sqrt{3} + 1}$$

Now rationalise the denominator...

$$\equiv \dfrac{1 - \sqrt{3}}{\sqrt{3} + 1} \times \dfrac{\sqrt{3} - 1}{\sqrt{3} - 1}$$

$$\equiv \dfrac{2\sqrt{3} - 4}{2} \equiv \sqrt{3} - 2$$

b) $\cos x = \cos x \cos\frac{\pi}{6} - \sin x \sin\frac{\pi}{6}$

$\Rightarrow \cos x - \frac{\sqrt{3}}{2}\cos x - \frac{1}{2}\sin x$

$\Rightarrow (2 - \sqrt{3})\cos x = -\sin x$

$\Rightarrow \dfrac{\sin x}{\cos x} = \tan x = \sqrt{3} - 2$

From a), $\tan\left(-\frac{\pi}{12}\right) = \sqrt{3} - 2$, so one solution for x is $-\frac{\pi}{12}$. To get an answer in the correct interval, add π, since $\tan x$ repeats itself every π radians. So $x = \frac{11\pi}{12}$.

Q5 $2\sin(x + 30°) = 2\sin x \cos 30° + 2\cos x \sin 30°$

$$\equiv 2\sin x \left(\frac{\sqrt{3}}{2}\right) + 2\cos x \left(\frac{1}{2}\right)$$

$$\equiv \sqrt{3}\sin x + \cos x$$

Q6 $\tan\left(\frac{\pi}{3} - x\right) \equiv \dfrac{\tan\frac{\pi}{3} - \tan x}{1 + \tan\frac{\pi}{3}\tan x} \equiv \dfrac{\sqrt{3} - \tan x}{1 + \sqrt{3}\tan x}$

Q7 $\tan(A + B) = \dfrac{\tan A + \tan B}{1 - \tan A \tan B} = \frac{1}{4}$

$\Rightarrow \dfrac{\frac{3}{8} + \tan B}{1 - \frac{3}{8}\tan B} = \frac{1}{4}$

$\Rightarrow \frac{3}{8} + \tan B = \frac{1}{4}\left(1 - \frac{3}{8}\tan B\right)$

$\Rightarrow \frac{3}{8} + \tan B = \frac{1}{4} - \frac{3}{32}\tan B$

$\Rightarrow \tan B + \frac{3}{32}\tan B = \frac{1}{4} - \frac{3}{8} = -\frac{1}{8}$

$\Rightarrow \frac{35}{32}\tan B = -\frac{1}{8} \Rightarrow \tan B = -\frac{1}{8} \times \frac{32}{35} = -\frac{4}{35}$

Q8 a) $\sin x \cos y + \cos x \sin y$
$= 4\cos x \cos y + 4\sin x \sin y$
Dividing through by $\cos x \cos y$ gives:
$\dfrac{\sin x}{\cos x} + \dfrac{\sin y}{\cos y} = 4 + \dfrac{4\sin x \sin y}{\cos x \cos y}$

$\Rightarrow \tan x + \tan y = 4 + 4\tan x \tan y$

$\Rightarrow \tan x - 4\tan x \tan y = 4 - \tan y$

$\Rightarrow \tan x (1 - 4\tan y) = 4 - \tan y$

$\Rightarrow \tan x = \dfrac{4 - \tan y}{1 - 4\tan y}$

b) $\tan x = \dfrac{4 - \tan\frac{\pi}{4}}{1 - 4\tan\frac{\pi}{4}}$

Comparing the equation you have to solve to the one in part a) you can see that $y = \frac{\pi}{4}$.

$\Rightarrow \tan x = \dfrac{4 - 1}{1 - 4} = -1$

$\Rightarrow x = \dfrac{3\pi}{4}$ and $\dfrac{7\pi}{4}$

Q9 a) Use the sin addition formula on $\sin(\theta + 45°)$:
$\sqrt{2}(\sin\theta\cos 45° + \cos\theta\sin 45°) = 3\cos\theta$

$\sqrt{2}\left(\frac{1}{\sqrt{2}}\sin\theta + \frac{1}{\sqrt{2}}\cos\theta\right) = 3\cos\theta$

$\sin\theta + \cos\theta = 3\cos\theta$

$\sin\theta = 2\cos\theta$

$\dfrac{\sin\theta}{\cos\theta} = 2$

$\tan\theta = 2$

So $\theta = 63.43°$ and $63.43° + 180° = 243.43°$.

b) Use the cos addition formula:
$2\cos\left(\theta - \frac{2\pi}{3}\right) - 5\sin\theta = 0$

$2\left(\cos\theta\cos\frac{2\pi}{3} + \sin\theta\sin\frac{2\pi}{3}\right) - 5\sin\theta = 0$

$2\left(-\frac{1}{2}\cos\theta + \frac{\sqrt{3}}{2}\sin\theta\right) - 5\sin\theta = 0$

$-\cos\theta + \sqrt{3}\sin\theta - 5\sin\theta = 0$

$-\cos\theta + (\sqrt{3} - 5)\sin\theta = 0$

$\cos\theta = (\sqrt{3} - 5)\sin\theta$

$\dfrac{1}{(\sqrt{3} - 5)} = \dfrac{\sin\theta}{\cos\theta} = \tan\theta$

So $\theta = -0.296... + \pi = 2.84$ to 2 d.p.
and $-0.296... + 2\pi = 5.99$ to 2 d.p.

c) Use the addition formulas:
$\sin(\theta - 30°) - \cos(\theta + 60°) = 0$
$(\sin\theta\cos 30° - \cos\theta\sin 30°)$
$\qquad - (\cos\theta\cos 60° - \sin\theta\sin 60°) = 0$
$\left(\frac{\sqrt{3}}{2}\sin\theta - \frac{1}{2}\cos\theta\right) - \left(\frac{1}{2}\cos\theta - \frac{\sqrt{3}}{2}\sin\theta\right) = 0$
$\frac{\sqrt{3}}{2}\sin\theta - \frac{1}{2}\cos\theta - \frac{1}{2}\cos\theta + \frac{\sqrt{3}}{2}\sin\theta = 0$
$\sqrt{3}\sin\theta - \cos\theta = 0$
$\sqrt{3}\sin\theta = \cos\theta$
$\dfrac{\sin\theta}{\cos\theta} = \dfrac{1}{\sqrt{3}} \Rightarrow \tan\theta = \dfrac{1}{\sqrt{3}}$
$\theta = 30°$ and $30° + 180° = 210°$

5. The Double Angle Formulas

Exercise 5.1 — Using the double angle formulas

Q1 a) $\sin 2A \equiv 2 \sin A \cos A$

$\Rightarrow 4 \sin A \cos A \equiv 2 \sin 2A$

$\Rightarrow 4 \sin \frac{\pi}{12} \cos \frac{\pi}{12} = 2 \sin \frac{\pi}{6} = 2 \times \frac{1}{2} = 1$

b) $\cos 2A \equiv 2 \cos^2 A - 1$

$\Rightarrow \cos \frac{2\pi}{3} = 2 \cos^2 \frac{\pi}{3} - 1 = 2\left(\frac{1}{2}\right)^2 - 1 = -\frac{1}{2}$

c) $\sin 2A \equiv 2 \sin A \cos A$

$\Rightarrow \frac{\sin 2A}{2} \equiv \sin A \cos A$

$\Rightarrow \frac{\sin 120°}{2} \equiv \sin 60° \cos 60° = \frac{\sqrt{3}}{2} \times \frac{1}{2} = \frac{\sqrt{3}}{4}$

d) $\tan 2A \equiv \frac{2 \tan A}{1 - \tan^2 A}$

$\Rightarrow \frac{\tan A}{2 - 2 \tan^2 A} \equiv \frac{\tan 2A}{4}$

$\Rightarrow \frac{\tan 15°}{2 - 2 \tan^2 15°} = \frac{\tan 30°}{4} = \frac{1}{4\sqrt{3}} = \frac{\sqrt{3}}{12}$

e) $\cos 2A \equiv 1 - 2 \sin^2 A$

$\Rightarrow 2 \sin^2 A - 1 \equiv -\cos 2A$

$\Rightarrow 2 \sin^2 15° - 1 = -\cos 30° = -\frac{\sqrt{3}}{2}$

Q2 a) $\cos 2A \equiv 1 - 2 \sin^2 A$

$\Rightarrow \cos 2x = 1 - 2 \sin^2 x = 1 - 2\left(\frac{1}{6}\right)^2 = \frac{17}{18}$

b) First find $\cos x$:

$\cos^2 x = 1 - \sin^2 x = 1 - \left(\frac{1}{6}\right)^2 = \frac{35}{36}$

$\Rightarrow \cos x = \frac{\sqrt{35}}{6}$

x is acute so take the positive root for cos x. Again, if you find it easier you can use the triangle method here.

$\sin 2A \equiv 2 \sin A \cos A$

$\Rightarrow \sin 2x = 2\left(\frac{1}{6} \times \frac{\sqrt{35}}{6}\right) = \frac{\sqrt{35}}{18}$

c) $\tan 2x = \frac{\sin 2x}{\cos 2x} = \frac{\sqrt{35}}{17}$

Q3 a) $\cos 2x = 1 - 2 \sin^2 x = 1 - 2\left(-\frac{1}{4}\right)^2 = \frac{7}{8}$

b) First find $\cos x$:

$\cos^2 x = 1 - \sin^2 x = 1 - \left(-\frac{1}{4}\right)^2 = \frac{15}{16}$

$\Rightarrow \cos x = -\frac{\sqrt{15}}{4}$

x is in the 3rd quadrant of the CAST diagram where cos x is negative, so take the negative root for cos x.

$\sin 2A \equiv 2 \sin A \cos A$

$\Rightarrow \sin 2x = 2\left(-\frac{1}{4} \times -\frac{\sqrt{15}}{4}\right) = \frac{\sqrt{15}}{8}$

c) $\tan 2x = \frac{\sin 2x}{\cos 2x} = \frac{\sqrt{15}}{7}$

Q4 a) Using the sin double angle formula:

$\frac{\sin 3\theta \cos 3\theta}{3} \equiv \frac{\sin 6\theta}{6}$

b) Using the cos double angle formula:

$\sin^2\left(\frac{2y}{3}\right) - \cos^2\left(\frac{2y}{3}\right) \equiv -\cos\left(\frac{4y}{3}\right)$

c) Using the tan double angle formula:

$\frac{1 - \tan^2\left(\frac{x}{2}\right)}{2 \tan\left(\frac{x}{2}\right)} \equiv \frac{1}{\tan x} \equiv \cot x$

Exercise 5.2 — Solving equations and proving identities

Q1 a) Using the double angle formula for cos involving sin:

$4(1 - 2 \sin^2 x) - 14 \sin x = 0$

$\Rightarrow 4 - 8 \sin^2 x - 14 \sin x = 0$

$\Rightarrow 8 \sin^2 x + 14 \sin x - 4 = 0$

$\Rightarrow 4 \sin^2 x + 7 \sin x - 2 = 0$

$\Rightarrow (4 \sin x - 1)(\sin x + 2) = 0$

So $\sin x = \frac{1}{4}$ or $\sin x = -2$ (not valid)

Solving $\sin x = \frac{1}{4}$ in the interval $0 \leq x \leq 360°$:

$x = 14.5°$ and $(180° - 14.5°) = 165.5°$

b) Using the double angle formula for cos involving cos:

$5(2 \cos^2 x - 1) + 9 \cos x + 7 = 0$

$\Rightarrow 10 \cos^2 x + 9 \cos x + 2 = 0$

$\Rightarrow (2 \cos x + 1)(5 \cos x + 2) = 0$

$\Rightarrow \cos x = -\frac{1}{2}$ or $\cos x = -\frac{2}{5}$

$\Rightarrow x = 113.6°, 120°, 240°, 246.4°$

c) Using the double angle formula for tan.

$\frac{4(1 - \tan^2 x)}{2 \tan x} + \frac{1}{\tan x} = 5$

$\Rightarrow 2(1 - \tan^2 x) + 1 = 5 \tan x$

$\Rightarrow 3 - 2 \tan^2 x = 5 \tan x$

$\Rightarrow 0 = 2 \tan^2 x + 5 \tan x - 3$

$\Rightarrow 0 = (2 \tan x - 1)(\tan x + 3)$

$\Rightarrow \tan x = \frac{1}{2}$ or $\tan x = -3$

$\Rightarrow x = 26.6°, 108.4°, 206.6°, 288.4°$

d) $\tan x - 5 (2 \sin x \cos x) = 0$

$\Rightarrow \frac{\sin x}{\cos x} = 10 \sin x \cos x$

$\Rightarrow \sin x = 10 \sin x \cos^2 x$

$\Rightarrow \sin x - 10 \sin x \cos^2 x = 0$

$\Rightarrow \sin x(1 - 10 \cos^2 x) = 0$

$\Rightarrow \sin x = 0$ or $\cos x = \pm\frac{1}{\sqrt{10}}$

Don't forget to find $\cos^{-1}$ of both the positive and negative root...

$x = 0°, 71.6°, 108.4°, 180°, 251.6°, 288.4°, 360°.$

Q2 a) $4(2 \cos^2 x - 1) - 10 \cos x + 1 = 0$

$\Rightarrow 8 \cos^2 x - 10 \cos x - 3 = 0$

$\Rightarrow (4 \cos x + 1)(2 \cos x - 3) = 0$

$\Rightarrow \cos x = -\frac{1}{4}$ or $\cos x = \frac{3}{2}$ (not valid)

$\Rightarrow x = 1.82$ and 4.46

b) $\cos 2x - 3 = 6 \sin^2 x - 3$

$\Rightarrow (1 - 2\sin^2 x) - 3 - 6\sin^2 x + 3 = 0$

$\Rightarrow 1 - 8\sin^2 x = 0$

$\Rightarrow \sin x = \pm \dfrac{1}{2\sqrt{2}}$

$\Rightarrow x = 0.361, 2.78, 3.50, 5.92$

Q3 a) $2\cos^2 x - 1 + 7\cos x = -4$

$\Rightarrow 2\cos^2 x + 7\cos x + 3 = 0$

$\Rightarrow (2\cos x + 1)(\cos x + 3) = 0$

$\Rightarrow \cos x = -\dfrac{1}{2}$ or $\cos x = -3$ (not valid)

$\Rightarrow x = \dfrac{2\pi}{3}$ and $\dfrac{4\pi}{3}$

b) $2\sin \dfrac{x}{2}\cos \dfrac{x}{2} + \cos \dfrac{x}{2} = 0$

$\Rightarrow \cos \dfrac{x}{2}(2\sin \dfrac{x}{2} + 1) = 0$

$\Rightarrow \cos \dfrac{x}{2} = 0$ or $\sin \dfrac{x}{2} = -\dfrac{1}{2}$

There are no solutions for $\sin \frac{x}{2} = -\frac{1}{2}$ in the interval $0 \le x \le \pi$ (they both lie in the 3rd and 4th quadrants of the CAST diagram, $\pi \le x \le 2\pi$) so...

$\Rightarrow \dfrac{x}{2} = \dfrac{\pi}{2} \Rightarrow x = \pi$

Q4 a) $\sin 2x \sec^2 x \equiv (2\sin x \cos x)\left(\dfrac{1}{\cos^2 x}\right)$

$\equiv \dfrac{2\sin x}{\cos x} \equiv 2\tan x$

b) $\dfrac{2}{1 + \cos 2x} = \dfrac{2}{1 + 2\cos^2 x - 1}$

$= \dfrac{2}{2\cos^2 x} = \dfrac{1}{\cos^2 x} = \sec^2 x$

c) $\cot x - 2\cot 2x = \dfrac{1}{\tan x} - \dfrac{2}{\tan 2x}$

$= \dfrac{1}{\tan x} - \dfrac{2(1 - \tan^2 x)}{2\tan x} \equiv \dfrac{1 - (1 - \tan^2 x)}{\tan x}$

$\equiv \dfrac{\tan^2 x}{\tan x} \equiv \tan x$

d) $\tan 2x + \cot 2x \equiv \dfrac{\sin 2x}{\cos 2x} + \dfrac{\cos 2x}{\sin 2x}$

$\equiv \dfrac{\sin^2 2x + \cos^2 2x}{\sin 2x \cos 2x}$

Use $\sin^2 x + \cos^2 x \equiv 1$, and $\sin 4x \equiv 2\sin 2x \cos 2x$...

$\equiv \dfrac{1}{\frac{1}{2}\sin 4x} \equiv \dfrac{2}{\sin 4x} \equiv 2\operatorname{cosec} 4x$

Q5 a) $\dfrac{1 + \cos 2x}{\sin 2x} \equiv \dfrac{1 + (2\cos^2 x - 1)}{2\sin x \cos x}$

$\equiv \dfrac{2\cos^2 x}{2\sin x \cos x} \equiv \dfrac{\cos x}{\sin x} \equiv \cot x$

b) Use $4\theta = 2x$, so $x = 2\theta$ and so $\dfrac{1 + \cos 4\theta}{\sin 4\theta} \equiv \cot 2\theta$

Solve $\cot 2\theta = 7$

$\Rightarrow \tan 2\theta = \dfrac{1}{7}$

$\Rightarrow 2\theta = 8.130°, 188.130°, 368.130°, 548.130°$

$\Rightarrow \theta = 4.1°, 94.1°, 184.1°, 274.1°$

Q6 a) $\operatorname{cosec} x - \cot \dfrac{x}{2} \equiv \dfrac{1}{\sin x} - \dfrac{\cos \frac{x}{2}}{\sin \frac{x}{2}}$

$\equiv \dfrac{1}{2\sin \frac{x}{2}\cos \frac{x}{2}} - \dfrac{\cos \frac{x}{2}}{\sin \frac{x}{2}} \equiv \dfrac{1 - 2\cos^2 \frac{x}{2}}{2\sin \frac{x}{2}\cos \frac{x}{2}}$

Here we've let $2A = x$ so $x = \frac{A}{2}$.

$\equiv \dfrac{-\left(2\cos^2 \frac{x}{2} - 1\right)}{2\sin \frac{x}{2}\cos \frac{x}{2}} \equiv \dfrac{-\cos x}{\sin x}$

$-\dfrac{1}{\left(\frac{\sin x}{\cos x}\right)} \equiv -\dfrac{1}{\tan x} \equiv -\cot x.$

b) Rearranging, $\operatorname{cosec} y - \cot \dfrac{y}{2} = -2 = -\cot y$

$\Rightarrow \cot y = 2 \Rightarrow \tan y = \dfrac{1}{2}.$

There are 2 solutions in the interval $-\pi \le y \le \pi$, at $y = 0.464$ and $y = 0.464 - \pi = -2.68$.

Q7 First find $\cos \theta$. You know $\sin \theta = \dfrac{5}{13}$ so using the triangle method $\cos \theta = \dfrac{12}{13}$.

a) (i) $\cos^2\left(\dfrac{\theta}{2}\right) = \dfrac{1}{2}(1 + \cos \theta) = \dfrac{1}{2}\left(1 + \dfrac{12}{13}\right) = \dfrac{25}{26}$

So $\cos\left(\dfrac{\theta}{2}\right) = \sqrt{\dfrac{25}{26}} = \dfrac{5}{\sqrt{26}}.$

θ is acute, so $\frac{\theta}{2}$ is also acute, and $\cos\left(\frac{\theta}{2}\right)$ is +ve so we can ignore the negative root.

(ii) $\sin^2\left(\dfrac{\theta}{2}\right) = \dfrac{1}{2}(1 - \cos \theta) = \dfrac{1}{2}\left(1 - \dfrac{12}{13}\right) = \dfrac{1}{26}$

So $\sin\left(\dfrac{\theta}{2}\right) = \sqrt{\dfrac{1}{26}} = \dfrac{1}{\sqrt{26}}.$

Again, θ is acute so $\sin\left(\frac{\theta}{2}\right)$ must be positive.

b) $\tan\left(\dfrac{\theta}{2}\right) = \dfrac{\sin\left(\frac{\theta}{2}\right)}{\cos\left(\frac{\theta}{2}\right)} = \dfrac{\left(\frac{1}{\sqrt{26}}\right)}{\left(\frac{5}{\sqrt{26}}\right)} = \dfrac{1}{5}$

6. The R Addition Formulas
Exercise 6.1 — Expressions of the form $a\cos\theta + b\sin\theta$

Q1 $3\sin x - 2\cos x \equiv R\sin(x - \alpha)$

$\Rightarrow 3\sin x - 2\cos x \equiv R\sin x \cos \alpha - R\cos x \sin \alpha$

$\Rightarrow$ **(1)** $R\cos \alpha = 3$ and **(2)** $R\sin \alpha = 2$

(2) $\div$ **(1)** gives $\tan \alpha = \dfrac{2}{3} \Rightarrow \alpha = 33.7°$ (to 1 d.p.)

(1)² + **(2)²** gives:

$R^2\cos^2 \alpha + R^2\sin^2 \alpha = 3^2 + 2^2 = 13$

$\Rightarrow R^2(\cos^2 \alpha + \sin^2 \alpha) = 13 \Rightarrow R^2 = 13 \Rightarrow R = \sqrt{13}$

So $3\sin x - 2\cos x \equiv \sqrt{13}\sin(x - 33.7°)$.

Q2 $6\cos x - 5\sin x \equiv R\cos(x + \alpha)$

$\Rightarrow 6\cos x - 5\sin x \equiv R\cos x \cos \alpha - R\sin x \sin \alpha$

$\Rightarrow$ **(1)** $R\cos \alpha = 6$ and **(2)** $R\sin \alpha = 5$

(2) $\div$ **(1)** gives $\tan \alpha = \dfrac{5}{6} \Rightarrow \alpha = 39.8°$ (to 1 d.p.)

(1)² + (2)² gives:

$R^2 \cos^2 \alpha + R^2 \sin^2 \alpha = 6^2 + 5^2 = 61 \Rightarrow R = \sqrt{61}$

So $6 \cos x - 5 \sin x \equiv \sqrt{61} \cos (x + 39.8°)$

Q3 $\sin x + \sqrt{7} \cos x \equiv R \sin (x + \alpha)$

$\Rightarrow \sin x + \sqrt{7} \cos x \equiv R \sin x \cos \alpha + R \cos x \sin \alpha$

$\Rightarrow$ **(1)** $R \cos \alpha = 1$ and **(2)** $R \sin \alpha = \sqrt{7}$

(2) ÷ (1) gives $\tan \alpha = \sqrt{7} \Rightarrow \alpha = 1.21$ (to 3 s.f.)

(1)² + (2)² gives:

$R^2 \cos^2 \alpha + R^2 \sin^2 \alpha = 1^2 + (\sqrt{7})^2 = 8$

$\Rightarrow R = \sqrt{8} = \sqrt{4 \times 2} = \sqrt{4} \times \sqrt{2} = 2\sqrt{2}$

So $\sin x + \sqrt{7} \cos x \equiv 2\sqrt{2} \sin (x + 1.21)$

Q4 $\sqrt{2} \sin x - \cos x \equiv R \sin (x - \alpha)$

$\Rightarrow \sqrt{2} \sin x - \cos x \equiv R \sin x \cos \alpha - R \cos x \sin \alpha$

$\Rightarrow$ **(1)** $R \cos \alpha = \sqrt{2}$ and **(2)** $R \sin \alpha = 1$

(2) ÷ (1) gives $\tan \alpha = \dfrac{1}{\sqrt{2}}$

(1)² + (2)² gives:

$R^2 \cos^2 \alpha + R^2 \sin^2 \alpha = (\sqrt{2})^2 + 1^2 = 3$

$\Rightarrow R^2 (\cos^2 \alpha + \sin^2 \alpha) = 3$

$\Rightarrow R^2 = 3 \Rightarrow R = \sqrt{3}$

So $\sqrt{2} \sin x - \cos x \equiv \sqrt{3} \sin (x - \alpha)$,

where $\tan \alpha = \dfrac{1}{\sqrt{2}}$.

Q5 $3 \cos 2x + 5 \sin 2x \equiv R \cos (2x - \alpha)$

$\Rightarrow 3 \cos 2x + 5 \sin 2x \equiv R \cos 2x \cos \alpha + R \sin 2x \sin \alpha$

$\Rightarrow$ **(1)** $R \cos \alpha = 3$ and **(2)** $R \sin \alpha = 5$

(2) ÷ (1) gives $\tan \alpha = \dfrac{5}{3}$

(1)² + (2)² gives:

$R^2 \cos^2 \alpha + R^2 \sin^2 \alpha = 3^2 + 5^2 = 34 \Rightarrow R = \sqrt{34}$

So $3 \cos 2x + 5 \sin 2x \equiv \sqrt{34} \cos (2x - \alpha)$, where $\tan \alpha = \dfrac{5}{3}$.

Q6 a) $\sqrt{3} \sin x + \cos x \equiv R \sin (x + \alpha)$

$\Rightarrow \sqrt{3} \sin x + \cos x \equiv R \sin x \cos \alpha + R \cos x \sin \alpha$

$\Rightarrow$ **(1)** $R \cos \alpha = \sqrt{3}$ and **(2)** $R \sin \alpha = 1$

(2) ÷ (1) gives $\tan \alpha = \dfrac{1}{\sqrt{3}} \Rightarrow \alpha = \dfrac{\pi}{6}$

(1)² + (2)² gives:

$R^2 \cos^2 \alpha + R^2 \sin^2 \alpha = (\sqrt{3})^2 + 1^2 = 4$

$\Rightarrow R = \sqrt{4} = 2$

So $\sqrt{3} \sin x + \cos x \equiv 2 \sin (x + \dfrac{\pi}{6})$

b) The graph of $y = 2 \sin (x + \dfrac{\pi}{6})$ is the graph of $y = \sin x$ transformed in the following way: a horizontal translation left by $\dfrac{\pi}{6}$, then a vertical stretch by a factor of 2.

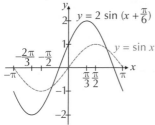

c) The graph of $y = \sin x$ has a minimum at

$(-\dfrac{\pi}{2}, -1)$, a maximum at $(\dfrac{\pi}{2}, 1)$, and cuts the x-axis at $(-\pi, 0)$, $(0, 0)$ and $(\pi, 0)$.

To describe the graph of $y = 2 \sin (x + \dfrac{\pi}{6})$, each of these points needs to have $\dfrac{\pi}{6}$ subtracted from the x-coordinates, and the y-coordinates multiplied by 2.

So the graph of $y = 2 \sin (x + \dfrac{\pi}{6})$ has a minimum at $(-\dfrac{2\pi}{3}, -2)$, a maximum at $(\dfrac{\pi}{3}, 2)$, and cuts the x-axis at $(-\dfrac{\pi}{6}, 0)$ and $(\dfrac{5\pi}{6}, 0)$.

To find the y-intercept, put $x = 0$ into the equation:

$y = 2 \sin (0 + \dfrac{\pi}{6}) = 2 \times \dfrac{1}{2} = 1$

So the y-intercept is at $(0, 1)$.

Exercise 6.2 — Applying the R addition formulas

For each of the questions below, use the methods shown in Exercise 6.1 to express the equations in R form.

Q1 a) $5 \cos \theta - 12 \sin \theta \equiv 13 \cos (\theta + 67.4°)$

b) $13 \cos (\theta + 67.4°) = 4$, in the interval $67.4° \le (\theta + 67.4°) \le 427.4°$.

$\cos (\theta + 67.4°) = \dfrac{4}{13}$

$\Rightarrow \theta + 67.4° = \cos^{-1} \dfrac{4}{13}$

$\qquad\qquad = 72.1°$ and $(360° - 72.1°) = 287.9°$

$\Rightarrow \theta = (72.1° - 67.4°)$ and $(287.9° - 67.4°)$

$\qquad = 4.7°$ and $220.5°$

c) The maximum and minimum values of $\cos \theta$ are at ± 1. So the maximum and minimum values of $13 \cos (\theta + 67.4°)$ are at ± 13.

Q2 a) $2 \sin 2\theta + 3 \cos 2\theta \equiv \sqrt{13} \sin (2\theta + 0.983)$

b) $\sqrt{13} \sin (2\theta + 0.983) = 1$ in the interval $0.983 \le (2\theta + 0.983) \le 13.549$.

$\sin (2\theta + 0.983) = \dfrac{1}{\sqrt{13}}$

$\Rightarrow 2\theta + 0.983 = 0.281$ (not in correct interval), $(\pi - 0.281)$, $(2\pi + 0.281)$, $(3\pi - 0.281)$, $(4\pi + 0.281)$.

There will be 4 solutions for θ between 0 and 2π because you're dealing with sin 2θ.

$\Rightarrow 2\theta + 0.983 = 2.861, 6.564, 9.144, 12.847$

$\Rightarrow \theta = 0.939, 2.79, 4.08, 5.93$

Q3 a) $3 \sin \theta - 2\sqrt{5} \cos \theta \equiv \sqrt{29} \sin (\theta - 56.1°)$

b) $\sqrt{29} \sin (\theta - 56.1°) = 5$ in the interval $-56.1° \le (\theta - 56.1°) \le 303.9°$.

$\sin (\theta - 56.1°) = \dfrac{5}{\sqrt{29}}$

$\Rightarrow \theta - 56.1° = 68.2°$, and $(180° - 68.2°) = 111.8°$

$\Rightarrow \theta = 124.3°$ and $167.9°$

c) $f(x) = \sqrt{29} \sin (x - 56.1°)$. The maximum of sin x is at 1, so the maximum value of f(x) is at $f(x) = \sqrt{29}$.

When $f(x) = \sqrt{29}$, $\sin(x - 56.1°) = 1$
$\Rightarrow x - 56.1° = 90° \Rightarrow x = 146.1°$

Q4 a) $3 \sin x + \cos x \equiv \sqrt{10} \sin(x + 18.4°)$

b) $\sqrt{10} \sin(x + 18.4°) = 2$ in the interval $18.4° \leq (x + 18.4°) \leq 378.4°$.

$\sin(x + 18.4°) = \dfrac{2}{\sqrt{10}}$

$\Rightarrow x + 18.4° = 39.2°$ or $(180° - 39.2°) = 140.8°$.

$\Rightarrow x = 20.8°$ and $122.4°$.

c) The maximum and minimum values of $f(x)$ are at $\pm\sqrt{10}$.

Q5 a) $4 \sin x + \cos x \equiv \sqrt{17} \sin(x + 0.245)$

b) Maximum value of $4 \sin x + \cos x = \sqrt{17}$, so the greatest value of $(4 \sin x + \cos x)^4 = (\sqrt{17})^4 = 289$.

c) $\sqrt{17} \sin(x + 0.245) = 1$ in the interval $0.245 \leq (x + 0.245) \leq 3.387$.

$\sin(x + 0.245) = \dfrac{1}{\sqrt{17}}$

$\Rightarrow x + 0.245 = 0.245$ and $(\pi - 0.245) = 2.897$

$\Rightarrow x = 0$ and 2.65

Q6 a) $f(x) = 8 \cos x + 15 \sin x = 17 \cos(x - 1.08)$.

b) So solve for $17 \cos(x - 1.08) = 5$ in the interval $-1.08 \leq (x - 1.08) \leq 5.20$.

$\cos(x - 1.08) = \dfrac{5}{17}$

$\Rightarrow x - 1.08 = 1.27$ or $(2\pi - 1.27) = 5.01$

$\Rightarrow x = 2.35$ and 6.09.

c) $g(x) = (8 \cos x + 15 \sin x)^2 = 17^2 \cos^2(x - 1.08)$
$= 289 \cos^2(x - 1.08)$

The function $\cos^2 x$ has a minimum value of 0 (since all negative values of $\cos x$ become positive when you square it) so the minimum of $g(x)$ is 0.
This minimum occurs when $\cos^2(x - 1.08) = 0$ so $\cos(x - 1.08) = 0$ so $x - 1.08 = \pi$ and $x = 2.06$.

Q7 a) $2 \cos x + \sin x \equiv R \cos(x - \alpha)$
$\equiv R \cos x \cos \alpha + R \sin x \sin \alpha$
$\Rightarrow$ **(1)** $R \cos \alpha = 2$ and **(2)** $R \sin \alpha = 1$

(2) $\div$ **(1)** gives $\tan \alpha = \dfrac{1}{2} \Rightarrow \alpha = 26.6°$ (to 3 s.f.)

(1)^2 + **(2)**^{2} gives:
$R^2 \cos^2 \alpha + R^2 \sin^2 \alpha = 2^2 + 1^2 = 5$
$\Rightarrow R^2 (\cos^2 \alpha + \sin^2 \alpha) = 5$
$\Rightarrow R^2 = 5 \Rightarrow R = \sqrt{5}$
So $2 \cos x + \sin x \equiv \sqrt{5} \cos(x - 26.6°)$.

b) The range of $g(x)$ is between the maximum and minimum values, which are at $\pm\sqrt{5}$.
So $-\sqrt{5} \leq g(x) \leq \sqrt{5}$.

Q8 $3 \sin \theta - \dfrac{3}{2} \cos \theta \equiv \dfrac{3\sqrt{5}}{2} \sin(\theta - 0.464)$

So solve $\dfrac{3\sqrt{5}}{2} \sin(\theta - 0.464) = 3$ in the interval $-0.464 \leq (\theta - 0.464) \leq 5.819$.

$\sin(\theta - 0.464) = \dfrac{2}{\sqrt{5}}$

$\Rightarrow \theta - 0.464 = 1.107$ and $(\pi - 1.107) = 2.034$
$\Rightarrow \theta = 1.57$ and 2.50

Q9 $4 \sin 2\theta + 3 \cos 2\theta \equiv 5 \sin(2\theta + 0.644)$
So solve $5 \sin(2\theta + 0.644) = 2$ in the interval $0.644 \leq (2\theta + 0.644) \leq 6.927$.

$\sin(2\theta + 0.644) = \dfrac{2}{5}$

$\Rightarrow 2\theta + 0.644 = 0.412$ (not in the interval), $(\pi - 0.412) = 2.730$, and $(2\pi + 0.412) = 6.695$
$\Rightarrow \theta = 1.04$ and 3.03

7. The Factor Formulas
Exercise 7.1 — Proving and using the factor formulas

Q1 Starting with the addition formulas for sin:
$\sin(x + y) \equiv \sin x \cos y + \cos x \sin y$
$\sin(x - y) \equiv \sin x \cos y - \cos x \sin y$

So $\sin(x + y) + \sin(x - y)$
$\equiv \sin x \cos y + \cos x \sin y + \sin x \cos y - \cos x \sin y$
$\equiv 2 \sin x \cos y$

Substitute $A = x + y$ and $B = x - y$

Then $A + B = 2x$ and $A - B = 2y$,
so $x = \left(\dfrac{A + B}{2}\right)$ and $y = \left(\dfrac{A - B}{2}\right)$.

Putting this back into the identity gives:
$\sin A + \sin B \equiv 2 \sin\left(\dfrac{A + B}{2}\right) \cos\left(\dfrac{A - B}{2}\right)$

Q2 Starting again with the addition formulas for sin, but subtracting this time gives:
$\sin(x + y) - \sin(x - y)$
$\equiv \sin x \cos y + \cos x \sin y - \sin x \cos y + \cos x \sin y$
$\equiv 2 \cos x \sin y$

Substituting as before for
$x = \left(\dfrac{A + B}{2}\right)$ and $y = \left(\dfrac{A - B}{2}\right)$, gives:
$\sin A - \sin B \equiv 2 \cos\left(\dfrac{A + B}{2}\right) \sin\left(\dfrac{A - B}{2}\right)$

Q3 Starting with the addition formulas for cos:
$\cos(x + y) \equiv \cos x \cos y - \sin x \sin y$
$\cos(x - y) \equiv \cos x \cos y + \sin x \sin y$

So $\cos(x + y) - \cos(x - y)$
$\equiv \cos x \cos y - \sin x \sin y - \cos x \cos y - \sin x \sin y$
$\equiv -2 \sin x \sin y$

Substitute $A = x + y$ and $B = x - y$
Then $A + B = 2x$ and $A - B = 2y$,
so $x = \left(\dfrac{A + B}{2}\right)$ and $y = \left(\dfrac{A - B}{2}\right)$.

Putting this back into the identity gives:
$\cos A - \cos B \equiv -2 \sin\left(\dfrac{A + B}{2}\right) \sin\left(\dfrac{A - B}{2}\right)$

Q4 $\sin 75° - \sin 15° = 2 \cos\left(\dfrac{75° + 15°}{2}\right) \sin\left(\dfrac{75° - 15°}{2}\right)$
$= 2 \cos 45° \sin 30°$
$= 2\left(\dfrac{1}{\sqrt{2}}\right)\left(\dfrac{1}{2}\right) = \dfrac{1}{\sqrt{2}}\left(\dfrac{\sqrt{2}}{\sqrt{2}}\right) = \dfrac{\sqrt{2}}{2}$

Q5 $\cos 165° - \cos 75°$

$$= -2 \sin \left(\frac{165°+75°}{2}\right) \sin \left(\frac{165°-75°}{2}\right)$$

$$= -2 \sin 120° \sin 45° = -2 \sin 60° \sin 45°$$

$$= -2\left(\frac{\sqrt{3}}{2}\right)\left(\frac{1}{\sqrt{2}}\right) = -\frac{\sqrt{3}}{\sqrt{2}} \left(\text{or} -\frac{\sqrt{6}}{2}\right)$$

Q6 a) $\cos \left(\frac{A+B}{2}\right) \cos \left(\frac{A-B}{2}\right) = \frac{1}{2}(\cos A + \cos B)$

$$\left(\frac{A+B}{2}\right) = 140° \Rightarrow A+B = 280°$$

$$\left(\frac{A-B}{2}\right) = 50° \Rightarrow A-B = 100°$$

Solving these equations: $A = 190°$ and $B = 90°$.

So $\cos 140° \cos 50° = \frac{1}{2}(\cos 190° + \cos 90°)$

$$= \frac{1}{2}(\cos 190° + 0) = \frac{1}{2}\cos 190°$$

So $\dfrac{\cos 140° \cos 50°}{\cos 190°} = \dfrac{\frac{1}{2}\cos 190°}{\cos 190°} = \dfrac{1}{2}$

b) $2 \cos \left(\frac{A+B}{2}\right) \sin \left(\frac{A-B}{2}\right) \equiv \sin A - \sin B$

So $2 \cos 75° \sin 15° = \sin A - \sin B$, where:

$$\left(\frac{A+B}{2}\right) = 75° \Rightarrow A+B = 150°$$

$$\left(\frac{A-B}{2}\right) = 15° \Rightarrow A-B = 30°$$

Solving these equations: $A = 90°$ and $B = 60°$.

So $2 \cos 75° \sin 15° = \sin 90° - \sin 60°$

$$= 1 - \frac{\sqrt{3}}{2} = \frac{2-\sqrt{3}}{2}$$

Q7 $4 \sin \left(\frac{A+B}{2}\right) \cos \left(\frac{A-B}{2}\right) \equiv 2 \sin A + 2 \sin B$

So $4 \sin 52.5° \cos 7.5° = 2 \sin A + 2 \sin B$, where:

$$\left(\frac{A+B}{2}\right) = 52.5° \Rightarrow A+B = 105°$$

$$\left(\frac{A-B}{2}\right) = 7.5° \Rightarrow A-B = 15°$$

Solving these equations: $A = 60°$ and $B = 45°$

So $4 \sin 52.5° \cos 7.5° = 2 \sin 60° + 2 \sin 45°$

$$= 2\left(\frac{\sqrt{3}}{2}\right) + 2\left(\frac{\sqrt{2}}{2}\right) = \sqrt{3} + \sqrt{2}$$

Q8 $\dfrac{\cos\frac{\pi}{12} - \cos\frac{5\pi}{12}}{\sin\frac{5\pi}{12} + \sin\frac{\pi}{12}} = \dfrac{-\left(\cos\frac{5\pi}{12} - \cos\frac{\pi}{12}\right)}{\sin\frac{5\pi}{12} + \sin\frac{\pi}{12}}$

$$= \frac{2 \sin\left(\frac{5\pi}{24} + \frac{\pi}{24}\right)\sin\left(\frac{5\pi}{24} - \frac{\pi}{24}\right)}{2 \sin\left(\frac{5\pi}{24} + \frac{\pi}{24}\right)\cos\left(\frac{5\pi}{24} - \frac{\pi}{24}\right)}$$

$$= \frac{\sin\frac{\pi}{6}}{\cos\frac{\pi}{6}} = \tan\frac{\pi}{6} = \frac{1}{\sqrt{3}}\left(\frac{\sqrt{3}}{\sqrt{3}}\right) = \frac{\sqrt{3}}{3}$$

Exercise 7.2 — Solving equations and proving other identities

Q1 a) $2 \sin 6\theta \cos 3\theta = 2 \sin \left(\frac{9\theta + 3\theta}{2}\right)\cos \left(\frac{9\theta - 3\theta}{2}\right)$

$$= \sin 9\theta + \sin 3\theta$$

b) $2 \sin 8\theta \cos 4\theta = 2 \sin \left(\frac{12\theta + 4\theta}{2}\right)\cos \left(\frac{12\theta - 4\theta}{2}\right)$

$$= \sin 12\theta + \sin 4\theta$$

c) $2 \sin 3\theta \cos \theta = 2 \sin \left(\frac{4\theta + 2\theta}{2}\right)\cos \left(\frac{4\theta - 2\theta}{2}\right)$

$$= \sin 4\theta + \sin 2\theta$$

d) $2 \cos 5\theta \sin 2\theta = 2 \cos \left(\frac{7\theta + 3\theta}{2}\right)\sin \left(\frac{7\theta - 3\theta}{2}\right)$

$$= \sin 7\theta - \sin 3\theta$$

e) $2 \cos 7\theta \sin 3\theta = 2 \cos \left(\frac{10\theta + 4\theta}{2}\right) \sin \left(\frac{10\theta - 4\theta}{2}\right)$

$$= \sin 10\theta - \sin 4\theta$$

f) $2 \cos 12\theta \sin \frac{5}{2}\theta$

$$= 2 \cos \left(\frac{\frac{29}{2}\theta + \frac{19}{2}\theta}{2}\right) \sin \left(\frac{\frac{29}{2}\theta - \frac{19}{2}\theta}{2}\right)$$

$$= \sin \frac{29}{2}\theta - \sin \frac{19}{2}\theta$$

Q2 a) $\cos 18\theta + \cos 8\theta$

b) $\cos 4\theta + \cos 3\theta$

c) $\cos 15\theta + \cos 19\theta$

d) $2\cos 16\theta + 2\cos 4\theta$

e) $\cos 22\theta - \cos 4\theta$

f) $\cos \frac{31}{2}\theta - \cos \frac{29}{2}\theta$

Q3 a) $\cos 5x - \cos 4x = -2 \sin \frac{9}{2}x \sin \frac{1}{2}x$

b) $\dfrac{\cos 5x}{\cos 4x} = 1 \Rightarrow \cos 5x - \cos 4x = 0$

$$\Rightarrow -2 \sin \frac{9}{2}x \sin \frac{1}{2}x = 0$$

So either $\sin \frac{9}{2}x = 0$ or $\sin \frac{1}{2}x = 0$

*Remember, $0 \le x \le 360°$ so $0 \le \frac{x}{2} \le 180°$
and $0 \le \frac{9x}{2} \le 1620°$.*

$$\Rightarrow \frac{9}{2}x = 0, 180°, 360°, 540°, 720°, 900°, 1080°,$$
$$1260°, 1440°, 1620°.$$

and $\frac{1}{2}x = 0, 180°$

So $x = 0, 40°, 80°, 120°, 160°, 200°, 240°, 280°,$
$320°, 360°$

Q4 a) $\cos 2x + \cos 3x = 2 \cos \frac{5}{2}x \cos \frac{1}{2}x$

b) $\cos 2x + \cos 3x = 0 \Rightarrow 2 \cos \frac{5}{2}x \cos \frac{1}{2}x = 0$

So either $\cos \frac{5}{2}x = 0$ or $\cos \frac{1}{2}x = 0$

*This time, $0 \le x \le 2\pi$ so $0 \le \frac{x}{2} \le \pi$
and $0 \le \frac{5x}{2} \le 5\pi$.*

$$\Rightarrow \frac{5}{2}x = \frac{\pi}{2}, \frac{3\pi}{2}, \frac{5\pi}{2}, \frac{7\pi}{2}, \frac{9\pi}{2}$$

and $\frac{1}{2}x = \frac{\pi}{2}$. So $x = \frac{\pi}{5}, \frac{3\pi}{5}, \pi, \frac{7\pi}{5}, \frac{9\pi}{5}$

Q5 $\sin(x + 15°)\cos(x - 15°) = 0.5$

$2\sin(x + 15°)\cos(x - 15°) = 1$

$\Rightarrow \sin A + \sin B = 1$, where:

$x + 15° = \left(\dfrac{A + B}{2}\right) \Rightarrow A = 2x + 30° - B$

and $x - 15° = \left(\dfrac{A - B}{2}\right)$

$\Rightarrow \left(\dfrac{2x + 30° - 2B}{2}\right) = x + 15° - B$

$\Rightarrow B = 30° \Rightarrow A = 2x$

So $\sin 2x + \sin 30° = 1 \Rightarrow \sin 2x = 0.5$

$\Rightarrow 2x = 30°, 150° \Rightarrow x = 15°, 75°$

Q6 $\cos 6x + \cos 4x = 2\cos 5x \cos x$

So write the equation as:

$2\cos 5x \cos x + \cos x = 0$

$\Rightarrow \cos x (2\cos 5x + 1) = 0$

$\Rightarrow \cos x = 0 \Rightarrow x = \dfrac{\pi}{2}$

or $2\cos 5x + 1 = 0 \Rightarrow \cos 5x = -\dfrac{1}{2}$

$\Rightarrow 5x = \dfrac{2\pi}{3}, \dfrac{4\pi}{3}, \dfrac{8\pi}{3}, \dfrac{10\pi}{3}, \dfrac{14\pi}{3}$

$\Rightarrow x = \dfrac{2\pi}{15}, \dfrac{4\pi}{15}, \dfrac{8\pi}{15}, \dfrac{2\pi}{3}, \dfrac{14\pi}{15}$

Q7 **a)** $\dfrac{\sin 9x + \sin x}{\sin 8x + \sin 2x} \equiv \dfrac{2\sin 5x \cos 4x}{2\sin 5x \cos 3x}$

$\equiv \dfrac{\cos 4x}{\cos 3x}$

b) $\dfrac{\sin 5x - \sin x}{\cos 5x + \cos x} \equiv \dfrac{2\cos 3x \sin 2x}{2\cos 3x \cos 2x}$

$\equiv \dfrac{\sin 2x}{\cos 2x} \equiv \tan 2x$

c) $\dfrac{\sin x + \sin y}{\cos x + \cos y} \equiv \dfrac{2\sin\left(\dfrac{x + y}{2}\right)\cos\left(\dfrac{x - y}{2}\right)}{2\cos\left(\dfrac{x + y}{2}\right)\cos\left(\dfrac{x - y}{2}\right)}$

$\equiv \dfrac{\sin\left(\dfrac{x + y}{2}\right)}{\cos\left(\dfrac{x + y}{2}\right)} \equiv \tan\left(\dfrac{x + y}{2}\right)$

Review Exercise — Chapter 2

Q1 **a)** $\sin^{-1}\dfrac{1}{\sqrt{2}} = \dfrac{\pi}{4}$ **b)** $\cos^{-1}0 = \dfrac{\pi}{2}$

c) $\tan^{-1}\sqrt{3} = \dfrac{\pi}{3}$

Q2

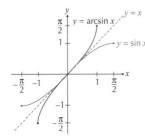

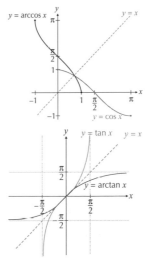

Q3 **a)** To find the inverse of $y = \dfrac{1}{1 + \cos x}$, first rearrange to make x the subject:

$1 + \cos x = \dfrac{1}{y} \Rightarrow \cos x = \dfrac{1}{y} - 1$

$\Rightarrow x = \cos^{-1}(\dfrac{1}{y} - 1)$

Then replace x with $f^{-1}(x)$ and y with x:

$f^{-1}(x) = \cos^{-1}(\dfrac{1}{x} - 1) = \arccos(\dfrac{1}{x} - 1)$.

b) $f(x)$ has domain $0 \le x \le \dfrac{\pi}{2}$ and range $\dfrac{1}{2} \le f(x) \le 1$.

The domain of $f(x)$ becomes the range of $f^{-1}(x)$ and the range of $f(x)$ becomes the domain of $f^{-1}(x)$, so the domain of $f^{-1}(x)$ is $\dfrac{1}{2} \le x \le 1$, and the range is $0 \le f^{-1}(x) \le \dfrac{\pi}{2}$.

c) $f^{-1}(x)$ is the reflection of $f(x)$ in the line $y = x$:

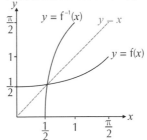

Q4 **a)** $\sin^{-1} 1 = \dfrac{\pi}{2}$, $\cos^{-1} 1 = 0$, $\tan^{-1} 1 = \dfrac{\pi}{4}$,

so $f(1) = \dfrac{\pi}{2} + 0 + \dfrac{\pi}{4} = \dfrac{3\pi}{4}$

b) $\sin^{-1}(-1) = -\dfrac{\pi}{2}$, $\cos^{-1}(-1) = \pi$, $\tan^{-1}(-1) = -\dfrac{\pi}{4}$,

so $f(-1) = -\dfrac{\pi}{2} + \pi - \dfrac{\pi}{4} - \dfrac{\pi}{4}$

Q5 **a)** $\csc 30° = 2$ (since $\sin 30° = 0.5$)

b) $\sec 30° = \dfrac{2}{\sqrt{3}}$ (since $\cos 30° = \dfrac{\sqrt{3}}{2}$)

c) $\cot 30° = \sqrt{3}$ (since $\tan 30° = \dfrac{1}{\sqrt{3}}$)

Q6

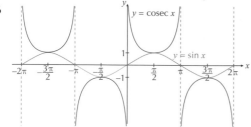

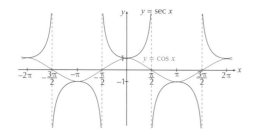

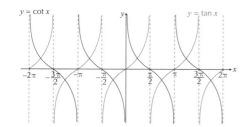

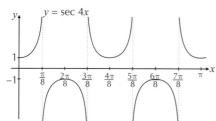

Q7 **a)** If $f(x) = \sec x$, then $y = \sec 4x = f(4x)$.
This is a horizontal stretch scale factor $\frac{1}{4}$.

b) The period of $y = \sec x$ is 2π, so the period of $y = \sec 4x$ is $2\pi \div 4 = \frac{\pi}{2}$.

c)

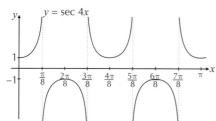

d) $y = \sec 4x$ is undefined when $x = \frac{\pi}{8}, \frac{3\pi}{8}, \frac{5\pi}{8}$ and $\frac{7\pi}{8}$.

Q8 Divide the whole identity by $\cos^2\theta$ to get:
$$\frac{\cos^2\theta}{\cos^2\theta} + \frac{\sin^2\theta}{\cos^2\theta} \equiv \frac{1}{\cos^2\theta}$$
$$\Rightarrow 1 + \tan^2\theta \equiv \sec^2\theta$$

(as sin/cos ≡ tan and 1/cos ≡ sec)

Q9 Using the identities $\csc^2\theta \equiv 1 + \cot^2\theta$ and $\sin^2\theta + \cos^2\theta \equiv 1$, the LHS becomes:
$(\csc^2\theta - 1) + (1 - \cos^2\theta) \equiv \csc^2\theta - \cos^2\theta$
which is the same as the RHS.

Q10 $y = \cot^2\theta = \csc^2\theta - 1 = x^2 - 1$

Q11 $y^2 = 4\tan^2\theta = 4(\sec^2\theta - 1) = 4(x^2 - 1)$
$\Rightarrow y = \pm 2\sqrt{x^2 - 1}$

Q12 **a)** $\csc^2 x = \frac{3\cot x + 4}{2}$
$\Rightarrow 2\csc^2 x = 3\cot x + 4$
$\Rightarrow 2(1 + \cot^2 x) = 3\cot x + 4$
$\Rightarrow 2\cot^2 x - 3\cot x + 2 - 4 = 0$
$\Rightarrow 2\cot^2 x - 3\cot x - 2 = 0$

b) Solve $2\cot^2 x - 3\cot x - 2 = 0$
This factorises to give $(2\cot x + 1)(\cot x - 2) = 0$
So $\cot x = -\frac{1}{2} \Rightarrow \tan x = -2$
and $\cot x = 2 \Rightarrow \tan x = \frac{1}{2}$
Solving these over the interval $0 \le x \le 2\pi$ gives:
$x = 0.46, 3.61, 2.03$ and 5.18 (to 2 d.p.)

Q13 **a)** $\sec\theta = \frac{1}{\cos\theta} = 2$

b) $\cos\theta = \frac{1}{2}$, so draw a right-angled triangle with the adjacent side having a length of 1 and the hypotenuse having a length of 2:

Using Pythagoras' Theorem, the missing side has a length of $\sqrt{(2^2 - 1^2)} = \sqrt{3}$.
So $\tan\theta = \frac{\text{OPP}}{\text{ADJ}} = \frac{\sqrt{3}}{1} = \sqrt{3}$

c) From a), $\sec\theta = 2$, so $\sec^2\theta = 4$
$\Rightarrow 1 + \tan^2\theta = 4$
$\Rightarrow \tan^2\theta = 3$
$\Rightarrow \tan\theta = \sqrt{3}$

d) $\cot\theta = \frac{1}{\tan\theta} = \frac{1}{\sqrt{3}}$

e) From d), $\cot\theta = \frac{1}{\sqrt{3}}$, so $\cot^2\theta = \frac{1}{3}$
$\Rightarrow \csc^2\theta - 1 = \frac{1}{3}$
$\Rightarrow \csc^2\theta = \frac{4}{3}$
$\Rightarrow \csc\theta = \frac{2}{\sqrt{3}} \Rightarrow \sin\theta = \frac{\sqrt{3}}{2}$

You can check that this is right by looking at the right-angled triangle in part b).

Q14 $\frac{\pi}{12} = \frac{\pi}{3} - \frac{\pi}{4}$, so use the addition
formula for $\cos(A - B)$:
$$\cos\frac{\pi}{12} = \cos\left(\frac{\pi}{3} - \frac{\pi}{4}\right)$$
$$= \cos\frac{\pi}{3}\cos\frac{\pi}{4} + \sin\frac{\pi}{3}\sin\frac{\pi}{4}$$
As $\cos\frac{\pi}{3} = \frac{1}{2}$, $\cos\frac{\pi}{4} = \frac{1}{\sqrt{2}}$,
$\sin\frac{\pi}{3} = \frac{\sqrt{3}}{2}$ and $\sin\frac{\pi}{4} = \frac{1}{\sqrt{2}}$

putting these values into the equation gives:

$$\cos\frac{\pi}{3}\cos\frac{\pi}{4} + \sin\frac{\pi}{3}\sin\frac{\pi}{4}$$

$$= \left(\frac{1}{2} \times \frac{1}{\sqrt{2}}\right) + \left(\frac{\sqrt{3}}{2} \times \frac{1}{\sqrt{2}}\right)$$

$$= \frac{1}{2\sqrt{2}} + \frac{\sqrt{3}}{2\sqrt{2}} = \frac{1 + \sqrt{3}}{2\sqrt{2}}$$

$$= \frac{\sqrt{2}(1 + \sqrt{3})}{4} = \frac{\sqrt{2} + \sqrt{6}}{4}$$

You could also have used $\frac{\pi}{12} = \frac{\pi}{4} - \frac{\pi}{6}$ in your answer.

Q15 $\sin(A + B) \equiv \sin A \cos B + \cos A \sin B$.

As $\sin A = \frac{4}{5}$, $\cos A = \frac{3}{5}$ (from the right-angled triangle with sides of length 3, 4 and 5) and as $\sin B = \frac{7}{25}$, $\cos B = \frac{24}{25}$ (from the right-angled triangle with sides of length 7, 24 and 25). Putting these values into the equation gives:

$$\sin A \cos B + \cos A \sin B = \left(\frac{4}{5} \cdot \frac{24}{25}\right) + \left(\frac{3}{5} \cdot \frac{7}{25}\right)$$

$$= \frac{96}{125} + \frac{21}{125} = \frac{117}{125} \ (= 0.936)$$

Q16 $\cos 2\theta \equiv \cos^2\theta - \sin^2\theta$
$\cos 2\theta \equiv 2\cos^2\theta - 1$
$\cos 2\theta \equiv 1 - 2\sin^2\theta$

Q17 $\sin 2\theta = \sqrt{3}\sin\theta \Rightarrow \sin 2\theta - \sqrt{3}\sin\theta = 0$
$2\sin\theta\cos\theta + \sqrt{3}\sin\theta = 0$
$\sin\theta(2\cos\theta + \sqrt{3}) = 0$

So either $\sin\theta = 0$, so $\theta = 0°$, 180°, 360° or

$$2\cos\theta + \sqrt{3} = 0 \Rightarrow \cos\theta = -\frac{\sqrt{3}}{2}$$

so $\theta = 150°$ or 210°. The set of values for θ is 0°, 150°, 180°, 210°, 360°.

Q18 a) $4(2\sin\frac{x}{2}\cos\frac{x}{2}) = \sin\frac{x}{2}$

$$\Rightarrow 8\sin\frac{x}{2}\cos\frac{x}{2} - \sin\frac{x}{2} = 0$$

$$\Rightarrow \sin\frac{x}{2}(8\cos\frac{x}{2} - 1) = 0$$

$$\Rightarrow \sin\frac{x}{2} = 0 \text{ or } \cos\frac{x}{2} = \frac{1}{8}$$

$$\Rightarrow \frac{x}{2} = 0, 1.445, 3.142 \Rightarrow x = 0, 2.89, 6.28$$

As you're solving for $\frac{x}{2}$ remember to halve the interval you're finding solutions in, so that when you double them to get solutions for x they'll lie in the right interval.

b) $$\frac{\tan\frac{x}{2}(2\tan\frac{x}{2})}{1 - \tan^2\frac{x}{2}} = 2 \Rightarrow \frac{2\tan^2\frac{x}{2}}{1 - \tan^2\frac{x}{2}} = 2$$

$$\Rightarrow 2\tan^2\frac{x}{2} = 2 - 2\tan^2\frac{x}{2} \Rightarrow \tan^2\frac{x}{2} = \frac{1}{2}$$

$$\Rightarrow \tan\frac{x}{2} = \pm\frac{1}{\sqrt{2}} \Rightarrow \frac{x}{2} = 0.615, 2.526$$

$$\Rightarrow x = 1.23, 5.05$$

Q19 a) $\dfrac{4\tan x}{1 - \tan^2 x} = \tan x \Rightarrow 4\tan x = \tan x(1 - \tan^2 x)$
$\Rightarrow \tan^3 x + 3\tan x = 0 \Rightarrow \tan x(\tan^2 x + 3) = 0$
$\Rightarrow \tan x = 0$ or $\tan^2 x + 3 = 0$ (not valid because $\tan^2 x = -3$ so $\tan x = \sqrt{-3}$)
$\Rightarrow x = 0, \pi, 2\pi$

b) $2\sin 3x\cos 3x - \cos 3x = 0$
$\cos 3x(2\sin 3x - 1) = 0$
$\cos 3x = 0$ or $\sin 3x = \frac{1}{2}$

You're solving for 3x, so find solutions between 0 and 6π.

$$3x = \frac{\pi}{2}, \frac{3\pi}{2}, \frac{5\pi}{2}, \frac{7\pi}{2}, \frac{9\pi}{2}, \frac{11\pi}{2} \text{ or}$$

$$\frac{\pi}{6}, \frac{5\pi}{6}, \frac{13\pi}{6}, \frac{17\pi}{6}, \frac{25\pi}{6}, \frac{29\pi}{6}$$

$$x = \frac{\pi}{6}, \frac{\pi}{2}, \frac{5\pi}{6}, \frac{7\pi}{6}, \frac{3\pi}{2}, \frac{11\pi}{6},$$

$$\frac{\pi}{18}, \frac{5\pi}{18}, \frac{13\pi}{18}, \frac{17\pi}{18}, \frac{25\pi}{18}, \frac{29\pi}{18}$$

Q20 $a\cos\theta + b\sin\theta \equiv R\cos(\theta - \alpha)$ or
$b\sin\theta + a\cos\theta \equiv R\sin(\theta + \alpha)$

Q21 $5\sin\theta - 6\cos\theta \equiv R\sin(\theta - \alpha)$
$\equiv R\sin\theta\cos\alpha - R\cos\theta\sin\alpha$ (using the addition rule for sin).
Equating coefficients of $\sin\theta$ and $\cos\theta$ gives:
1) $R\cos\alpha = 5$ and 2) $R\sin\alpha = 6$.

Dividing 2. by 1. to find α:
$$\frac{R\sin\alpha}{R\cos\alpha} = \tan\alpha, \text{ so } \frac{6}{5} = \tan\alpha$$

Solving this gives $\alpha = 50.19°$.
To find R, square equations 1. and 2., add, then square root:
$$R = \sqrt{5^2 + 6^2} = \sqrt{25 + 36} = \sqrt{61}, \text{ so}$$
$5\sin\theta - 6\cos\theta \equiv \sqrt{61}\sin(\theta - 50.19°)$.

Q22 Start by putting the LHS over a common denominator:
$$\frac{\cos\theta}{\sin\theta} + \frac{\sin\theta}{\cos\theta} \equiv \frac{\cos\theta\cos\theta}{\sin\theta\cos\theta} + \frac{\sin\theta\sin\theta}{\sin\theta\cos\theta}$$

$$\equiv \frac{\cos^2\theta + \sin^2\theta}{\sin\theta\cos\theta} \equiv \frac{1}{\sin\theta\cos\theta}$$

(using the identity $\sin^2\theta + \cos^2\theta \equiv 1$).
Now, $\sin 2\theta \equiv 2\sin\theta\cos\theta$, so $\sin\theta\cos\theta = \frac{1}{2}\sin 2\theta$.
So $$\frac{1}{\sin\theta\cos\theta} \equiv \frac{1}{\frac{1}{2}\sin 2\theta} \equiv 2\operatorname{cosec} 2\theta,$$

which is the same as the RHS.

Exam-Style Questions — Chapter 2

1 a)

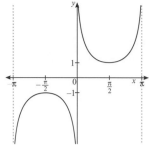

[3 marks available — 1 mark for n-shaped curve in third quadrant and u-shaped curve in first quadrant, 1 mark for asymptotes at 0 and ±π and 1 mark for max/min points of the curves at −1 and 1]

b) If $\csc x = \dfrac{5}{4} \Rightarrow \dfrac{1}{\sin x} = \dfrac{5}{4} \Rightarrow \sin x = \dfrac{4}{5}$

[1 mark]. Solving this for x gives $x = 0.927, 2.21$

[1 mark for each solution, lose a mark if answers aren't given to 3 s.f.].

The second solution can be found by sketching $y = \sin x$:

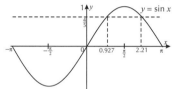

You can see that there are two solutions, one at 0.927, and the other at $\pi - 0.927 = 2.21$. You could also use the CAST diagram and find the other positive solution for sin in the 2nd quadrant.

c) $\csc x = 3\sec x \Rightarrow \dfrac{1}{\sin x} = \dfrac{3}{\cos x} \Rightarrow \dfrac{\cos x}{\sin x} = 3$

$\Rightarrow \dfrac{1}{\tan x} = 3$ so $\tan x = \dfrac{1}{3}$

Solving for x gives $x = -2.82, 0.322,$

[1 mark for appropriate rearranging, 1 mark for each solution.].

Again, you can sketch a graph to find the second solution (or use a CAST diagram).

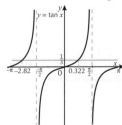

You can see that there are two solutions in the given range, one at 0.322 (this is the one you get from your calculator) and one at $-\pi + 0.322 = -2.82$.

2 a) $9\sin\theta + 12\cos\theta \equiv R\sin(\theta + \alpha)$.
Using the sin addition formula,
$9\sin\theta + 12\cos\theta \equiv R\sin\theta\cos\alpha + R\cos\theta\sin\alpha$.
Equating coefficients of $\sin\theta$ and $\cos\theta$ gives:
$R\cos\alpha = 9$ and $R\sin\alpha = 12$ *[1 mark]*.

$\dfrac{R\sin\alpha}{R\cos\alpha} = \tan\alpha$, so $\tan\alpha = \dfrac{12}{9} = \dfrac{4}{3}$

Solving this gives $\alpha = 0.927$
[1 mark — no other solutions in given range].
$R = \sqrt{9^2 + 12^2} = \sqrt{81 + 144} = \sqrt{225} = 15$
[1 mark],
so $9\sin\theta + 12\cos\theta = 15\sin(\theta + 0.927)$.

b) If $9\sin\theta + 12\cos\theta = 3$, then from part a),
$15\sin(\theta + 0.927) = 3$, so $\sin(\theta + 0.927) = 0.2$.
The range for θ is $0 \le \theta \le 2\pi$, which becomes
$0.927 \le \theta + 0.927 \le 7.210$. Solving the equation
gives $(\theta + 0.927) = 0.201$ *[1 mark]*.

As this is outside the range, use a sketch to find values that are in the range:

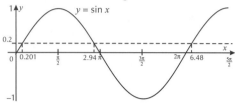

There are solutions at
$\pi - 0.201 = 2.94$ and at $2\pi + 0.201 = 6.48$, so
$(\theta + 0.927) = 2.940, 6.48$ *[1 mark for each]*,
so $\theta = 2.01, 5.56$ *[1 mark for each solution]*.

Be careful with the range — if you hadn't extended the range to $2\pi + 0.927$, you would have missed one of the solutions.

3 $\sin 3x \equiv \sin(2x + x)$
$\equiv \sin 2x \cos x + \cos 2x \sin x$ *[1 mark]*
$\equiv (2\sin x \cos x)\cos x + (1 - 2\sin^2 x)\sin x$
[1 mark]
$\equiv 2\sin x \cos^2 x + \sin x - 2\sin^3 x$
$\equiv 2\sin x(1 - \sin^2 x) + \sin x - 2\sin^3 x$ *[1 mark]*
$\equiv 2\sin x - 2\sin^3 x + \sin x - 2\sin^3 x$
$\equiv 3\sin x - 4\sin^3 x$ *[1 mark]*

4 a) Use the double angle formula:
$\cos 2\theta \equiv 1 - 2\sin^2\theta$ to replace $\cos 2\theta$:
$DE^2 = 4 - 4(1 - 2\sin^2\theta)$ *[1 mark]*
$DE^2 = 4 - 4 + 8\sin^2\theta \Rightarrow DE^2 = 8\sin^2\theta$
$DE = \sqrt{8}\,\sin\theta = 2\sqrt{2}\,\sin\theta$ *[1 mark]*

b) $P = 2DE + 2DG$
To find DG, use triangle BDG:

$\cos\theta = \dfrac{DG}{\sqrt{2}}$, so $DG = \sqrt{2}\,\cos\theta$ *[1 mark]*

So $P = 2(2\sqrt{2}\,\sin\theta) + 2(\sqrt{2}\,\cos\theta)$
$= 4\sqrt{2}\,\sin\theta + 2\sqrt{2}\,\cos\theta$ *[1 mark]*

c) $4\sqrt{2}\,\sin\theta + 2\sqrt{2}\,\cos\theta \equiv R\sin(\theta + \alpha)$
$\Rightarrow 4\sqrt{2}\,\sin\theta + 2\sqrt{2}\,\cos\theta$
$\equiv R\sin\theta\cos\alpha + R\cos\theta\sin\alpha$
$\Rightarrow$ **(1)** $R\cos\alpha = 4\sqrt{2}$
and **(2)** $R\sin\alpha = 2\sqrt{2}$ *[1 mark]*

(2) ÷ **(1)** gives $\tan\alpha = \dfrac{1}{2}$
$\Rightarrow \alpha = 0.464$ (to 3 s.f.) *[1 mark]*
(1)^2 + **(2)**^{2} gives:
$R^2\cos^2\alpha + R^2\sin^2\alpha = (4\sqrt{2})^2 + (2\sqrt{2})^2 = 40$
$\Rightarrow R = \sqrt{40} = 2\sqrt{10}$ *[1 mark]*
So $4\sqrt{2}\,\sin\theta + 2\sqrt{2}\,\cos\theta \equiv 2\sqrt{10}\,\sin(\theta + 0.464)$

5 a) The start and end points of the cos curve (with restricted domain) are $(0, 1)$ and $(\pi, -1)$, so the coordinates of the start point of arccos (point A) are $(-1, \pi)$ *[1 mark]* and the coordinates of the end point (point B) are $(1, 0)$ *[1 mark]*.

b) $y = \arccos x$, so $y = \cos^{-1}x$, so $x = \cos y$ *[1 mark]*.

c) $\arccos x = 2$, so $x = \cos 2$ *[1 mark]*
so $x = -0.416$ *[1 mark]*.

6 a) $\dfrac{2\sin x}{1 - \cos x} - \dfrac{2\cos x}{\sin x}$

$\equiv \dfrac{2\sin^2 x - 2\cos x + 2\cos^2 x}{\sin x(1 - \cos x)}$ *[1 mark]*

$= \dfrac{2 - 2\cos x}{\sin x(1 - \cos x)}$ *[1 mark]*

$\equiv \dfrac{2(1 - \cos x)}{\sin x(1 - \cos x)}$ *[1 mark]*

$\equiv \dfrac{2}{\sin x} \equiv 2\csc x$ *[1 mark]*

b) $2\csc x = 4$
$\csc x = 2$ OR $\sin x = \dfrac{1}{2}$ *[1 mark]*
$x = \dfrac{\pi}{6}$ *[1 mark]*, $x = \dfrac{5\pi}{6}$ *[1 mark]*.

7 a) $5\cos\theta + 12\sin\theta \equiv R\cos(\theta - \alpha)$.
$5\cos\theta + 12\sin\theta \equiv R\cos\theta\cos\alpha + R\sin\theta\sin\alpha$.
Equating coefficients gives:
$R\cos\alpha = 5$ and $R\sin\alpha = 12$ *[1 mark]*.
$\dfrac{R\sin\alpha}{R\cos\alpha} = \tan\alpha$, so $\tan\alpha = \dfrac{12}{5}$ *[1 mark]*.
Solving this gives $\alpha = 67.38°$ *[1 mark]*.
$R = \sqrt{5^2 + 12^2} = \sqrt{25 + 144} = \sqrt{169} = 13$ *[1 mark]*,
so $5\cos\theta + 12\sin\theta = 13\cos(\theta - 67.38°)$.

b) From part a), if $5\cos\theta + 12\sin\theta = 2$, that means $13\cos(\theta - 67.38°) = 2$, so:
$\cos(\theta - 67.38°) = \dfrac{2}{13}$ *[1 mark]*.

The range for θ is $0 \le \theta \le 360°$, which becomes
$-67.38° \le \theta - 67.38° \le 292.62°$ *[1 mark]*.

Solving the equation gives
$\theta - 67.38 = 81.15, 278.85$ *[1 mark]*,
so $\theta = 148.53°, 346.23°$ *[1 mark for each value]*.

You can look at the cos graph to get the second solution of $\theta - 67.38°$ (or use the CAST diagram).

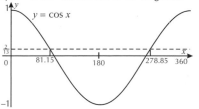

There are two solutions, one at 81.15°, and the other at $360 - 81.15 = 278.85°$.

c) The minimum points of the cos curve have a value of -1,
so as $5\cos\theta + 12\sin\theta = 13\cos(\theta - 67.38°)$, the minimum value of $5\cos\theta + 12\sin\theta$ is -13 *[1 mark]*. Hence the minimum value of $(5\cos\theta + 12\sin\theta)^3$ is $(-13)^3 = -2197$ *[1 mark]*.

8 a) (i) Rearrange the identity $\sec^2\theta \equiv 1 + \tan^2\theta$ to get $\sec^2\theta - 1 \equiv \tan^2\theta$, then replace $\tan^2\theta$ in the equation:
$3\tan^2\theta - 2\sec\theta = 5$
$3(\sec^2\theta - 1) - 2\sec\theta - 5 = 0$ *[1 mark]*
$3\sec^2\theta - 3 - 2\sec\theta - 5 = 0$
so $3\sec^2\theta - 2\sec\theta - 8 = 0$ *[1 mark]*

(ii) To factorise this, let $y = \sec\theta$, so the equation becomes $3y^2 - 2y - 8 = 0$, so
$(3y + 4)(y - 2) = 0$ *[1 mark]*.
Solving for y gives $y = -\dfrac{4}{3}$ or $y = 2$.
As $y = \sec\theta$, this means that $\sec\theta = -\dfrac{4}{3}$ or $\sec\theta = 2$ *[1 mark]*.
$\sec\theta = \dfrac{1}{\cos\theta}$, so $\cos\theta = -\dfrac{3}{4}$ or $\cos\theta = \dfrac{1}{2}$ *[1 mark]*.

b) Let $\theta = 2x$. From above, we know that the solutions to $3\tan^2\theta - 2\sec\theta = 5$ satisfy
$\cos\theta = -\dfrac{3}{4}$ or $\cos\theta = \dfrac{1}{2}$.
The range for x is $0 \le x \le 180°$, so as $\theta = 2x$, the range for θ is $0 \le \theta \le 360°$ *[1 mark]*.
Solving these equations for θ gives
$\theta = 138.59°, 221.41°$ and $\theta = 60°, 300°$ *[1 mark]*.
So, as $\theta = 2x$, $x = \dfrac{1}{2}\theta$,
so $x = 69.30°, 110.70°, 30°, 150°$ *[1 mark]*.

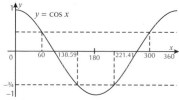

There is a solution at $360 - 60 = 300°$, and another at $360 - 138.59 = 221.41°$. Don't be fooled by the 2x in this question — you don't need to use the double angle formulas for this one.

Chapter 3: Exponentials and Logarithms

1. Exponential and Logarithmic Graphs

Exercise 1.1 — Transformations

Q1 a) – c)

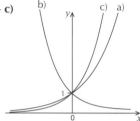

Q2 a)

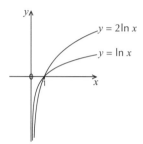

b)

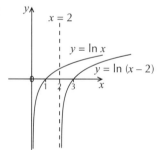

c)

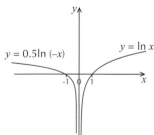

d)

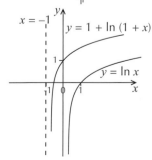

Q3 a)

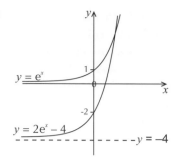

b)

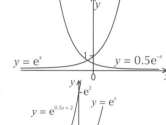

c)

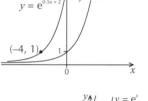

d)

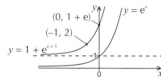

Q4 a) $A = 2$ b) $B = -\frac{1}{3}$ c) $C = 3$

Q5 a) $A = (0, 3)$, $D: y = 0$.

     b) $B = (0, 3)$, $E: y = 2$.

     c) $C = (0, 2)$, $F: y = 3$.

Q6 a) Asymptote at $y = -3$ and y intercept at $(0, -2)$. So $y = e^x$ has been translated down the y-axis by 3 so the function is $f(x) = e^x - 3$.

     b) Asymptote at $x = -2$ and passes through the x-axis at $x = -1$. So $y = \ln x$ has been translated by 2 units left on the x-axis. So $g(x) = \ln (x + 2)$.

     c) Asymptote at $y = 0$ and goes through point $(-1, 1)$. So $y = e^x$ has been translated left on the x-axis by 1 so the function is $h(x) = e^{(x + 1)}$

2. Using Exponentials and Logarithms

Exercise 2.1 — Solving Equations

Q1 a) If $y = e^x$ then $x = \ln y$

     b) If $a = \ln b$ then $b = e^a$

Q2 a) $e^x = 7 \Rightarrow \ln e^x = \ln 7 \Rightarrow x = \ln 7$.

     b) $5e^{3t} = 11 \Rightarrow e^{3t} = \frac{11}{5} \Rightarrow \ln e^{3t} = \ln \left(\frac{11}{5}\right)$
        $\Rightarrow 3t = \ln \left(\frac{11}{5}\right) \Rightarrow t = \frac{1}{3} \ln \left(\frac{11}{5}\right)$

c) $2e^{(-2x)} = 6 \Rightarrow e^{(-2x)} = 3 \Rightarrow \ln e^{(-2x)} = \ln 3$
$\Rightarrow -2x = \ln 3 \Rightarrow x = -\frac{1}{2}\ln 3$

d) $e^{(0.5x + 3)} = 9 \Rightarrow \ln e^{(0.5x + 3)} = \ln 9 \Rightarrow 0.5x + 3 = \ln 9$
$\Rightarrow 0.5x = \ln 9 - 3 \Rightarrow x = 2(\ln 9 - 3)$

e) $10 - 3e^{(1-2x)} = 8 \Rightarrow 3e^{(1-2x)} = 2 \Rightarrow e^{(1-2x)} = \frac{2}{3} \Rightarrow$
$\ln e^{(1-2x)} = \ln \frac{2}{3} \Rightarrow 1 - 2x = \ln \frac{2}{3} \Rightarrow -2x = \ln \frac{2}{3} - 1$
$\Rightarrow x = -\frac{1}{2}(\ln \frac{2}{3} - 1)$

Q3 a) (i) $\ln x = -2 \Rightarrow e^{\ln x} = e^{-2} \Rightarrow x = e^{-2}$
(ii) $x = 0.135$ to 3 s.f.

b) (i) $3\ln (2x) = 7 \Rightarrow \ln (2x) = \frac{7}{3} \Rightarrow e^{\ln (2x)} = e^{\frac{7}{3}} \Rightarrow$
$2x = e^{\frac{7}{3}} \Rightarrow x = \frac{1}{2}e^{\frac{7}{3}}$
(ii) $x = 5.16$ to 3 s.f.

c) (i) $\ln (5t - 3) - 4 \Rightarrow e^{\ln (5t - 3)} = e^4 \Rightarrow 5t \quad 3 = e^4 \rightarrow$
$t = \frac{1}{5}(e^4 + 3)$
(ii) $t = 11.5$ to 3 s.f.

d) (i) $6\ln (8 - 2t) = 10 \Rightarrow \ln (8 - 2t) = \frac{5}{3}$
$\rightarrow e^{\ln (8 \quad 2t)} = e^{\frac{5}{3}} \Rightarrow 8 - 2t = e^{\frac{5}{3}}$
$\Rightarrow t = -\frac{1}{2}(e^{\frac{5}{3}} - 8)$
(ii) $t = 1.35$ to 3 s.f.

e) (i) $6 - \ln (0.5x) = 3 \Rightarrow \ln (0.5x) = 3 \Rightarrow e^{\ln (0.5x)} = e^3$
$\Rightarrow 0.5x = e^3 \Rightarrow x = 2e^3$
(ii) $x = 40.2$

Q4 a) $e^{3x} = 27 \Rightarrow \ln (e^{3x}) = \ln 27 \rightarrow 3x = \ln 27 = \ln (3^3)$
$\Rightarrow 3x = 3\ln 3 \Rightarrow x = \ln 3$

If you're asked to give your answer in the form ln a where a is a number, try and write the number inside the logarithm as a power of a and use the third log law to get it in the form you want

b) $e^{-4x} = 9 \Rightarrow \ln (e^{-4x}) = \ln 9 \Rightarrow -4x = \ln 9$
$\Rightarrow x = -\frac{1}{4}\ln 9 = -\frac{1}{4}\ln (3^2) = -\frac{1}{2}\ln 3$

c) $e^{(6x - 1)} = \frac{1}{3} \Rightarrow \ln e^{(6x - 1)} = \ln \left(\frac{1}{3}\right) \Rightarrow 6x - 1 = \ln (3^{-1})$
$\Rightarrow 6x = 1 - \ln 3 \Rightarrow x = \frac{1}{6}(1 - \ln 3)$

d) $3e^{(2x + 3)} = \frac{1}{27} \Rightarrow e^{(2x + 3)} = \frac{1}{81} \Rightarrow \ln e^{(2x + 3)} = \ln \left(\frac{1}{81}\right)$
$\Rightarrow 2x + 3 = \ln (3^{-4}) \Rightarrow 2x + 3 = -4\ln (3)$
$\rightarrow 2x = -4\ln 3 - 3 \Rightarrow x = \frac{1}{2}(-4\ln 3 - 3)$

e) $\frac{1}{3}e^{(1 - x)} - 3 = 0 \Rightarrow e^{(1 - x)} = 9 \Rightarrow \ln e^{(1 - x)} = \ln 9$
$\Rightarrow 1 - x = \ln 9 \Rightarrow x = 1 - \ln (3^2) \Rightarrow x = 1 - 2\ln 3$

Q5 a) (i) Substitute $y = e^x \rightarrow y^2 - 7y + 12 = 0$
$\Rightarrow (y - 3)(y - 4) = 0 \Rightarrow y = 3$ or $y = 4$
$\Rightarrow e^x = 3$ or $e^x = 4 \Rightarrow x = \ln 3$ or $x = \ln 4$
(ii) $x = 1.10$ or $x = 1.39$

b) (i) $e^{7x} - 3e^{5x} = 0 \Rightarrow e^{5x}(e^{2x} - 3) = 0 \Rightarrow e^{5x} = 0$
or $e^{2x} = 3$. $e^{5x} = 0$ is impossible so $e^{2x} = 3$
$\Rightarrow 2x = \ln 3 \Rightarrow x = 0.5\ln 3$

The graph of $y = be^{ax}$ has an asymptote at $y = 0$ for any values of a or b, so it never reaches 0. Therefore anytime you have $be^a = 0$ where a and b are any real numbers, there's no solution.

(ii) $x = 0.549$

c) (i) Substitute $y = e^x \Rightarrow 3y^2 + 10y + 3 = 0$
$\Rightarrow (3y + 1)(y + 3) = 0 \Rightarrow e^x = -\frac{1}{3}$ or $e^x = -3$
both of which are impossible since $e^x > 0$.
There are no solutions.
(ii) No solutions.

d) (i) Substitute $y = e^{2x} \Rightarrow y^2 + 4y + 5 = 0$.
Using the quadratic formula:
$$x = \frac{-4 \pm \sqrt{4^2 - (4 \times 5 \times 1)}}{2}$$
$$= \frac{4 \pm \sqrt{16 - 20}}{2} = \frac{-4 \pm \sqrt{-4}}{2}$$
there are no real solutions since there is a negative square root.
(ii) No solutions.

e) (i) $e^x + e^{-x} = 6 \Rightarrow e^{2x} + 1 - 6e^x = 0$

If you have an equation with e^{-x} in it, then you can multiply everything through by e^x to get rid of it.

$\Rightarrow$ Substitute $y = e^x \Rightarrow y^2 + 1 - 6y = 0$
The quadratic formula gives solutions:
$y = \frac{6 \pm \sqrt{32}}{2} = 3 \pm 2\sqrt{2}$
$\Rightarrow e^x = 3 \pm 2\sqrt{2}$
$\Rightarrow x = \ln (3 \pm 2\sqrt{2})$
(ii) $x = 1.76$ or -1.76

Q6 a) $\ln 5 + \ln x = 7 \Rightarrow \ln(5x) = 7 \Rightarrow e^{\ln (5x)} = e^7$
$\rightarrow 5x = e^7 \Rightarrow x = \frac{e^7}{5}$

b) $\ln (2x) + \ln (3x) = 15 \Rightarrow \ln (2x \times 3x) = 15$
$\Rightarrow \ln(6x^2) = 15 \Rightarrow e^{\ln 6x^2} = e^{15} \Rightarrow 6x^2 = e^{15}$
$\Rightarrow x = \sqrt{\frac{1}{6}e^{15}} = \frac{1}{\sqrt{6}}e^{\frac{15}{2}}$

c) $\ln (x^2 - 4) - \ln (2x) = 0 \Rightarrow \ln \left(\frac{x^2 - 4}{2x}\right) = 0$
$\Rightarrow \frac{x^2 - 4}{2x} = e^0 = 1 \Rightarrow x^2 - 4 = 2x$
$\Rightarrow x^2 - 2x - 4 = 0$
$\Rightarrow x = \frac{2 \pm \sqrt{20}}{2} = 1 \pm \sqrt{5}$
But $x > 0$ otherwise $\ln 2x$ would be undefined so $x = 1 + \sqrt{5}$.

d) $3\ln (x^2) + 5\ln x = 2 \Rightarrow 6\ln x + 5\ln x = 2$
$\Rightarrow 11\ln x = 2 \Rightarrow \ln x = \frac{2}{11} \Rightarrow x = e^{\frac{2}{11}}$

Exercise 2.2 — Modelling Growth and Decay

Q1 In 1953, $t = 0$, $P = 52$ (million). So $52 = P_0e^0$, so $P_0 = 52$. $P = 52e^{nt}$ so in 1993 when $t = 40$, $P = 60$ (million) so $60 = 52e^{40n}$
$\Rightarrow n = \ln \left(\frac{15}{13}\right) \div 40 = 0.003577... = 0.00358$ (3.s.f.)

a) In 2020, $t = 67$,
$P = 52 \, e^{(0.00357... \times 67)} = 66.1$ (million) (3 s.f.)

b) In 2050, $t = 97$,
$P = 52 \, e^{(0.00357... \times 97)} = 73.6$ (million) (3 s.f.)

c) In 2100, $t = 147$,
$P = 52 \, e^{(0.00357... \times 147)} = 88.0$ (million) (3 s.f.)

Q2 When $t = 10$, $M = \frac{M_0}{2}$ so $\frac{M_0}{2} = M_0 e^{-10k} \Rightarrow \frac{1}{2} = e^{-10k}$
$\Rightarrow k = -\frac{1}{10} \ln\left(\frac{1}{2}\right) = 0.0693... = 0.0693$ (3 s.f.)

a) Want to find t when $M = \frac{M_0}{4}$,
so $\frac{M_0}{4} = M_0 e^{(-0.0693... \times t)} \Rightarrow \frac{1}{4} = e^{(-0.0693... \times t)} \Rightarrow$
$t = -\frac{1}{0.0693...} \ln\left(\frac{1}{4}\right) = 20.0$ years (3 s.f.).
So after 20 years the substance will be reduced to a quarter of its mass.

Note that a much easier way to do this would be to think of it as 'half and half again'. The substance will be a quarter of it's mass after two half lives which is 2 × 10 = 20 years.

b) When $t = 5$, $M = 200$, so $200 = M_0 e^{(-0.0693... \times 5)}$ so $M_0 = 200 e^{(0.0693... \times 5)} = 283$ grams (3 s.f.).
So the original mass is 283 grams.

c) Let $t = 15$, then $M = 283 \times e^{(-0.0693... \times 15)} = 100$ (3 s.f.). So after 15 years, 100 g is remaining.

Q3 **a)** If $t = 0$, $T = 225 - 207e^0 = 18$. So the oven was 18 °C to begin with.

b) As $t \to \infty$, $e^{\left(-\frac{t}{8}\right)} \to 0$ so $T \to 225 - 0 = 225$. The oven would approach 225 °C if left on indefinitely.

c) Let $t = 5$, then $T = 225 - 207e^{\left(-\frac{5}{8}\right)} = 114$ °C. (3 s.f.). So after 5 minutes the oven will be at 114 °C.

d) Let $T = 190$ °C. Then $190 = 225 - 207e^{\left(-\frac{t}{8}\right)}$
$\Rightarrow e^{\left(-\frac{t}{8}\right)} = \frac{190 - 225}{-207} = \frac{35}{207}$
$\Rightarrow -\frac{t}{8} = \ln\left(\frac{35}{207}\right) \Rightarrow t = -8 \ln\left(\frac{35}{207}\right) = 14.2$ min (to 3 s.f.). So the oven reaches 190 °C just after 12:14.

e)
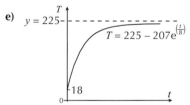

Q4 **a)** When $t = 0$, $F = 4$, so $F_0 = 4$.
When $t = 6$, $F = 10$ so $10 = 4e^{6g}$ so
$g = \frac{1}{6} \ln\left(\frac{10}{4}\right) = 0.1527... = 0.153$ (3 s.f.).

b) Let $t = 12$, then $F = 4e^{(12 \times 0.1527...)} = 25$. So after 12 hours the fungus will be 25 mm².

c) Let $F = 15$. Then $15 = 4e^{(0.1527... \times t)}$
$\Rightarrow e^{(0.1527... \times t)} = \frac{15}{4}$
$\Rightarrow t = \frac{1}{0.1527...} \ln\left(\frac{15}{4}\right) = 8.66$ (3 s.f.). The fungus will take 8.66 hours to grow to 15 mm².

Q5 When $t = 0$, $N = 3$. So $3 = Ae^0$ so $A = 3$.

a) Let $t = 0.5$ (hours).
Then $N = 3e^{-t} = 3e^{-0.5} = 1.82$ mg/l.
The concentration after 30 minutes is 1.82 mg/l.

b) Let $N = 0.1$. Then $0.1 = 3e^{-t}$ so
$t = -\ln\left(\frac{0.1}{3}\right) = 3.40$ hours (3 s.f.).

c)
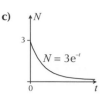

Q6 **a)** When $t = 0$, $V = 1500 + 9000e^0 = 10500$. The car was £10500 when new.

b) Let $t = 5$, then $V = 1500 + 9000e^{\left(-\frac{5}{3}\right)} = 3200$ (3 s.f.). The car's value after 5 years is £3200.

c) Let $V = 2500$, then $2500 = 1500 + 9000e^{\left(-\frac{t}{3}\right)}$
$\Rightarrow 1000 = 9000e^{\left(-\frac{t}{3}\right)} \Rightarrow \frac{1}{9} = e^{\left(-\frac{t}{3}\right)}$
$\Rightarrow t = -3\ln\left(\frac{1}{9}\right) = 6.59$ (3 s.f.). The car will have a value less than £2500 after 7 whole years.
Note: After 6 years the car will still have a value above £2500 so the answer is 7 and not 6.

d)
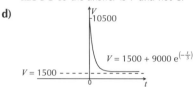

Q7 **a)** $b = \ln 1.8 = 0.5877... = 0.588$ (3 s.f.)

b) Let $t = 3$ then $H = 20e^{(0.5877... \times 3)} = 117$ (3 s.f.). So after 3 hours, 117 hectares will be burnt.

c) If $H = 500$, $500 = 20e^{(0.5877... \times t)} \Rightarrow 25 = e^{(0.5877... \times t)}$
$\Rightarrow \ln 25 = 0.5877... \times t$
$\Rightarrow t = \frac{1}{0.5877...} \ln 25 = 5.48$ (3 s.f.)
So it would take 5.48 hours to burn 500 hectares of land.

d) At $t = k$, $H = H_k = 20e^{(\ln 1.8)k}$
At $t = k + 1$, $H = H_{k+1} = 20e^{(\ln 1.8)(k + 1)}$
$= 20e^{(\ln 1.8)k + \ln 1.8} = 20e^{(\ln 1.8)k}e^{\ln 1.8} = H_k \times 1.8$
Every hour the burnt area is multiplied by 1.8. This represents a percentage increase of 80%.

Q8 **a)** When $t = 0$, $y = 5 \Rightarrow 5 = pe^0 = p \Rightarrow p = 5$.
When $t = 3$, $y = 20 \Rightarrow 20 = 5e^{3q} \Rightarrow 4 = e^{3q} \Rightarrow$
$\ln 4 = 3q \Rightarrow q = \frac{1}{3}\ln 4 = 0.462... = 0.462$ (3 s.f.).

b) When $t = 6$, $y = 5 \Rightarrow 5 = pe^{6q}$
When $t = 9$, $y = 20 \Rightarrow 20 = pe^{9q}$
$\frac{20}{5} = \frac{pe^{9q}}{pe^{6q}} \Rightarrow 4 = e^{3q}$
$3q = \ln 4 \Rightarrow q = \left(\frac{1}{3}\right)\ln 4$
$q = 0.462... = 0.462$ (3 s.f.)
So $5 = p e^{(6 \times 0.462...)}$ and $p = 5 e^{-(6 \times 0.462...)} = 0.3125$
$= 0.313$ (3 s.f.). So $y = 0.313 e^{0.462... \times t}$

You could also do this question by noticing that the graph for part a) has been translated up the x-axis by 6, giving the equation $y = 5e^{0.462...\times(t - 6)}$.

Q9 **a)** If $t = 0$, then $\theta = 65e^0 + 18 = 83$ °C. The initial temperature is 83 °C.

b) When $t = 60$, $\theta = 83 - 8 = 75$ $\to$

$75 = 65e^{-60c} + 18$

$\Rightarrow 65e^{-60c} = 75 - 18 = 57 \Rightarrow e^{-60c} = \dfrac{57}{65}$

$\Rightarrow 60c = -\ln\left(\dfrac{57}{65}\right) \Rightarrow c = -\dfrac{1}{60}\ln\left(\dfrac{57}{65}\right) = 0.002188...$

$c = 0.00219$ (3 s.f.)

c) Let $t = 3$ min $= 3 \times 60$ seconds $= 180$ seconds.

$\Rightarrow \theta = 65e^{(-0.002188... \times 180)} + 18 = 61.8$ (3 s.f.)

After 3 minutes the soup will be 61.8 °C.

d) Let $\theta = 40$. Then $40 = 65e^{(-0.002188... \times t)} + 18$

$\Rightarrow \dfrac{40 - 18}{65} = e^{(-0.002188... \times t)}$

$\Rightarrow \ln\left(\dfrac{22}{65}\right) = -0.002188... \times t$

$\Rightarrow t = -\dfrac{1}{0.002188...}\ln\left(\dfrac{22}{65}\right) = 495$ (3 s.f.)

So the soup will take 495 seconds to cool down.

e)

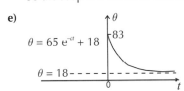

$\theta = 65\,e^{-ct} + 18$

$\theta = 18$

Q10 a) At 8:00, let $t = 0$. Then at $t = 0$, $p = 0.05$.

So $0.05 = \dfrac{1}{1 + Re^0} = \dfrac{1}{1 + R} \Rightarrow 1 + R = \dfrac{1}{0.05} = 20$

$R = 19$

At 10:00, $t = 2$ and $p = 0.3$

So $0.3 = \dfrac{1}{1 + 19e^{-2q}} \Rightarrow 0.3(1 + 19e^{-2q}) = 1$

$\Rightarrow 19e^{-2q} = \dfrac{1}{0.3} - 1 = \dfrac{7}{3} \Rightarrow e^{-2q} = \dfrac{7}{57}$

$\Rightarrow q = -0.5\ln\dfrac{7}{57} = 1.048... = 1.05$ (3 s.f.)

b) At 14:00, $t = 6$. $p = \dfrac{1}{1 + 19e^{(-1.048... \times 6)}} = 0.966$

By 14:00, 96.6% of the population have heard of the King's death.

c) Let $p = 0.7$ then $0.7 = \dfrac{1}{1 + 19e^{(-1.048... \times t)}} \to$

$1 + 19e^{(-1.048... \times t)} = \dfrac{1}{0.7} \Rightarrow 19e^{(-1.048... \times t)} = \dfrac{1}{0.7} - 1$

$\Rightarrow e^{(-1.048... \times t)} = \dfrac{1}{19}\left(\dfrac{1}{0.7} - 1\right) = 0.0225...$

$= 0.0226$ (3 s.f.)

$\Rightarrow -1.048... \times t = \ln(0.0225...)$

$\Rightarrow t = -\dfrac{1}{1.048...}\ln(0.0225...) = 3.62$ (3 s.f.)

So the time taken is 3.62 hours

$= 3$ hours 37 minutes. So the time will be 11:37.

Review Exercise — Chapter 3

Q1 a) The graph still has an asymptote at $y = 0$ but it goes through (0, 2) instead of (0, 1) so the graph has been stretched by a factor of 2 along the y-axis, so the function is $y = 2e^x$.

b) The graph has a negative gradient and so represents an exponential decay. It has an asymptote at $y = 1$ and goes through the point (0, 2), so the graph $y = e^{-x}$ has been translated up the y-axis by 1 unit, so it is the function $y = 1 + e^{-x}$.

Q2 a) $A = (-1, 0)$, C: $x = -2$

b) $B = (1, 3)$, D: $x = 0$

Q3 a)-d)

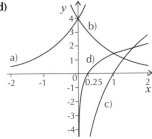

Q4 a) The transformation from $y = e^x$ to $y = 2 + e^x$ is a translation 2 units vertically up.

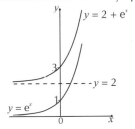

b) The transformation from $y = e^x$ to $y = e^{\frac{x}{2}} - 1$ is a stretch horizontally by a scale factor of 2 and a translation 1 unit vertically down.

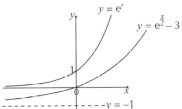

c) The transformation from $y = e^x$ to $y = e^{3x} - 0.5$ is a stretch horizontally by a scale factor of $\dfrac{1}{3}$ and a translation 0.5 units vertically down.

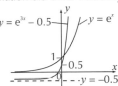

d) The transformation from $y = e^x$ to $y = 5 - 3e^x$ is a stretch vertically by a scale factor of 3, a reflection in the x-axis and a translation 5 units vertically up.

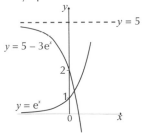

Q5 **a)** The transformation from $y = \ln x$ to $y = 1 + \ln x$ is a translation 1 unit up.

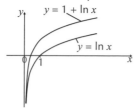

b) The transformation from $y = \ln x$ to $y = \ln (2x)$ is a stretch horizontally of scale factor $\frac{1}{2}$.

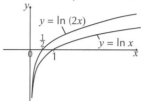

c) The transformation from $y = \ln x$ to $y = 3\ln x - 1$ is a stretch vertically of scale factor 3 and a translation of 1 unit vertically down.

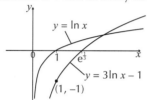

d) The transformation from $y = \ln x$ to $y = 5\ln (-x)$ is a reflection in the y-axis and a stretch vertically of scale factor 5.

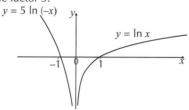

Q6 **a)** $e^{2x} = 6 \Rightarrow 2x = \ln 6 \Rightarrow x = \ln 6 \div 2 = 0.8959$ to 4 d.p.

b) $\ln (x + 3) = 0.75 \Rightarrow x + 3 = e^{0.75} \Rightarrow x = e^{0.75} - 3 = -0.8830$ to 4 d.p.

c) $3e^{-4x+1} = 5 \Rightarrow e^{-4x+1} = \frac{5}{3} \Rightarrow e^{4x-1} = \frac{3}{5}$
$\Rightarrow 4x - 1 = \ln \frac{3}{5}$
$\Rightarrow x = (\ln \frac{3}{5} + 1) \div 4 = 0.1223$ to 4 d.p.

d) $\ln x + \ln 5 = \ln 4 \Rightarrow \ln (5x) = \ln 4 \Rightarrow 5x = 4$
$\Rightarrow x = 0.8000$ to 4 d.p.

Q7 **a)** $2\ln x - \ln (2x) = 2 \Rightarrow \ln (x^2) - \ln (2x) = 2$
$\Rightarrow \ln \left(\frac{x^2}{2x} \right) = 2 \Rightarrow \frac{x^2}{2x} = e^2 \Rightarrow \frac{x}{2} = e^2 \Rightarrow x = 2e^2$

b) $\ln (2x - 7) + \ln 4 = -3 \Rightarrow \ln (4(2x - 7)) = -3$
$\Rightarrow 8x - 28 = e^{-3} \Rightarrow x = \frac{e^{-3} + 28}{8}$ or $\frac{1}{8e^3} + \frac{7}{2}$.

Q8 **a)** $y = 2 - e^{x+1}$

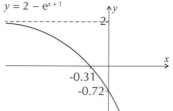

Goes through $(0, -0.72)$ and $(-0.31, 0)$, with asymptote at $y = 2$.

b) $y = 5e^{0.5x} + 5$

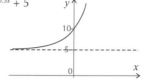

Goes through $(0, 10)$, with asymptote at $y = 5$.

c) $y = \ln (2x) + 1$

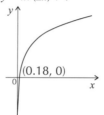

Goes through $(0.18, 0)$, with asymptote at $x = 0$.

d) $y = \ln (x + 5)$

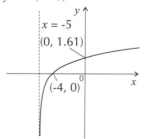

Goes through $(0, 1.61)$ and $(-4, 0)$, with asymptote at $x = -5$.
You can use your 'graph transformation' skills to work out what they'll look like — e.g. d) is just $y = \ln x$ shifted 5 to the left.

Q9 **a)** $2e^{2x} + e^x = 3$. Let $y = e^x$, $2y^2 + y - 3 = 0$, which will factorise to: $(2y + 3)(y - 1) = 0$, so $e^x = -1.5$ (not possible), and $e^x = 1$, so $x = 0$ is the only solution.

b) $e^{8x} - e^{4x} - 6 = 0 \Rightarrow$ Substitute $y = e^{4x}$
$\Rightarrow y^2 - y - 6 = 0 \Rightarrow (y - 3)(y + 2) = 0 \Rightarrow y = 3$
or $y = -2 \Rightarrow e^{4x} = 3$ or $e^{4x} = -2$. $e^{4x} = -2$ is impossible since $e^{4x} > 0$, so $e^{4x} = 3 \Rightarrow 4x = \ln 3$
$\Rightarrow x = \frac{1}{4} \ln 3$.

Q10 a) $V = 7500e^{-0.2t}$, so when $t = 0$,
$V = 7500 \times e^0 = £7500$.

b) $V = 7500 \times e^{(-0.2 \times 10)} = £1015$ to the nearest £.

c) When $V = 500$, $500 = 7500e^{-0.2t}$
$\Rightarrow e^{-0.2t} = \dfrac{500}{7500} \Rightarrow e^{0.2t} = \dfrac{7500}{500} \Rightarrow 0.2t$
$= \ln \dfrac{7500}{500} = 2.7080...$
$\Rightarrow t = 2.7080... \div 0.2 = 13.5$ years.
So it will be 14 years old before the value falls
below £500.

d)

Goes through (0, 7500) with an asymptote at
$y = 0$.

Q11 a) $L = 20e^{\left(\frac{10}{12}\right)} = 46.02$, so the model predicts the
reserve will have 46 leopards after 10 years.

b) Let $L = 60$, then $60 = 20e^{\frac{t}{12}} \Rightarrow 3 = e^{\frac{t}{12}}$
$\Rightarrow t = 12\ln 3 = 13.18$. So the reserve
will run out of space after 13 years.

c) $W = 15e^{\left(-\frac{5}{3}\right)} = 2.83$. So the model predicts that
only 2 or 3 leopards will be left in the wild after
5 years.

Q12 a) $Z = 10 + 20e^0 = 30$. There were 30 zombies to
begin with.

b) $Z = 10 + 20e^2 = 157.8$, so around 160 people will
have been turned into zombies after 2 weeks.

c) $60\,000\,000 = 10 + 20e^t$
$\Rightarrow t = \ln\left(\dfrac{60\,000\,000 - 10}{20}\right) = 14.9$
So after 15 weeks more than 60 million will be
zombies.

d) A graph of $Z = 10 + 20e^t$ with intersect.

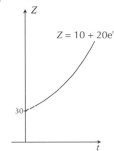

Exam-Style Questions — Chapter 3

1 a) $6e^x = 3 \Rightarrow e^x = 0.5$ *[1 mark]*
$\rightarrow x = \ln 0.5$ *[1 mark]*.

b) $e^{2x} - 8e^x + 7 = 0$.
(This looks like a quadratic, so use $y = e^x$...)
If $y = e^x$, then $y^2 - 8y + 7 = 0$. This will factorise
to give: $(y - 7)(y - 1) = 0 \Rightarrow y = 7$ and $y = 1$.
So $e^x = 7 \Rightarrow x = \ln 7$, and $e^x = 1 \Rightarrow x = \ln 1 = 0$.
*[4 marks available — 1 mark for factorisation of
a quadratic, 1 mark for both solutions for e^x, and
1 mark for each correct solution for x.]*

c) $4\ln x = 3 \Rightarrow \ln x = 0.75$ *[1 mark]*
$\rightarrow x = e^{0.75}$ *[1 mark]*.

d) $\ln x + \dfrac{24}{\ln x} = 10$
(You need to get rid of the fraction, so multiply through
by $\ln x$...)
$(\ln x)^2 + 24 = 10\ln x \Rightarrow (\ln x)^2 - 10\ln x + 24 = 0$
(...which looks like a quadratic, so use $y = \ln x$...)
$y^2 - 10y + 24 = 0 \Rightarrow (y - 6)(y - 4) = 0$
$\Rightarrow y = 6$ or $y = 4$.
So $\ln x = 6 \Rightarrow x = e^6$, or $\ln x = 4 \Rightarrow x = e^4$.
*[4 marks available — 1 mark for factorisation of
a quadratic, 1 mark for both solutions for $\ln x$,
and 1 mark for each correct solution for x.]*

2 $y = e^{ax} + b$
The sketch shows that when $x = 0$, $y = -6$, so:
$-6 = e^0 + b$ *[1 mark]* $-6 = 1 + b \Rightarrow b = -7$ *[1 mark]*.

The sketch also shows that when $y = 0$, $x = \frac{1}{4}\ln 7$, so:
$0 = e^{\left(\frac{a}{4}\ln 7\right)} - 7$ *[1 mark]* $\Rightarrow e^{\left(\frac{a}{4}\ln 7\right)} = 7$
$\Rightarrow \frac{a}{4}\ln 7 = \ln 7 \Rightarrow \frac{a}{4} = 1 \Rightarrow a = 4$ *[1 mark]*.
The asymptote occurs as $x \rightarrow -\infty$, so $e^{4x} \rightarrow 0$,
and since $y = e^{4x} - 7$, $y \rightarrow -7$.
So the equation of the asymptote is $y = -7$ *[1 mark]*.

3 a) When $t = 0$ (i.e. when the mink were introduced
to the habitat) $M = 74 \times e^0 = 74$, so there were 74
mink originally *[1 mark]*.

b) After 3 years, $M = 74 \times e^{0.6 \times 3}$ *[1 mark]* $= 447.67$
i.e. 447 mink (rounding down) *[1 mark]*.

c) For $M = 10\,000$: $10\,000 = 74e^{0.6t}$
$\Rightarrow e^{0.6t} = 10\,000 \div 74 = 135.1351$
$\Rightarrow 0.6t = \ln 135.1351 = 4.9063$ *[1 mark]*
$\Rightarrow t = 4.9063 \div 0.6 = 8.2$ years to reach
10 000, so it would take 9 complete years for the
population to exceed 10 000 *[1 mark]*.

d)

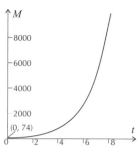

[2 marks available — 1 mark for correct shape, 1 mark for (0, 74) as a point on the graph.]

4 a) $y = \ln(4x - 3)$, and $x = a$ when $y = 1$.
$1 = \ln(4a - 3) \Rightarrow e^1 = 4a - 3$ *[1 mark]*
$\Rightarrow a = (e^1 + 3) \div 4 = 1.43$ to 2 d.p. *[1 mark]*.

b) The curve can only exist when $4x - 3 > 0$
[1 mark] so $x > 3 \div 4$, $x > 0.75$. If $x > b$, then
$b = 0.75$ *[1 mark]*.

c)

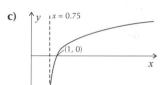

When $y = 0$, $4x - 3 = e^0 = 1$, so $x = 1$.
As $x \to \infty$, $y \to \infty$ gradually.
From (b), there will be an asymptote at $x = 0.75$.

[2 marks available — 1 mark for correct shape including asymptote at x = 0.75, 1 mark for (1, 0) as a point on the graph.]

5 a) $2e^x + 18e^{-x} = 20$
(Multiply through by e^x to remove the e^{-x}, since $e^x \times e^{-x} = 1$)
$2e^{2x} + 18 = 20e^x$
$\Rightarrow 2e^{2x} - 20e^x + 18 = 0 \Rightarrow e^{2x} - 10e^x + 9 = 0$
(This now looks like a quadratic equation, so use $y = e^x$ to simplify...)
$y^2 - 10y + 9 = 0$
$\Rightarrow (y - 1)(y - 9) = 0 \Rightarrow y = 1$ or $y = 9$.
So $e^x = 1 \Rightarrow x = 0$ or $e^x = 9 \Rightarrow x = \ln 9$.

[4 marks available — 1 mark for factorisation of a quadratic, 1 mark for both solutions for e^x, and 1 mark for each correct exact solution for x.]

b) $2\ln x - \ln 3 = \ln 12 \Rightarrow 2\ln x = \ln 12 + \ln 3$
(Use the log laws to simplify at this point...)
$\Rightarrow \ln x^2 = \ln 36$ *[1 mark]* $\Rightarrow x^2 = 36$ *[1 mark]*
$\Rightarrow x = 6$ *[1 mark]* (x must be positive as $\ln(-6)$ does not exist.)

6 a) B is the value of A when $t = 0$.
From the table, $B = 50$ *[1 mark]*.

b) Substitute $t = 5$ and $A = 42$ into $A = 50e^{-kt}$:
$42 = 50e^{-5k} \Rightarrow e^{-5k} = \frac{42}{50} \Rightarrow e^{5k} = \frac{50}{42}$ *[1 mark]*
$\Rightarrow 5k = \ln\left(\frac{50}{42}\right) = 0.17435$
$\Rightarrow k = 0.17435 \div 5 = 0.0349$ to 3 s.f. *[1 mark]*.

c) $A = 50e^{-0.0349t}$ (using values from (a) and (b)),
so when $t = 10$, $A = 50 \times e^{-0.0349 \times 10}$ *[1 mark]*
$= 35$ to the nearest whole *[1 mark]*.

d) The half-life will be the value of t when A reaches
half of the original value of 50, i.e. when $A = 25$.
$25 = 50e^{-0.0349t} \Rightarrow \frac{25}{50} = e^{-0.0349t} \Rightarrow \frac{50}{25} = e^{0.0349t}$
$\Rightarrow e^{0.0349t} = 2$ *[1 mark]* $\Rightarrow 0.0349t = \ln 2$ *[1 mark]*
$\Rightarrow t = \ln 2 \div 0.0349 = 20$ days to the nearest day
[1 mark].

7 a) $27 = 3e^{2-2x} \Rightarrow 9 = e^{2-2x} \Rightarrow \ln 9 = 2 - 2x$ *[1 mark]*
$\Rightarrow 2x = 2 - \ln 9 \Rightarrow x = 1 - 0.5\ln 9$ *[1 mark]*
$\Rightarrow x = 1 - 0.5\ln 3^2 = 1 - \ln 3$ *[1 mark]*.

b) Sketch of the graph $y = 3e^{2-2x}$ with asymptote and
y-intercept labelled.

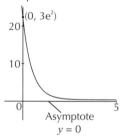

[3 marks available — 1 mark for correct shape of graph, 1 mark for (0, 3e²) as a point on the graph, 1 mark for asymptote at y = 0.]

c) $y = 3e^{2-2x} \Rightarrow e^{2-2x} = \frac{y}{3} \Rightarrow 2 - 2x = \ln\left(\frac{y}{3}\right)$
$\Rightarrow 2x = 2 - \ln\left(\frac{y}{3}\right) \Rightarrow x = 1 - 0.5\ln\left(\frac{y}{3}\right)$

[2 marks — 1 mark for taking logarithms of each side and 1 mark for the final answer.]

Chapter 4: Differentiation

1. Chain Rule

Exercise 1.1 — The chain rule

Q1 a) $y = (x + 7)^2$, so let $y = u^2$ where $u = x + 7$

$\Rightarrow \dfrac{dy}{du} = 2u = 2(x + 7)$, $\dfrac{du}{dx} = 1$

$\dfrac{dy}{dx} = \dfrac{du}{dx} \times \dfrac{dy}{du} = 1 \times 2(x + 7) = 2(x + 7)$

b) $y = (2x - 1)^5$, so let $y = u^5$ where $u = 2x - 1$

$\Rightarrow \dfrac{dy}{du} = 5u^4 = 5(2x - 1)^4$, $\dfrac{du}{dx} = 2$

$\dfrac{dy}{dx} = \dfrac{du}{dx} \times \dfrac{dy}{du} = 2 \times 5(2x - 1)^4 = 10(2x - 1)^4$

c) $y = 3(4 - x)^8$, so let $y = 3u^8$ where $u = 4 - x$

$\Rightarrow \dfrac{dy}{du} = 24u^7 = 24(4 - x)^7$, $\dfrac{du}{dx} = -1$

$\dfrac{dy}{dx} = \dfrac{du}{dx} \times \dfrac{dy}{du} = (-1) \times 24(4 - x)^7 = -24(4 - x)^7$

d) $y = (3 - 2x)^7$, so let $y = u^7$ where $u = 3 - 2x$

$\Rightarrow \dfrac{dy}{du} = 7u^6 = 7(3 - 2x)^6$, $\dfrac{du}{dx} = -2$

$\dfrac{dy}{dx} = \dfrac{du}{dx} \times \dfrac{dy}{du} = (-2) \times 7(3 - 2x)^6 = -14(3 - 2x)^6$

e) $y = (x^2 + 3)^5$, so let $y = u^5$ where $u = x^2 + 3$

$\Rightarrow \dfrac{dy}{du} = 5u^4 = 5(x^2 + 3)^4$, $\dfrac{du}{dx} = 2x$

$\dfrac{dy}{dx} = \dfrac{du}{dx} \times \dfrac{dy}{du} = 2x \times 5(x^2 + 3)^4 = 10x(x^2 + 3)^4$

f) $y = (5x^2 + 3)^2$, so let $y = u^2$ where $u = 5x^2 + 3$

$\Rightarrow \dfrac{dy}{du} = 2u = 2(5x^2 + 3)$, $\dfrac{du}{dx} = 10x$

$\dfrac{dy}{dx} = \dfrac{du}{dx} \times \dfrac{dy}{du} = 10x \times 2(5x^2 + 3) = 20x(5x^2 + 3)$

Q2 a) $f(x) = (4x^3 - 9)^8$, so let $y = u^8$ where $u = 4x^3 - 9$

$\Rightarrow \dfrac{dy}{du} = 8u^7 = 8(4x^3 - 9)^7$, $\dfrac{du}{dx} = 12x^2$

$f'(x) = \dfrac{du}{dx} \times \dfrac{dy}{du} = 12x^2 \times 8(4x^3 - 9)^7$

$\qquad = 96x^2(4x^3 - 9)^7$

b) $f(x) = (6 - 7x^2)^4$, so let $y = u^4$ where $u = 6 - 7x^2$

$\Rightarrow \dfrac{dy}{du} = 4u^3 = 4(6 - 7x^2)^3$, $\dfrac{du}{dx} = -14x$

$f'(x) = \dfrac{du}{dx} \times \dfrac{dy}{du} = (-14x) \times 4(6 - 7x^2)^3$

$\qquad = -56x(6 - 7x^2)^3$

c) $f(x) = (x^2 + 5x + 7)^6$, so let $y = u^6$
where $u = x^2 + 5x + 7$

$\Rightarrow \dfrac{dy}{du} = 6u^5 = 6(x^2 + 5x + 7)^5$, $\dfrac{du}{dx} = 2x + 5$

$f'(x) = \dfrac{du}{dx} \times \dfrac{dy}{du} = (2x + 5) \times 6(x^2 + 5x + 7)^5$

$\qquad = (12x + 30)(x^2 + 5x + 7)^5$

d) $f(x) = (x + 4)^{-3}$, so let $y = u^{-3}$ where $u = x + 4$

$\Rightarrow \dfrac{dy}{du} = -3u^{-4} = -3(x + 4)^{-4}$, $\dfrac{du}{dx} = 1$

$f'(x) = \dfrac{du}{dx} \times \dfrac{dy}{du} = 1 \times (-3)(x + 4)^{-4} = -3(x + 4)^{-4}$

e) $f(x) = (5 - 3x)^{-2}$, so let $y = u^{-2}$ where $u = 5 - 3x$

$\Rightarrow \dfrac{dy}{du} = -2u^{-3} = -2(5 - 3x)^{-3}$, $\dfrac{du}{dx} = -3$

$f'(x) = \dfrac{du}{dx} \times \dfrac{dy}{du} = (-3) \times (-2)(5 - 3x)^{-3} = 6(5 - 3x)^{-3}$

f) $f(x) = \dfrac{1}{(5 - 3x)^4} = (5 - 3x)^{-4}$,

so let $y = u^{-4}$ where $u = 5 - 3x$

$\Rightarrow \dfrac{dy}{du} = -4u^{-5} = -4(5 - 3x)^{-5}$, $\dfrac{du}{dx} = -3$

$f'(x) = \dfrac{du}{dx} \times \dfrac{dy}{du} = (-3) \times (-4)(5 - 3x)^{-5} = \dfrac{12}{(5 - 3x)^5}$

g) $f(x) = (3x^2 + 4)^{\frac{3}{2}}$, so let $y = u^{\frac{3}{2}}$ where $u - 3x^2 + 4$

$\Rightarrow \dfrac{dy}{du} = \dfrac{3}{2}u^{\frac{1}{2}} = \dfrac{3}{2}(3x^2 + 4)^{\frac{1}{2}}$, $\dfrac{du}{dx} = 6x$

$f'(x) = \dfrac{du}{dx} \times \dfrac{dy}{du} = 6x \times \dfrac{3}{2}(3x^2 + 4)^{\frac{1}{2}} = 9x(3x^2 + 4)^{\frac{1}{2}}$

h) $f(x) = \dfrac{1}{\sqrt{5 - 3x}} = (5 - 3x)^{-\frac{1}{2}}$,

so let $y = u^{-\frac{1}{2}}$ where $u = 5 - 3x$

$\Rightarrow \dfrac{dy}{du} = -\dfrac{1}{2}u^{-\frac{3}{2}} = -\dfrac{1}{2}(5 - 3x)^{-\frac{3}{2}}$, $\dfrac{du}{dx} = -3$

$f'(x) = \dfrac{du}{dx} \times \dfrac{dy}{du} = (-3) \times (-\dfrac{1}{2})(5 - 3x)^{-\frac{3}{2}}$

$\qquad = \dfrac{3}{2(\sqrt{5 - 3x})^3}$

Q3 a) $y = (5x - 3x^2)^{-\frac{1}{2}}$, so let $y = u^{-\frac{1}{2}}$ where $u = 5x - 3x^2$

$\Rightarrow \dfrac{dy}{du} = -\dfrac{1}{2}u^{-\frac{3}{2}} = -\dfrac{1}{2}(5x - 3x^2)^{-\frac{3}{2}}$, $\dfrac{du}{dx} = 5 - 6x$

$\dfrac{dy}{dx} = \dfrac{du}{dx} \times \dfrac{dy}{du} = (5 - 6x) \times -\dfrac{1}{2}(5x - 3x^2)^{-\frac{3}{2}}$

$\qquad = -\dfrac{5 - 6x}{2(\sqrt{5x - 3x^2})^3}$

When $x = 1$, $\dfrac{dy}{dx} = -\dfrac{5 - (6 \times 1)}{2(\sqrt{(5 \times 1) - (3 \times 1^2)})^3} = \dfrac{1}{4\sqrt{2}}$

b) $y = \dfrac{12}{\sqrt[3]{x + 6}} = 12(x + 6)^{-\frac{1}{3}}$,

so let $y = 12u^{-\frac{1}{3}}$ where $u = x + 6$

$\Rightarrow \dfrac{dy}{du} = -4u^{-\frac{4}{3}} = -4(x + 6)^{-\frac{4}{3}}$, $\dfrac{du}{dx} = 1$

$\dfrac{dy}{dx} = \dfrac{du}{dx} \times \dfrac{dy}{du} = 1 \times -4(x + 6)^{-\frac{4}{3}} = -\dfrac{4}{\sqrt[3]{(x + 6)^4}}$

When $x = 1$, $\dfrac{dy}{dx} = -\dfrac{4}{\sqrt[3]{(1 + 6)^4}} = -\dfrac{4}{7(\sqrt[3]{7})}$

Q4 a) $(\sqrt{x} + \dfrac{1}{\sqrt{x}})^2 = \sqrt{x}\sqrt{x} + 2\sqrt{x}\dfrac{1}{\sqrt{x}} + \dfrac{1}{\sqrt{x}}\dfrac{1}{\sqrt{x}}$

$\qquad = x + \dfrac{1}{x} + 2$

$\dfrac{d}{dx}(x + \dfrac{1}{x} + 2) = 1 - \dfrac{1}{x^2}$

Remember $\dfrac{1}{x} = x^{-1}$

b) $y = (\sqrt{x} + \frac{1}{\sqrt{x}})^2$, so let $y = u^2$ where $u = \sqrt{x} + \frac{1}{\sqrt{x}}$

$\Rightarrow \dfrac{dy}{du} = 2u = 2(\sqrt{x} + \frac{1}{\sqrt{x}})$,

$\dfrac{du}{dx} = \frac{1}{2}x^{-\frac{1}{2}} - \frac{1}{2}x^{-\frac{3}{2}} = \dfrac{1}{2\sqrt{x}} - \dfrac{1}{2(\sqrt{x})^3}$

$\dfrac{dy}{dx} = \dfrac{du}{dx} \times \dfrac{dy}{du} = (\dfrac{1}{2\sqrt{x}} - \dfrac{1}{2(\sqrt{x})^3}) \times 2(\sqrt{x} + \frac{1}{\sqrt{x}})$

$= 2(\frac{1}{2} + \frac{1}{2x} - \frac{1}{2x} - \frac{1}{2x^2}) = 1 - \dfrac{1}{x^2}$

Using powers notation makes this question easier to handle.

Q5 $y = (x - 3)^5$, so let $y = u^5$ where $u = x - 3$

$\Rightarrow \dfrac{dy}{du} = 5u^4 = 5(x-3)^4$, $\dfrac{du}{dx} = 1$

$\dfrac{dy}{dx} = \dfrac{du}{dx} \times \dfrac{dy}{du} = 1 \times 5(x-3)^4 = 5(x-3)^4$

At the point (1, −32), gradient $= 5(1-3)^4 = 80$

The equation of a straight line is $y = mx + c$

$\Rightarrow -32 = (80 \times 1) + c \Rightarrow c = -112$

So the equation of the tangent is $y = 80x - 112$

Q6 $y = (2x - 3)^7$, so let $y = u^7$ where $u = 2x - 3$

$\Rightarrow \dfrac{dy}{du} = 7u^6 = 7(2x-3)^6$, $\dfrac{du}{dx} = 2$

$\dfrac{dy}{dx} = \dfrac{du}{dx} \times \dfrac{dy}{du} = 2 \times 7(2x-3)^6 = 14(2x-3)^6$

At the point (2, 1), gradient $= 14(4 - 3)^6 = 14$

The equation of a straight line is $y = mx + c$

$\Rightarrow 1 = (14 \times 2) + c \Rightarrow c = -27$

So the equation of the tangent is $y = 14x - 27$.

Q7 $y = \frac{1}{4}(x - 7)^4$, so let $y = \frac{1}{4}u^4$ where $u = x - 7$

$\Rightarrow \dfrac{dy}{du} = u^3 = (x-7)^3$, $\dfrac{du}{dx} = 1$

$\dfrac{dy}{dx} = \dfrac{du}{dx} \times \dfrac{dy}{du} = 1 \times (x-7)^3 = (x-7)^3$

When $x = 6$, $y = \frac{1}{4}(6-7)^4 = \frac{1}{4}$

and $\dfrac{dy}{dx} = (6-7)^3 = -1$

The gradient of the normal is $-1 \div -1 = 1$

The equation of a straight line is $y = mx + c$

$\Rightarrow \frac{1}{4} = (1 \times 6) + c \Rightarrow c = -\frac{23}{4}$

So the equation of the normal is $y = x - \frac{23}{4}$

Q8 $y = (\frac{x}{4} - 2)^3$, so let $y = u^3$ where $u = \frac{x}{4} - 2$

$\Rightarrow \dfrac{dy}{du} = 3u^2 = 3(\frac{x}{4} - 2)^2$, $\dfrac{du}{dx} = \frac{1}{4}$

$\dfrac{dy}{dx} = \dfrac{du}{dx} \times \dfrac{dy}{du} = \frac{1}{4} \times 3(\frac{x}{4} - 2)^2 = \frac{3}{4}(\frac{x}{4} - 2)^2$

At the point (4, −1), gradient $= \frac{3}{4}(\frac{4}{4} - 2)^2 = \frac{3}{4}$

So the gradient of the normal is $-\frac{4}{3}$

$-1 = (-\frac{4}{3} \times 4) + c \Rightarrow c = \frac{13}{3}$

So the equation of the normal is $y = -\frac{4}{3}x + \frac{13}{3}$

To write it in the form $ax + by + c = 0$, where a, b and c are integers, multiply by 3 and rearrange:

$y = (-\frac{4}{3}x + \frac{13}{3}) \Rightarrow 3y = -4x + 13 \Rightarrow 4x + 3y - 13 = 0$

Q9 $y = (7x^2 - 3)^{-4}$, so let $y = u^{-4}$ where $u = 7x^2 - 3$

$\Rightarrow \dfrac{dy}{du} = -4u^{-5} = -4(7x^2 - 3)^{-5}$, $\dfrac{du}{dx} = 14x$

$\dfrac{dy}{dx} = \dfrac{du}{dx} \times \dfrac{dy}{du} = 14x \times -4(7x^2 - 3)^{-5} = -56x(7x^2 - 3)^{-5}$

When $x = 1$, $\dfrac{dy}{dx} = -56(1)(7(1)^2 - 3)^{-5} = -56(4^{-5})$

$= -\dfrac{7}{128}$

Q10 $y = \dfrac{7}{\sqrt[3]{3 - 2x}}$, so let $y = 7u^{-\frac{1}{3}}$ where $u = 3 - 2x$

$\Rightarrow \dfrac{dy}{du} = -\frac{7}{3}u^{-\frac{4}{3}} = -\dfrac{7}{3(\sqrt[3]{3 - 2x})^4}$, $\dfrac{du}{dx} = -2$

$f'(x) = \dfrac{du}{dx} \times \dfrac{dy}{du} = -2 \times -\dfrac{7}{3(\sqrt[3]{3 - 2x})^4} = \dfrac{14}{3(\sqrt[3]{3 - 2x})^4}$

$f'(x)$ could also be written as $\frac{14}{3}(3 - 2x)^{-\frac{4}{3}}$.

Q11 $y = \sqrt{5x - 1}$, so let $y = u^{\frac{1}{2}}$ where $u = 5x - 1$

$\Rightarrow \dfrac{dy}{du} = \frac{1}{2}u^{-\frac{1}{2}} = \frac{1}{2}\dfrac{1}{\sqrt{5x - 1}}$, $\dfrac{du}{dx} = 5$

$\dfrac{dy}{dx} = \dfrac{du}{dx} \times \dfrac{dy}{du} = 5 \times \frac{1}{2}\dfrac{1}{\sqrt{5x - 1}} = \dfrac{5}{2\sqrt{5x - 1}}$

when $x = 2$, $\dfrac{dy}{dx} = \dfrac{5}{2\sqrt{10 - 1}} = \frac{5}{6}$

and $y = \sqrt{10 - 1} = 3$

$y = mx + c \Rightarrow 3 = (\frac{5}{6} \times 2) + c \Rightarrow c = \frac{4}{3}$

So the equation of the tangent is $y = \frac{5}{6}x + \frac{4}{3}$

In the form $ax + by + c = 0$, $5x - 6y + 8 = 0$

Q12 $y = \sqrt[3]{3x - 7}$, so let $y = u^{\frac{1}{3}}$ where $u = 3x - 7$

$\Rightarrow \dfrac{dy}{du} = \frac{1}{3}u^{-\frac{2}{3}} = \dfrac{1}{3(\sqrt[3]{3x - 7})^2}$, $\dfrac{du}{dx} = 3$

$\dfrac{dy}{dx} = \dfrac{du}{dx} \times \dfrac{dy}{du} = 3 \times \dfrac{1}{3(\sqrt[3]{3x - 7})^2} = \dfrac{1}{(\sqrt[3]{3x - 7})^2}$

when $x = 5$, $\dfrac{dy}{dx} = \dfrac{1}{(\sqrt[3]{(3 \times 5) - 7})^2} = \frac{1}{4}$, $y = \sqrt[3]{15 - 7} = 2$

Gradient of normal $= \dfrac{-1}{\frac{1}{4}} = -4$

$y = mx + c \Rightarrow 2 = (-4 \times 5) + c \Rightarrow c = 22$

So the equation of the normal is $y = 22 - 4x$

Q13 $y = (x^4 + x^3 + x^2)^2$, so let $y = u^2$ where $u = x^4 + x^3 + x^2$

$\Rightarrow \dfrac{dy}{du} = 2u = 2(x^4 + x^3 + x^2)$, $\dfrac{du}{dx} = 4x^3 + 3x^2 + 2x$

$\dfrac{dy}{dx} = \dfrac{du}{dx} \times \dfrac{dy}{du} = (4x^3 + 3x^2 + 2x) \times 2(x^4 + x^3 + x^2)$

At $x = -1$ $\dfrac{dy}{dx} = (-4 + 3 + -2) \times 2(1 - 1 + 1) = -6$

$y = ((-1)^4 + (-1)^3 + (-1)^2)^2 = 1$

$y = mx + c \Rightarrow 1 = (-6 \times -1) + c \Rightarrow c = -5$

So the equation of the tangent is $y = -6x - 5$.

Exercise 1.2 — Finding $\frac{dy}{dx}$ when $x = f(y)$

Q1 a) $\frac{dx}{dy} = 6y + 5 \Rightarrow \frac{dy}{dx} = \frac{1}{6y + 5}$

At $(5, -1)$, $y = -1$ so $\frac{dy}{dx} = \frac{1}{-1} = -1$.

b) $\frac{dx}{dy} = 3y^2 - 2 \Rightarrow \frac{dy}{dx} = \frac{1}{3y^2 - 2}$

At $(-4, -2)$, $y = -2$ so $\frac{dy}{dx} = \frac{1}{10} = 0.1$.

c) $x = (2y + 1)(y - 2) = 2y^2 - 3y - 2$

$\frac{dx}{dy} = 4y - 3 \Rightarrow \frac{dy}{dx} = \frac{1}{4y - 3}$

At $(3, -1)$ $y = -1$ so $\frac{dy}{dx} = -\frac{1}{7}$.

d) $x = \frac{4 + y^2}{y} = 4y^{-1} + y$

$\frac{dx}{dy} = -4y^{-2} + 1 \Rightarrow \frac{dy}{dx} = \frac{1}{1 - 4y^{-2}} = \frac{y^2}{y^2 - 4}$

At $(5, 4)$, $y = 4$ so $\frac{dy}{dx} = \frac{4}{3}$.

Q2 $x = (2y^3 - 5)^3$, so let $x = u^3$ where $u = 2y^3 - 5$

$\Rightarrow \frac{dx}{du} = 3u^2 = 3(2y^3 - 5)^2$, $\frac{du}{dy} = 6y^2$

$\frac{dx}{dy} = \frac{du}{dy} \times \frac{dx}{du} = 6y^2 \times 3(2y^3 - 5)^2 = 18y^2(2y^3 - 5)^2$

$\frac{dy}{dx} = \frac{1}{18y^2(2y^3 - 5)^2}$

Q3 a) $x = \sqrt{4 + y} \Rightarrow x = u^{\frac{1}{2}}$, $u = 4 + y$

$\Rightarrow \frac{dx}{du} = \frac{1}{2}u^{-\frac{1}{2}} = \frac{1}{2}\frac{1}{\sqrt{4 + y}}$, $\frac{du}{dy} = 1$

$\frac{dx}{dy} = \frac{du}{dy} \times \frac{dx}{du} = 1 \times \frac{1}{2}\frac{1}{\sqrt{4 + y}} = \frac{1}{2\sqrt{4 + y}} = \frac{1}{2x}$

$\Rightarrow \frac{dy}{dx} = 2x$

If you look back at the question, $x = \sqrt{4 + y}$, so you can just replace this with x on the bottom row when finding dx/dy.

b) $x = \sqrt{4 + y} \Rightarrow x^2 = 4 + y \Rightarrow y = x^2 - 4$

$\frac{dy}{dx} = 2x$

2. Differentiation of e^x and $\ln x$
Exercise 2.1 — Differentiating e^x

Q1 a) $y = e^{f(x)}$, where $f(x) = 3x$, so $f'(x) = 3$

$\frac{dy}{dx} = f'(x)e^{f(x)} = 3 \times e^{3x} = 3e^{3x}$

b) $\frac{dy}{dx} = f'(x)e^{f(x)} = 2 \times e^{2x - 5} = 2e^{2x - 5}$

c) $\frac{dy}{dx} = f'(x)e^{f(x)} = 1 \times e^{x + 7} = e^{x + 7}$

d) $\frac{dy}{dx} = f'(x)e^{f(x)} = 3 \times e^{3x + 9} = 3e^{3x + 9}$

e) $\frac{dy}{dx} = f'(x)e^{f(x)} = (-2) \times e^{7 - 2x} = -2e^{7 - 2x}$

f) $\frac{dy}{dx} = f'(x)e^{f(x)} = 3x^2 \times e^{x^3} = 3x^2e^{x^3}$

Q2 $f'(x) = g'(x)e^{g(x)} = (3x^2 + 3)e^{x^3 + 3x}$

Q3 $f'(x) = g'(x)e^{g(x)} = (3x^2 - 3)e^{x^3 - 3x - 5}$

Q4 $f(x) = e^{2x^2 + x}$, so:

$f'(x) = g'(x)e^{g(x)} = (4x + 1) \times e^{2x^2 + x} = (4x + 1)e^{x(2x + 1)}$

Q5 e^x differentiates to e^x and e^{-x} differentiates to $-e^{-x}$ so

$f'(x) = \frac{1}{2} \times (e^x - (-e^{-x})) = \frac{1}{2}(e^x + e^{-x})$

Q6 $f(x) = e^{x^2 + 7x + 12}$

$f'(x) = g'(x)e^{g(x)} = (2x + 7)e^{x^2 + 7x + 12}$

Q7 $\frac{d}{dx}(e^{x^4 + 3x^2}) = (4x^3 + 6x)e^{x^4 + 3x^2}$ and

$\frac{d}{dx}(2e^{2x}) = 4e^{2x}$

So $f'(x) = (4x^3 + 6x)e^{x^4 + 3x^2} + 4e^{2x}$

Q8 $\frac{dy}{dx} = f'(x)e^{f(x)} = 2 \times e^{2x} = 2e^{2x}$

At $x = 0$, $\frac{dy}{dx} = 2 \times e^{2 \times 0} = 2 \times 1 = 2$

$y = mx + c \Rightarrow 1 = (2 \times 0) + c \Rightarrow c = 1$

So the equation of the tangent is $y = 2x + 1$

There's no real need to use the $y = mx + c$ formula here as we already know the place it crosses the y-axis is $(0, 1)$ (it's given in the question), but it's good to be safe.

Q9 $\frac{dy}{dx} = f'(x)e^{f(x)} = 3 \times e^{3(x - 2)} = 3e^{3(x - 2)}$

When $x = 2$, $\frac{dy}{dx} = 3e^{3(2 - 2)} = 3e^0 = 3$

$y = mx + c \Rightarrow 1 = (3 \times 2) + c \Rightarrow c = -5$

So the equation of the tangent is $y = 3x - 5$.

Q10 $\frac{dy}{dx} = f'(x)e^{f(x)} = 4xe^{2x^2}$

At $x = 1$, $\frac{dy}{dx} = 4 \times 1 \times e^2 = 4e^2$ and $y = e^2$

$y = mx + c \Rightarrow e^2 = (4e^2 \times 1) + c \Rightarrow c = -3e^2$

So the equation of the tangent is $y = 4e^2x - 3e^2$.

Q11 $\frac{dy}{dx} = f'(x)e^{f(x)} = 2e^{2x - 4}$

When $x = 2$, $\frac{dy}{dx} = 2e^{4 - 4} = 2e^0 = 2$

$\Rightarrow$ Gradient of the normal $= -\frac{1}{2}$

$y = mx + c \Rightarrow 1 = (-\frac{1}{2} \times 2) + c \Rightarrow c = 1 - (-1) = 2$

So the equation of the normal is $y - 2 - \frac{1}{2}x$.

Q12 $\frac{dy}{dx} = f'(x)e^{f(x)} = (3 \times e^{3x}) = 3e^{3x}$

When it crosses the y-axis, $x = 0$, so $y = e^{3 \times 0} + 3 = 4$

$\frac{dy}{dx} = (3 \times e^{3 \times 0}) = (3 \times 1) = 3$

$\Rightarrow$ Gradient of the normal $= -\frac{1}{3}$

$y = mu + c \rightarrow 4 = (-\frac{1}{3} \times 0) + c \rightarrow c = 4$

So the equation of the normal is $y = -\frac{1}{3}x + 4$.

Q13 $\frac{dy}{dx} = f'(x)e^{f(x)} = 3 \times e^{3(x-1)} = 3e^{3(x-1)}$

When $x = 2$, $y = e^3$ and $\frac{dy}{dx} = 3e^3$

So the gradient of the normal is $-\frac{1}{3e^3} = -\frac{1}{3}e^{-3}$

$y = mx + c \Rightarrow e^3 = 2 \times -\frac{1}{3}e^{-3} + c$

$\Rightarrow c = e^3 + \frac{2}{3}e^{-3}$

So the equation of the normal is

$y = -\frac{1}{3}e^{-3}x + e^3 + \frac{2}{3}e^{-3}$.

Q14 If y has a turning point the gradient $\frac{dy}{dx}$ will be 0.

$\frac{dy}{dx} = f'(x)e^{f(x)} = (3x^2 - 3)e^{x^3 - 3x - 5}$

So if $\frac{dy}{dx} = 0$, either $3x^2 - 3 = 0$ or $e^{x^3 - 3x - 5} = 0$.

If $3x^2 - 3 = 0 \Rightarrow 3(x^2 - 1) = 0 \Rightarrow x^2 = 1$

$\Rightarrow x = \pm 1$ and if $e^{x^3 - 3x - 5} = 0$, there are no solutions.

So the gradient is 0 when $x = \pm 1 \Rightarrow$ the curve has turning points at $x = \pm 1$.

Q15 Turning points occur when the gradient is 0.

$\frac{dy}{dx} = f'(x)e^{f(x)} - 6 = 3e^{3x} - 6$

$3e^{3x} - 6 = 0 \Rightarrow e^{3x} = 2 \Rightarrow 3x = \ln 2 \Rightarrow x = \frac{1}{3}\ln 2$

Take ln of both sides to get rid of the exponential.

To find the nature of the root, calculate $\frac{d^2y}{dx^2}$

$\frac{d^2y}{dx^2} = 3f'(x)e^{f(x)} = 9e^{3x}$

When $x = \frac{1}{3}\ln 2$, $\frac{d^2y}{dx^2} = 9e^{\ln 2} = 9 \times 2 = 18$

$\frac{d^2y}{dx^2}$ is positive, so it's a minimum turning point.

Exercise 2.2 — Differentiating ln x

Q1 a) $y = \ln(3x) = \ln 3 + \ln x \Rightarrow \frac{dy}{dx} = \frac{1}{x}$

You could use that the derivative of ln (f(x)) is $\frac{f'(x)}{f(x)}$ — it'd give the same answer.

b) $\frac{dy}{dx} = 3 \times \frac{1}{x} = \frac{3}{x}$

c) $\frac{dy}{dx} = \frac{f'(x)}{f(x)} = \frac{1}{1 + x}$

The coefficient of x is 1 so it's a 1 on top of the fraction.

d) $\frac{dy}{dx} = \frac{f'(x)}{f(x)} = \frac{1}{5 + x}$

e) $\frac{dy}{dx} = \frac{f'(x)}{f(x)} = \frac{5}{1 + 5x}$

f) $\frac{dy}{dx} = 4 \times \frac{f'(x)}{f(x)} = 4 \times \frac{4}{4x - 2} = \frac{16}{4x - 2} = \frac{8}{2x - 1}$

Don't forget to simplify your answers if you can.

Q2 a) $\frac{dy}{dx} = \frac{f'(x)}{f(x)} = \frac{2x}{1 + x^2}$

b) $\frac{dy}{dx} = \frac{f'(x)}{f(x)} = \frac{-4x}{4 - 2x^2} = \frac{-2x}{2 - x^2}$

c) $y = \ln(2 + x)^2 = 2\ln(2 + x)$

$\frac{dy}{dx} = 2\frac{f'(x)}{f(x)} = 2 \times \frac{1}{2 + x} = \frac{2}{2 + x}$

d) $3\ln x^3 = 9\ln x \Rightarrow \frac{dy}{dx} = \frac{9}{x}$

e) $\frac{dy}{dx} = 2 \times \frac{f'(x)}{f(x)} = 2 \times \frac{6x + 3}{3x^2 + 3x}$

$= \frac{12x + 6}{3x^2 + 3x} = \frac{4x + 2}{x^2 + x}$

f) $\frac{dy}{dx} = \frac{f'(x)}{f(x)} = \frac{3x^2 + 2x}{x^3 + x^2} = \frac{3x + 2}{x^2 + x}$

Q3 $f(x) = \ln \frac{1}{x} = \ln x^{-1} = -\ln x \Rightarrow f'(x) = -\frac{1}{x}$

Q4 $f(x) = \ln \sqrt{x} = \ln x^{\frac{1}{2}} = \frac{1}{2}\ln x \Rightarrow f'(x) = \frac{1}{2x}$

Q5 $\ln\left(\frac{\sqrt{1 - x}}{\sqrt{1 + x}}\right) = \ln \sqrt{1 - x} - \ln \sqrt{1 + x}$

First part:

$f(x) = \ln \sqrt{1 - x} = \ln(1 - x)^{\frac{1}{2}} = \frac{1}{2}\ln(1 - x)$

$f'(x) = -\frac{1}{2(1 - x)}$

Second part:

$f(x) = \ln \sqrt{1 + x} = \ln(1 + x)^{\frac{1}{2}} = \frac{1}{2}\ln(1 + x)$

$f'(x) = \frac{1}{2(1 + x)}$

Putting it all together:

$f'(x) = -\frac{1}{2(1 - x)} - \frac{1}{2(1 + x)} = \frac{-(1 + x) - (1 - x)}{2(1 - x)(1 + x)}$

$= -\frac{1}{(1 - x)(1 + x)}$

Q6 $\ln((2x + 1)^2 \sqrt{x - 4}) = \ln(2x + 1)^2 + \ln \sqrt{x - 4}$

$= 2\ln(2x + 1) + \frac{1}{2}\ln(x - 4)$

First part:

$f'(x) = 2 \times \frac{2}{2x + 1} = \frac{4}{2x + 1}$

Second part:

$f'(x) = \frac{1}{2} \times \frac{1}{x - 4} = \frac{1}{2(x - 4)}$

Putting it all together:

$f'(x) = \frac{4}{2x + 1} + \frac{1}{2(x - 4)} = \frac{8(x - 4) + 2x + 1}{2(2x + 1)(x - 4)}$

$= \frac{10x - 31}{2(2x + 1)(x - 4)}$

Q7 $g(x) = x - \sqrt{x - 4} \Rightarrow g'(x) = 1 - \left(\frac{dy}{du} \times \frac{du}{dx}\right)$

$= 1 - \frac{1}{2\sqrt{x - 4}}$

$f'(x) = \frac{g'(x)}{g(x)} = \frac{1 - \frac{1}{2\sqrt{x - 4}}}{x - \sqrt{x - 4}} = \frac{2\sqrt{x - 4} - 1}{2(x\sqrt{x - 4} - x + 4)}$

Q8 $\ln\left(\frac{(3x + 1)^2}{\sqrt{2x + 1}}\right) = \ln(3x + 1)^2 - \ln \sqrt{2x + 1}$

$= 2\ln(3x + 1) - \frac{1}{2}\ln(2x + 1)$

First part:

$f'(x) = 2 \times \frac{3}{3x + 1} = \frac{6}{3x + 1}$

Second part:

$f'(x) = \frac{1}{2} \times \frac{2}{2x+1} = \frac{1}{2x+1}$

Putting it all together:

$f'(x) = \frac{6}{3x+1} - \frac{1}{2x+1} = \frac{6(2x+1) - 3x - 1}{(3x+1)(2x+1)}$

$= \frac{9x+5}{(3x+1)(2x+1)}$

You could have left your answer as 2 fractions.

Q9 $\ln(x\sqrt{x+4}) = \ln x + \ln\sqrt{x+4} = \ln x + \frac{1}{2}\ln(x+4)$

First part:

$\frac{dy}{dx} = \frac{1}{x}$

Second part:

$\frac{dy}{dx} = \frac{1}{2} \times \frac{1}{x+4} = \frac{1}{2(x+4)}$

Putting it all together:

$f'(x) = \frac{1}{x} + \frac{1}{2(x+4)} = \frac{2x+8+x}{2x(x+4)} = \frac{3x+8}{2x(x+4)}$

Q10 $y = \ln(3x) = \ln 3 + \ln x \Rightarrow \frac{dy}{dx} = \frac{1}{x}$

This is just the derivative from 1 a).

When $x = \frac{1}{3}$, $\frac{dy}{dx} = \frac{1}{\left(\frac{1}{3}\right)} = 3$

$y = mx + c \Rightarrow 0 = (3 \times \frac{1}{3}) + c \Rightarrow c = -1$

So the equation of the tangent is $y = 3x - 1$.

Q11 a) $y = \ln(3x)^2 = 2\ln(3x) = 2\ln 3 + 2\ln x$

$\Rightarrow \frac{dy}{dx} = \frac{2}{x}$

When $x = -2$, $\frac{dy}{dx} = -1$ and $y = \ln 36$

$y = mx + c \Rightarrow \ln 36 = [(-1) \times (-2)] + c$

$\Rightarrow c = \ln 36 - 2$

So the equation of the tangent is

$y = -x + \ln 36 - 2$

b) When $x = 2$, $\frac{dy}{dx} = 1$ and $y = \ln 36$

$y = mx + c \Rightarrow \ln 36 = [1 \times 2] + c$

$\Rightarrow c = \ln 36 - 2$

So the equation of the tangent is
$y = x + \ln 36 - 2$

Q12 a) $y = \ln(x+6)^2 = 2\ln(x+6) \Rightarrow \frac{dy}{dx} = 2\frac{f'(x)}{f(x)} = \frac{2}{x+6}$

When $x = -3$, $\frac{dy}{dx} = \frac{2}{3}$ and $y = \ln 9$

So the gradient of the normal $= -\frac{1}{\left(\frac{2}{3}\right)} = -\frac{3}{2}$

$y = mx + c \Rightarrow \ln 9 = (-\frac{3}{2} \times -3) + c$

$\Rightarrow c = \ln 9 - \frac{9}{2}$

so the equation of the normal is

$y = -\frac{3}{2}x + \ln 9 - \frac{9}{2}$.

b) When $x = 0$, $\frac{dy}{dx} = \frac{2}{6} = \frac{1}{3}$ and $y = \ln 36$

So the gradient of the normal $= -\frac{1}{\left(\frac{1}{3}\right)} = -3$

$y = mx + c \Rightarrow \ln 36 = (-3 \times 0) + c \Rightarrow c = \ln 36$

So the equation of the normal is

$y = -3x + \ln 36$

Q13 Turning points occur when the gradient is 0.

$\frac{dy}{dx} = \frac{f'(x)}{f(x)} = \frac{3x^2 - 6x + 3}{x^3 - 3x^2 + 3x}$

so $3x^2 - 6x + 3 = 0 \Rightarrow 3(x-1)(x-1) = 0$

You can ignore the denominator here, as it's only the top part that affects when it's equal to 0.

So the gradient is 0 when $x = 1$. When $x = 1$, $y = 0$
so the turning point is at $(1, 0)$.

3. Differentiation of Trig Functions

Exercise 3.1 — Differentiating sin, cos and tan

Q1 a) $y = \sin(3x)$, so let $y = \sin u$ where $u = 3x$

$\Rightarrow \frac{dy}{du} = \cos u = \cos(3x)$, $\frac{du}{dx} = 3$

$\frac{dy}{dx} = \frac{dy}{du} \times \frac{du}{dx} = 3\cos(3x)$

b) $y = \cos(-2x)$, so let $y = \cos u$ where $u = -2x$

$\Rightarrow \frac{dy}{du} = -\sin(u) = -\sin(-2x)$, $\frac{du}{dx} = -2$

$\frac{dy}{dx} = \frac{dy}{du} \times \frac{du}{dx} = (-2) \times (-\sin(-2x)) = 2\sin(-2x)$

As you can see, the number at the front is always just the coefficient of x inside the trig function.

c) $\frac{dy}{dx} = \frac{dy}{du} \times \frac{du}{dx} = -\sin\frac{x}{2} \times \frac{1}{2} = -\frac{1}{2}\sin\frac{x}{2}$

d) $\frac{dy}{dx} = \frac{dy}{du} \times \frac{du}{dx} = 1 \times \cos(x + \frac{\pi}{4}) = \cos(x + \frac{\pi}{4})$

e) $\frac{dy}{dx} = \frac{dy}{du} \times \frac{du}{dx} = 6 \times \frac{1}{2} \times \sec^2\frac{x}{2} = 3\sec^2\frac{x}{2}$

f) $\frac{dy}{dx} = \frac{dy}{du} \times \frac{du}{dx} = 3 \times 5 \times \sec^2(5x) = 15\sec^2(5x)$

Q2 $f'(x) = \frac{dy}{du} \times \frac{du}{dx} = 3 \times 2 \times \sec^2(2x-1)$
$= 6\sec^2(2x-1)$

Q3 First part: $\frac{dy}{dx} = 3\sec^2 x$

Second part: $\frac{dy}{dx} = \frac{dy}{du} \times \frac{du}{dx} = 3\sec^2(3x)$

Putting it all together:

$f'(x) = 3(\sec^2 x + \sec^2(3x))$

Q4 $f'(x) = \frac{dy}{du} \times \frac{du}{dx} = 2x\cos(x^2 + \frac{\pi}{3})$

Q5 $f(x) = \sin^2 x$, so let $y = u^2$ where $u = \sin x$

$f'(x) = \dfrac{dy}{du} \times \dfrac{du}{dx} = (2 \sin x) \times \cos x = 2 \sin x \cos x$

Q6 $f(x) = 2 \sin^3 x$, so let $y = 2u^3$ where $u = \sin x$

$f'(x) = \dfrac{dy}{du} \times \dfrac{du}{dx} = 6 \sin^2 x \cos x$

Q7 **a)** $f'(x) = 3 \cos x - 2 \sin x$

b) $f'(x) = 0 \Rightarrow 3 \cos x - 2 \sin x = 0$

$\Rightarrow 3 \cos x = 2 \sin x$

$\Rightarrow \dfrac{3}{2} = \tan x \Rightarrow x = \tan^{-1} \dfrac{3}{2} = 0.983$ (3 s.f.)

Remember that tan x = sin x / cos x

Q8 $y = \dfrac{1}{\cos x} = (\cos x)^{-1}$, so let $y = u^{-1}$ where $u = \cos x$

$\Rightarrow \dfrac{dy}{du} = -u^{-2} = -\dfrac{1}{\cos^2 x}$, $\dfrac{du}{dx} = -\sin x$

$\dfrac{dy}{dx} = \dfrac{dy}{du} \times \dfrac{du}{dx} = -\dfrac{1}{\cos^2 x} \times -\sin x$

$= \dfrac{\sin x}{\cos^2 x} = \sec x \tan x$

Remember that 1/cos x = sec x

Q9 **a)** $y = \cos^2 x$, so let $y = u^2$ where $u = \cos x$.

$\dfrac{dy}{dx} = \dfrac{dy}{du} \times \dfrac{du}{dx} = (2 \cos x) \times (-\sin x)$

$= -2 \sin x \cos x$

b) Using the double angle formula:

$\cos (2x) \equiv 2 \cos^2 x - 1 \Rightarrow \cos^2 x = \dfrac{1}{2}(\cos (2x) + 1)$

$\dfrac{dy}{dx} = \dfrac{1}{2} \times 2 \times (-\sin (2x)) = -\sin (2x)$

As the original function was in terms of cos x rather than cos (2x), it would be better to rearrange this.

From the double angle formula for sin:

$-\sin (2x) \equiv -2 \sin x \cos x$

Q10 First part:

$y = 6 \cos^2 x = 6(\cos x)^2$, so let $y = 6u^2$ where $u = \cos x$

$\Rightarrow \dfrac{dy}{du} = 12u = 12 \cos x$, $\dfrac{du}{dx} = -\sin x$

$\dfrac{dy}{dx} = \dfrac{dy}{du} \times \dfrac{du}{dx} = -12 \sin x \cos x$

Second part:

$y = 2 \sin (2x)$, so let $y = 2 \sin u$ where $u = 2x$

$\Rightarrow \dfrac{dy}{du} = 2 \cos u = 2 \cos (2x)$, $\dfrac{du}{dx} = 2$

$\dfrac{dy}{dx} = \dfrac{dy}{du} \times \dfrac{du}{dx} = 4 \cos (2x)$

Putting it all together:

$\dfrac{dy}{dx} = -12 \sin x \cos x - 4 \cos (2x)$

Double angle formula: $2 \sin x \cos x \equiv \sin (2x)$

$\Rightarrow -12 \sin x \cos x - 4 \cos (2x) = -6 \sin (2x) - 4 \cos (2x)$

Q11 $\dfrac{dy}{dx} = \cos x$. When $x = \dfrac{\pi}{4}$, $\dfrac{dy}{dx} = \dfrac{1}{\sqrt{2}}$

Q12 $\dfrac{dy}{dx} = -2 \sin (2x)$

When $x = \dfrac{\pi}{4}$, $y = 0$ and $\dfrac{dy}{dx} = -2$

So the gradient of the normal is $\dfrac{-1}{-2} = \dfrac{1}{2}$.

$y = mx + c \Rightarrow 0 = (\dfrac{1}{2} \times \dfrac{\pi}{4}) + c \Rightarrow c = -\dfrac{\pi}{8}$

So the equation of the normal is $y = \dfrac{1}{2}x - \dfrac{\pi}{8}$

$\Rightarrow 8y = 4x - \pi$

Q13 **a)** $\dfrac{dx}{dy} = 2 \cos (2y)$, $\dfrac{dy}{dx} = \dfrac{1}{2 \cos (2y)} = \dfrac{1}{2} \sec (2y)$

At the point $\left(\dfrac{\sqrt{3}}{2}, \dfrac{\pi}{6}\right)$, $\dfrac{dy}{dx} = \dfrac{1}{2 \cos \dfrac{\pi}{3}} = 1$

$y = mx + c \Rightarrow \dfrac{\pi}{6} = \dfrac{\sqrt{3}}{2} + c \Rightarrow c = \dfrac{\pi}{6} - \dfrac{\sqrt{3}}{2}$

So the equation of the tangent is $y = x + \dfrac{\pi}{6} - \dfrac{\sqrt{3}}{2}$.

b) from part a), $\dfrac{dy}{dx} = 1$ so the normal gradient is -1.

$y = mx + c \Rightarrow \dfrac{\pi}{6} = -\dfrac{\sqrt{3}}{2} + c \Rightarrow c = \dfrac{\pi}{6} + \dfrac{\sqrt{3}}{2}$

So the equation of the normal is $y = -x + \dfrac{\pi}{6} + \dfrac{\sqrt{3}}{2}$.

Q14 **a)** $y = 2 \sin (2x) \cos x \Rightarrow y = 4 \sin x \cos^2 x$

(From double angle formula sin (2x) ≡ 2 sin x cos x)

$\Rightarrow y = 4 \sin x (1 - \sin^2 x)$ *(from sin² x + cos² x = 1)*

$\Rightarrow y = 4 \sin x - 4 \sin^3 x$

b) First part:

$\dfrac{dy}{dx} = 4 \cos x$

Second part:

$y = 4 \sin^3 x = 4 (\sin x)^3$, so let $y = 4u^3$ where $u = \sin x$

$\dfrac{dy}{dx} = \dfrac{dy}{du} \times \dfrac{du}{dx} = 12 \sin^2 x \cos x$

Putting it all together:

$\dfrac{dy}{dx} = 4 \cos x - 12 \sin^2 x \cos x$

Exercise 3.2 — Differentiating by using the chain rule twice

Q1 **a)** $y = \sin (\cos (2x))$, so let $y = \sin u$ where $u = \cos (2x)$

$\dfrac{dy}{du} = \cos u = \cos (\cos (2x))$

Using the chain rule again on $\dfrac{du}{dx}$ gives:

$u = \cos (2x) \Rightarrow \dfrac{du}{dx} = -2 \sin (2x)$

Putting it all together:

$\dfrac{dy}{dx} = \dfrac{dy}{du} \times \dfrac{du}{dx} = -2 \sin (2x) \cos (\cos (2x))$

b) $y = 2\ln f(x) \Rightarrow \dfrac{dy}{dx} = 2\dfrac{f'(x)}{f(x)}$

$f(x) = \cos (3x) \Rightarrow f'(x) = -3 \sin (3x)$

$\dfrac{dy}{dx} = 2\dfrac{-3 \sin (3x)}{\cos (3x)} = -6 \tan (3x)$

c) $y = \ln (\tan^2 x) = \ln (f(x)) \Rightarrow \dfrac{dy}{dx} = \dfrac{f'(x)}{f(x)}$

$f(x) = \tan^2 x = (\tan x)^2$, so let $y = u^2$ where $u = \tan x$

$\dfrac{dy}{du} = 2u = 2 \tan x$, $\dfrac{du}{dx} = \sec^2 x$

$f'(x) = \dfrac{dy}{du} \times \dfrac{du}{dx} = 2 \tan x \sec^2 x$

Putting it all together:

$\dfrac{dy}{dx} = \dfrac{2 \tan x \sec^2 x}{\tan^2 x} = 2 \sec x \operatorname{cosec} x$

You could've written $\ln (\tan^2 x)$ as $2 \ln (\tan x)$ using the laws of logs and then differentiated — you'd end up with the same answer.

d) $y = e^{f(x)} \Rightarrow \dfrac{dy}{dx} = f'(x) e^{f(x)}$

$f(x) = \tan (2x)$, so let $y = \tan u$ where $u = 2x$

$\dfrac{dy}{du} = \sec^2 u - \sec^2 (2x)$, $\dfrac{du}{dx} = 2$

$\Rightarrow f'(x) = \dfrac{dy}{du} \times \dfrac{du}{dx} = 2 \sec^2 (2x)$

$\Rightarrow \dfrac{dy}{dx} = 2 \sec^2 (2x) e^{\tan (2x)}$

e) $y = \sin^4 x^2 = (\sin x^2)^4$, so let $y = u^4$ where $u = \sin x^2$

$\dfrac{dy}{du} = 4u^3 = 4 \sin^3 x^2$

For $\dfrac{du}{dx}$, set up another chain rule:

$u - \sin x^2$ so let $u = \sin v$, $v = x^2$

$\dfrac{du}{dv} = \cos v = \cos x^2$, $\dfrac{dv}{dx} = 2x$

$\dfrac{du}{dx} = \dfrac{du}{dv} \times \dfrac{dv}{dx} = 2x \cos x^2$

Putting it all together:

$\dfrac{dy}{dx} = \dfrac{dy}{du} \times \dfrac{du}{dx} = 8x \sin^3 x^2 \cos x^2$

f) $\dfrac{dy}{dx} = f'(x) e^{f(x)}$

$f(x) = \sin^2 x = (\sin x)^2$, so let $y = u^2$ where $u = \sin x$

$f'(x) = \dfrac{dy}{du} \times \dfrac{du}{dx} = (2 \sin x) \times (\cos x)$
$\qquad\qquad = 2 \sin x \cos x$

$\Rightarrow \dfrac{dy}{dx} = 2 e^{\sin^2 x} \sin x \cos x$

g) First part:

$y = \tan^2 (3x) = (\tan (3x))^2$,

so let $y = u^2$ where $u = \tan (3x)$

$\dfrac{dy}{du} = 2u = 2 \tan (3x)$

For $\dfrac{du}{dx}$ set up the chain rule again:

$u = \tan (3x)$, so let $u = \tan v$ where $v = 3x$

$\dfrac{du}{dv} = \sec^2 v = \sec^2 (3x)$, $\dfrac{dv}{dx} = 3$

$\Rightarrow \dfrac{du}{dx} = \dfrac{du}{dv} \times \dfrac{dv}{dx} = 3 \sec^2 (3x)$

$\Rightarrow \dfrac{dy}{dx} = \dfrac{dy}{du} \times \dfrac{du}{dx} = 6 \tan (3x) \sec^2 (3x)$

Second part:

$\dfrac{dy}{dx} = \cos x$

Putting it all together:

$\dfrac{dy}{dx} = 6 \tan (3x) \sec^2 (3x) + \cos x$

With practice, you should be able to do some of the simpler chain rule calculations in your head, e.g. $\tan^2 (3x) = 6 \tan (3x) \sec^2 (3x)$, which will make these questions much quicker.

h) First part:

$y = e^{f(x)}$, $f(x) = 2 \cos (2x) \Rightarrow \dfrac{dy}{dx} = f'(x) e^{f(x)}$

$f(x) = 2 \cos (2x) \Rightarrow f'(x) = -4 \sin (2x)$

So $\dfrac{dy}{dx} = -4 \sin (2x) e^{2 \cos (2x)}$

Second part:

$y = \cos^2 (2x) = (\cos (2x))^2$,

so let $y = u^2$ where $u = \cos (2x)$

$\dfrac{dy}{du} = 2u = 2 \cos (2x)$

For $\dfrac{du}{dx}$, set up the chain rule again:

$u = \cos (2x) \Rightarrow \dfrac{du}{dx} - 2 \sin (2x)$

$\Rightarrow \dfrac{dy}{dx} = \dfrac{dy}{du} \times \dfrac{du}{dx} = -4 \sin (2x) \cos (2x)$

Putting it all together:

$\dfrac{dy}{dx} = -4 \sin (2x) e^{2 \cos (2x)} - 4 \sin (2x) \cos (2x)$

4. Product Rule

Exercise 4.1 — Differentiating functions multiplied together

Q1 a) $y = x(x + 2) = x^2 + 2x$

$\dfrac{dy}{dx} = 2x + 2$

b) $u = x$, $v = x + 2 \Rightarrow \dfrac{du}{dx} = 1$, $\dfrac{dv}{dx} = 1$

$\dfrac{dy}{dx} = u\dfrac{dv}{dx} + v\dfrac{du}{dx} = x + (x + 2) = 2x + 2$

Q2 a) $u = x^2$, $v = (x + 6)^3 \Rightarrow \dfrac{du}{dx} = 2x$, $\dfrac{dv}{dx} = 3(x + 6)^2$

$\dfrac{dy}{dx} = u\dfrac{dv}{dx} + v\dfrac{du}{dx} = [x^2 \times 3(x + 6)^2] + [2x(x + 6)^3]$

$= 3x^2(x + 6)^2 + 2x(x + 6)^3 = x(x + 6)^2[3x + 2(x + 6)]$

$= x(x + 6)^2(5x + 12)$

Here the chain rule was used to find $\dfrac{dv}{dx}$ — write out all the steps if you're struggling.

b) $u = x^3$, $v = (5x + 2)^4 \Rightarrow \dfrac{du}{dx} = 3x^2$, $\dfrac{dv}{dx} = 20(5x + 2)^3$

$\dfrac{dy}{dx} = u\dfrac{dv}{dx} + v\dfrac{du}{dx} = [x^3 \times 20(5x + 2)^3]$
$\qquad\qquad\qquad\qquad\quad + [3x^2 \times (5x + 2)^4]$

$= 20x^3(5x + 2)^3 + 3x^2(5x + 2)^4$

$= x^2(5x + 2)^3[20x + 3(5x + 2)]$

$= x^2(5x + 2)^3(35x + 6)$

c) $u = x^3$, $v = e^x \Rightarrow \dfrac{du}{dx} = 3x^2$, $\dfrac{dv}{dx} = e^x$

$\dfrac{dy}{dx} = u\dfrac{dv}{dx} + v\dfrac{du}{dx} = x^3 e^x + 3x^2 e^x = x^2 e^x(x + 3)$

d) $u = x$, $v = e^{4x} \Rightarrow \dfrac{du}{dx} = 1$, $\dfrac{dv}{dx} = 4e^{4x}$

$\dfrac{dy}{dx} = u\dfrac{dv}{dx} + v\dfrac{du}{dx} = 4xe^{4x} + e^{4x} = e^{4x}(4x + 1)$

e) $u = x$, $v = e^{x^2} \Rightarrow \dfrac{du}{dx} = 1$, $\dfrac{dv}{dx} = 2xe^{x^2}$

$\dfrac{dy}{dx} = u\dfrac{dv}{dx} + v\dfrac{du}{dx} = x \times 2xe^{x^2} + e^{x^2} = e^{x^2}(2x^2 + 1)$

f) $u = e^{2x}$, $v = \sin x \Rightarrow \dfrac{du}{dx} = 2e^{2x}$, $\dfrac{dv}{dx} = \cos x$

$\dfrac{dy}{dx} = u\dfrac{dv}{dx} + v\dfrac{du}{dx} = e^{2x}\cos x + 2e^{2x}\sin x$

$= e^{2x}(\cos x + 2\sin x)$

Q3 a) $u = x^3$, $v = (x + 3)^{\frac{1}{2}}$

$\Rightarrow \dfrac{du}{dx} = 3x^2$, $\dfrac{dv}{dx} = \dfrac{1}{2}(x + 3)^{-\frac{1}{2}}$

$f'(x) = u\dfrac{dv}{dx} + v\dfrac{du}{dx}$

$= [x^3 \times \dfrac{1}{2}(x + 3)^{-\frac{1}{2}}] + [3x^2 \times (x + 3)^{\frac{1}{2}}]$

$= \dfrac{x^3}{2\sqrt{x + 3}} + 3x^2\sqrt{x + 3}$

b) $u = x^2$, $v = (x - 7)^{-\frac{1}{2}}$

$\Rightarrow \dfrac{du}{dx} = 2x$, $\dfrac{dv}{dx} = -\dfrac{1}{2}(x - 7)^{-\frac{3}{2}}$

$f'(x) = u\dfrac{dv}{dx} + v\dfrac{du}{dx}$

$= [x^2 \times (-\dfrac{1}{2}) \times (x - 7)^{-\frac{3}{2}}] + [2x(x - 7)^{-\frac{1}{2}}]$

$= -\dfrac{x^2}{2(\sqrt{x - 7})^3} + \dfrac{2x}{\sqrt{x - 7}}$

c) $u = x^4$, $v = \ln x \Rightarrow \dfrac{du}{dx} = 4x^3$, $\dfrac{dv}{dx} = \dfrac{1}{x}$

$f'(x) = u\dfrac{dv}{dx} + v\dfrac{du}{dx} = [x^4 \times \dfrac{1}{x}] + [4x^3\ln x]$

$= x^3 + 4x^3\ln x = x^3(1 + 4\ln x)$

d) $u = 4x$, $v = \ln x^2 = 2\ln x \Rightarrow \dfrac{du}{dx} = 4$, $\dfrac{dv}{dx} = \dfrac{2}{x}$

$f'(x) = u\dfrac{dv}{dx} + v\dfrac{du}{dx} = [4x \times \dfrac{2}{x}] + [4\ln x^2] = 8 + 4\ln x^2$

e) $u = 2x^3$, $v = \cos x$

$\Rightarrow \dfrac{du}{dx} = 6x^2$, $\dfrac{dv}{dx} = -\sin x$

$f'(x) = u\dfrac{dv}{dx} + v\dfrac{du}{dx} = -2x^3\sin x + 6x^2\cos x$

f) $u = x^2$, $v = \cos(2x) \Rightarrow \dfrac{du}{dx} = 2x$, $\dfrac{dv}{dx} = -2\sin(2x)$

$f'(x) = u\dfrac{dv}{dx} + v\dfrac{du}{dx}$

$= [x^2 \times -2\sin(2x)] + [2x\cos(2x)]$

$= 2x\cos(2x) - 2x^2\sin(2x)$

$= 2x(\cos(2x) - x\sin(2x))$

Q4 a) $u = (x + 1)^2$, $v = x^2 - 1 \Rightarrow \dfrac{du}{dx} = 2(x + 1)$, $\dfrac{dv}{dx} = 2x$

$\dfrac{dy}{dx} = u\dfrac{dv}{dx} + v\dfrac{du}{dx}$

$= [(x + 1)^2 \times 2x] + [2(x + 1) \times (x^2 - 1)]$

$= 2x(x + 1)^2 + 2(x + 1)(x^2 - 1)$

$= 2x^3 + 4x^2 + 2x + 2x^3 + 2x^2 - 2x - 2$

$= 4x^3 + 6x^2 - 2$

b) $u = (x + 1)^3$, $v = x - 1 \Rightarrow \dfrac{du}{dx} = 3(x + 1)^2$, $\dfrac{dv}{dx} = 1$

$\dfrac{dy}{dx} = u\dfrac{dv}{dx} + v\dfrac{du}{dx}$

$= [(x + 1)^3 \times 1] + [3(x + 1)^2(x - 1)]$

$= (x + 1)^3 + 3(x + 1)^2(x - 1)$

$= (x^3 + 3x^2 + 3x + 1) + (3x^3 + 6x^2 + 3x - 3x^2 - 6x - 3)$

$= 4x^3 + 6x^2 - 2$

Use the binomial theorem to expand $(x + 1)^3$. Using Pascal's triangle you'll get the coefficients 1, 3, 3, 1.

c) $y = (x + 1)^2(x^2 - 1) = (x + 1)^2(x + 1)(x - 1)$

$= (x + 1)^3(x - 1)$

Q5 a) $u = x$, $v = e^x \Rightarrow \dfrac{du}{dx} = 1$, $\dfrac{dv}{dx} = e^x$

$\dfrac{dy}{dx} = u\dfrac{dv}{dx} + v\dfrac{du}{dx} = xe^x + e^x$

At the point $(0, 0)$, $\dfrac{dy}{dx} = 0 + 1 = 1$

$y = mx + c \Rightarrow 0 = 0 + c \Rightarrow c = 0$

So the equation of the tangent is $y = x$.

b) Gradient of the normal $= -1$

$y = mx + c \Rightarrow 0 = 0 + c \Rightarrow c = 0$

So the equation of the normal is $y = -x$

Q6 $u = \sqrt{x + 2}$, $v = \sqrt{x + 7}$

$\Rightarrow \dfrac{du}{dx} = \dfrac{1}{2\sqrt{x + 2}}$, $\dfrac{dv}{dx} = \dfrac{1}{2\sqrt{x + 7}}$

$\dfrac{dy}{dx} = u\dfrac{dv}{dx} + v\dfrac{du}{dx} = \dfrac{\sqrt{x + 2}}{2\sqrt{x + 7}} + \dfrac{\sqrt{x + 7}}{2\sqrt{x + 2}}$

At the point $(2, 6)$, $\dfrac{dy}{dx} = \dfrac{\sqrt{4}}{2\sqrt{9}} + \dfrac{\sqrt{9}}{2\sqrt{4}} = \dfrac{13}{12}$

$y = mx + c \Rightarrow 6 = (2 \times \dfrac{13}{12}) + c \Rightarrow c = \dfrac{23}{6}$

So the equation of the tangent is $y = \dfrac{13}{12}x + \dfrac{23}{6}$.

To write this in the form $ax + by + c = 0$ where a, b and c are integers, multiply by 12 and rearrange.

$y = \dfrac{13}{12}x + \dfrac{23}{6} \Rightarrow 12y = 13x + 46$

$\Rightarrow 13x - 12y + 46 = 0$

Q7 a) $u = (x - 1)^{\frac{1}{2}}$, $v = (x + 4)^{-\frac{1}{2}}$

$\Rightarrow \dfrac{du}{dx} = \dfrac{1}{2\sqrt{x - 1}}$, $\dfrac{dv}{dx} = -\dfrac{1}{2(\sqrt{x + 4})^3}$

$\dfrac{dy}{dx} = u\dfrac{dv}{dx} + v\dfrac{du}{dx}$

$= \dfrac{1}{2\sqrt{x - 1}\sqrt{x + 4}} - \dfrac{\sqrt{x - 1}}{2(\sqrt{x + 4})^3}$

When $x = 5$, $\dfrac{dy}{dx} = \dfrac{1}{2\sqrt{4}\sqrt{9}} - \dfrac{\sqrt{4}}{2(\sqrt{9})^3} = \dfrac{5}{108}$

and $y = \dfrac{\sqrt{4}}{\sqrt{9}} = \dfrac{2}{3}$

$y = mx + c \Rightarrow \dfrac{2}{3} = (5 \times \dfrac{5}{108}) + c \Rightarrow c = \dfrac{47}{108}$

So the equation of the tangent is $y = \frac{5}{108}x + \frac{47}{108}$

To write this in the form $ax + by + c = 0$ where a, b and c are integers, multiply by 108 and rearrange.

$y = \frac{5}{108}x + \frac{47}{108} \Rightarrow 108y = 5x + 47$

$\Rightarrow 5x - 108y + 47 = 0$

b) Gradient of the normal $= -\frac{1}{\left(\frac{5}{108}\right)} = -\frac{108}{5}$

$y = mx + c \Rightarrow \frac{2}{3} = (5 \times (-\frac{108}{5})) + c \Rightarrow c = \frac{326}{3}$

So the equation of the normal is $y = -\frac{108}{5}x + \frac{326}{3}$.

To write this in the form $ax + by + c = 0$ where a, b and c are integers, multiply by 15 and rearrange.

$y = -\frac{108}{5}x + \frac{326}{3} \Rightarrow 15y = -324x + 1630$

$\Rightarrow 324x + 15y - 1630 = 0$

Q8 Turning points occur when the gradient is 0.

$u = (x - 2)^2, v = (x + 4)^3$

$\Rightarrow \frac{du}{dx} = 2(x - 2), \frac{dv}{dx} = 3(x + 4)^2$

$\frac{dy}{dx} = u\frac{dv}{dx} + v\frac{du}{dx}$

$= [(x - 2)^2 \times 3(x + 4)^2] + [2(x - 2) \times (x + 4)^3]$

$= 3(x - 2)^2(x + 4)^2 + 2(x - 2)(x + 4)^3$

$= (x - 2)(x + 4)^2[3x - 6 + 2x + 8]$

$= (x - 2)(x + 4)^2(5x + 2)$

So the turning points occur when:

$x - 2 = 0 \Rightarrow x = 2$

and $x + 4 = 0 \Rightarrow x = -4$

and $5x + 2 = 0 \Rightarrow x = -\frac{2}{5}$

When $x = 2, y = 0 \times 6^3 = 0$

When $x = -4, y = (-6)^2 \times 0 = 0$

When $x = -\frac{2}{5}, y = (-\frac{12}{5})^2(\frac{18}{5})^3 = 268.74$ (to 2 d.p.)

So the turning points are $(2, 0)$, $(-4, 0)$ and $(-\frac{2}{5}, 268.74)$.

Q9 First use chain rule:

$\frac{dy}{dx} = f'(x)e^{f(x)}$ where $f(x) = x^2\sqrt{x + 3}$.

Then use the product rule to find $f'(x)$:

$u = x^2, v = \sqrt{x + 3} \Rightarrow \frac{du}{dx} = 2x, \frac{dv}{dx} = \frac{1}{2\sqrt{x + 3}}$

$\frac{dy}{dx} = u\frac{dv}{dx} + v\frac{du}{dx} = [x^2 \times \frac{1}{2\sqrt{x + 3}}] + [\sqrt{x + 3} \times 2x]$

$= \frac{x^2 + 4x(x + 3)}{2\sqrt{x + 3}} = \frac{5x^2 + 12x}{2\sqrt{x + 3}}$

Now putting it all together:

$\frac{dy}{dx} = \frac{5x^2 + 12x}{2\sqrt{x + 3}} e^{x^2\sqrt{x + 3}}$

Q10 Turning points occur when the gradient is 0.
Differentiate with the product rule:

$u = x, v = e^{x - x^2} \Rightarrow \frac{du}{dx} = 1, \frac{dv}{dx} = (1 - 2x)e^{x - x^2}$

$\frac{dy}{dx} = u\frac{dv}{dx} + v\frac{du}{dx} = [x(1 - 2x)e^{x - x^2}] + [1 \times e^{x - x^2}]$

$= e^{x - x^2}(x - 2x^2 + 1)$

$e^{x - x^2}$ cannot be 0, so the turning points occur when $-2x^2 + x + 1 = 0$

$\Rightarrow (2x + 1)(-x + 1) = 0 \Rightarrow x = 1$ or $x = -\frac{1}{2}$

When $x = 1, y = 1 \times e^0 = 1$.

When $x = -\frac{1}{2}, y = -\frac{1}{2} \times e^{-\frac{3}{4}} = -\frac{e^{-\frac{3}{4}}}{2}$.

So the turning points are $(1, 1)$ and $(-\frac{1}{2}, -\frac{e^{-\frac{3}{4}}}{2})$.

5. Quotient Rule

Exercise 5.1 — Differentiating a function divided by a function

Q1 a) $u = x + 5, v = x - 3 \Rightarrow \frac{du}{dx} = 1, \frac{dv}{dx} = 1$

$\frac{dy}{dx} = \frac{v\frac{du}{dx} - u\frac{dv}{dx}}{v^2} = \frac{((x - 3) \times 1) - ((x + 5) \times 1)}{(x - 3)^2}$

$= -\frac{8}{(x - 3)^2}$

b) $u = (x - 7)^4, v = (5 - x)^3$

$\Rightarrow \frac{du}{dx} = 4(x - 7)^3, \frac{dv}{dx} = -3(5 - x)^2$

$\frac{dy}{dx} = \frac{v\frac{du}{dx} - u\frac{dv}{dx}}{v^2}$

$= \frac{4(5 - x)^3(x - 7)^3 + 3(x - 7)^4(5 - x)^2}{(5 - x)^6}$

$= \frac{(x - 7)^3[4(5 - x) + 3(x - 7)]}{(5 - x)^4}$

$= \frac{(x - 7)^3(-x - 1)}{(5 - x)^4}$

c) $u = e^x, v = x^2 \Rightarrow \frac{du}{dx} = e^x, \frac{dv}{dx} = 2x$

$\frac{dy}{dx} = \frac{v\frac{du}{dx} - u\frac{dv}{dx}}{v^2} = \frac{x^2e^x - e^x2x}{x^4} = \frac{xe^x - 2e^x}{x^3}$

d) $u = 3x, v = (x - 1)^2 \Rightarrow \frac{du}{dx} = 3, \frac{dv}{dx} = 2(x - 1)$

$\frac{dy}{dx} = \frac{v\frac{du}{dx} - u\frac{dv}{dx}}{v^2}$

$= \frac{3(x - 1)^2 - 6x(x - 1)}{(x - 1)^4}$

$= \frac{3x - 3 - 6x}{(x - 1)^3} = \frac{-3x - 3}{(x - 1)^3}$

Q2 $u = x^3, v = (x + 3)^3 \Rightarrow \frac{du}{dx} = 3x^2, \frac{dv}{dx} = 3(x + 3)^2$

$f'(x) = \frac{v\frac{du}{dx} - u\frac{dv}{dx}}{v^2}$

$= \frac{[(x + 3)^3 \times 3x^2] - [x^3 \times 3(x + 3)^2]}{(x + 3)^6}$

$= \frac{3x^2(x + 3) - 3x^3}{(x + 3)^4} = \frac{9x^2}{(x + 3)^4}$

Q3 $u = x^2$, $v = \sqrt{x-7}$ $\Rightarrow$ $\dfrac{du}{dx} = 2x$, $\dfrac{dv}{dx} = \dfrac{1}{2\sqrt{x-7}}$

$$f'(x) = \dfrac{v\dfrac{du}{dx} - u\dfrac{dv}{dx}}{v^2}$$

$$= \dfrac{[\sqrt{x-7} \times 2x] - [x^2\dfrac{1}{2\sqrt{x-7}}]}{x-7}$$

$$= \dfrac{4x(x-7) - x^2}{2(\sqrt{x-7})^3} = \dfrac{3x^2 - 28x}{2(\sqrt{x-7})^3}$$

Q4 $u = e^{2x}$, $v = e^{2x} + e^{-2x}$ $\Rightarrow$ $\dfrac{du}{dx} = 2e^{2x}$, $\dfrac{dv}{dx} = 2e^{2x} - 2e^{-2x}$

$$f'(x) = \dfrac{v\dfrac{du}{dx} - u\dfrac{dv}{dx}}{v^2}$$

$$= \dfrac{[(e^{2x} + e^{-2x})2e^{2x}] - [e^{2x}(2e^{2x} - 2e^{-2x})]}{(e^{2x} + e^{-2x})^2}$$

$$= \dfrac{2e^{4x} + 2 - 2e^{4x} + 2}{e^{4x} + e^{-4x} + 2} = \dfrac{4}{e^{4x} + e^{-4x} + 2}$$

Q5 $u = x$, $v = \sin x$ $\Rightarrow$ $\dfrac{du}{dx} = 1$, $\dfrac{dv}{dx} = \cos x$

$$f'(x) = \dfrac{v\dfrac{du}{dx} - u\dfrac{dv}{dx}}{v^2} = \dfrac{\sin x - x\cos x}{\sin^2 x}$$

Q6 $u = \sin x$, $v = x$ $\Rightarrow$ $\dfrac{du}{dx} = \cos x$, $\dfrac{dv}{dx} = 1$

$$f'(x) = \dfrac{v\dfrac{du}{dx} - u\dfrac{dv}{dx}}{v^2} = \dfrac{x\cos x - \sin x}{x^2}$$

Q7 $u = x^2$, $v = \tan x$ $\Rightarrow$ $\dfrac{du}{dx} = 2x$, $\dfrac{dv}{dx} = \sec^2 x$

$$f'(x) = \dfrac{v\dfrac{du}{dx} - u\dfrac{dv}{dx}}{v^2} = \dfrac{[\tan x \times 2x] - [x^2 \times \sec^2 x]}{\tan^2 x}$$

$$= \dfrac{2x\tan x - x^2\sec^2 x}{\tan^2 x}$$

$$= 2x\cot x - x^2\cosec^2 x$$

Here the answer was simplified using:
$\sec^2 x/\tan^2 x = (1/\cos^2 x) \times (\cos^2 x/\sin^2 x) = 1/\sin^2 x = \cosec^2 x$

Q8 a) $u = x$, $v = \cos(2x)$ $\Rightarrow$ $\dfrac{du}{dx} = 1$, $\dfrac{dv}{dx} = -2\sin(2x)$

$$\dfrac{dy}{dx} = \dfrac{v\dfrac{du}{dx} - u\dfrac{dv}{dx}}{v^2}$$

$$= \dfrac{\cos(2x) - [x \times -2\sin(2x)]}{\cos^2(2x)}$$

$$= \dfrac{\cos(2x) + 2x\sin(2x)}{\cos^2(2x)}$$

b) $\dfrac{dy}{dx} = 0$ if $\cos(2x) + 2x\sin(2x) = 0$

$\Rightarrow -\cos(2x) = 2x\sin(2x) \Rightarrow 2x = -\cot(2x)$

$\Rightarrow x = -\dfrac{1}{2}\cot(2x)$

Remember cos x/sin x = 1/tan x = cot x.

Q9 a) $u = 1$, $v = 1 + 4\cos x$ $\Rightarrow$ $\dfrac{du}{dx} = 0$, $\dfrac{dv}{dx} = -4\sin x$

$$\dfrac{dy}{dx} = \dfrac{v\dfrac{du}{dx} - u\dfrac{dv}{dx}}{v^2}$$

$$= \dfrac{[(1 + 4\cos x) \times 0] - [1 \times (-4\sin x)]}{(1 + 4\cos x)^2}$$

$$= \dfrac{4\sin x}{(1 + 4\cos x)^2}$$

When $x = \dfrac{\pi}{2}$, $\dfrac{dy}{dx} = \dfrac{4}{(1)^2} = 4$ and $y = \dfrac{1}{1} = 1$

$y = mx + c \Rightarrow 1 = 4\dfrac{\pi}{2} + c \Rightarrow c = 1 - 2\pi$

So the equation of the tangent is $y = 4x + 1 - 2\pi$.

b) From part a), the gradient of the normal must be $-\dfrac{1}{4}$. Equation of a straight line:

$y = mx + c \Rightarrow 1 = -\dfrac{1}{4}\dfrac{\pi}{2} + c \Rightarrow c = 1 + \dfrac{\pi}{8}$

So the equation of the normal is

$$y = -\dfrac{1}{4}x + 1 + \dfrac{\pi}{8}$$

Q10 $u = 2x$, $v = \cos x$ $\Rightarrow$ $\dfrac{du}{dx} = 2$, $\dfrac{dv}{dx} = -\sin x$

$$\dfrac{dy}{dx} = \dfrac{v\dfrac{du}{dx} - u\dfrac{dv}{dx}}{v^2}$$

$$= \dfrac{[\cos x \times 2] - [2x \times (-\sin x)]}{\cos^2 x}$$

$$= \dfrac{2\cos x + 2x\sin x}{\cos^2 x}$$

When $x = \dfrac{\pi}{3}$, $\dfrac{dy}{dx} = \dfrac{1 + \dfrac{\pi\sqrt{3}}{3}}{(\frac{1}{2})^2} = 4 + \dfrac{4\pi\sqrt{3}}{3}$

Q11 $u = x - \sin x$, $v = 1 + \cos x$,

$\Rightarrow \dfrac{du}{dx} = 1 - \cos x$, $\dfrac{dv}{dx} = -\sin x$

$$\dfrac{dy}{dx} = \dfrac{v\dfrac{du}{dx} - u\dfrac{dv}{dx}}{v^2}$$

$$= \dfrac{[(1 + \cos x)(1 - \cos x)] - [(x - \sin x)(-\sin x)]}{(1 + \cos x)^2}$$

$$= \dfrac{1 - \cos^2 x - \sin^2 x + x\sin x}{(1 + \cos x)^2}$$

$$= \dfrac{1 - 1 + x\sin x}{(1 + \cos x)^2} = \dfrac{x\sin x}{(1 + \cos x)^2}$$

The identity $\sin^2 x + \cos^2 x \equiv 1$ was used to simplify the expression here.

Q12 Turning points occur when the gradient is 0.

$u = \cos x$, $v = 4 - 3\cos x$, $\Rightarrow \dfrac{du}{dx} = -\sin x$, $\dfrac{dv}{dx} = 3\sin x$

$$\dfrac{dy}{dx} = \dfrac{v\dfrac{du}{dx} - u\dfrac{dv}{dx}}{v^2}$$

$$= \dfrac{[(4 - 3\cos x)(-\sin x)] - [\cos x(3\sin x)]}{(4 - 3\cos x)^2}$$

$$= \dfrac{-4\sin x}{(4 - 3\cos x)^2}$$

$\frac{dy}{dx} = 0 \Rightarrow -4\sin x = 0 \Rightarrow x = \sin^{-1} 0 = 0, \pi$ and 2π.

When $x = 0$, $y = \frac{1}{4-3} = 1$

When $x = \pi$, $y = \frac{-1}{4-(-3)} = -\frac{1}{7}$

When $x = 2\pi$, $y = \frac{1}{4-3} = 1$

So the turning points are $(0, 1)$, $(\pi, -\frac{1}{7})$ and $(2\pi, 1)$.

Q13 First use chain rule: $y = e^{f(x)} \Rightarrow \frac{dy}{dx} = f'(x)e^{f(x)}$

Then use the quotient rule to find $f'(x)$:

$u = 1 + x$, $v = 1 - x \Rightarrow \frac{du}{dx} = 1$, $\frac{dv}{dx} = -1$

$\frac{v\frac{du}{dx} - u\frac{dv}{dx}}{v^2} = \frac{[(1-x)(1)] - [(1+x)(-1)]}{(1-x)^2} = \frac{2}{(1-x)^2}$

So $\frac{dy}{dx} = f'(x)e^{f(x)} = \frac{2e^{\frac{1+x}{1-x}}}{(1-x)^2}$

6. More Differentiation

Exercise 6.1 — Differentiating cosec, sec and cot

Q1 a) $\frac{dy}{dx} = 2\text{cosec}\,(2x)\cot\,(2x)$

b) $\frac{dy}{dx} = \frac{dy}{du} \times \frac{du}{dx} = (2\text{cosec}\,x)(-\text{cosec}\,x\cot x)$
$= -2\text{cosec}^2\,x\cot x$

c) $\frac{dy}{dx} = \frac{dy}{du} \times \frac{du}{dx} = -7\text{cosec}^2\,(7x)$

d) $\frac{dy}{dx} = \frac{dy}{du} \times \frac{du}{dx} = (7\cot^6 x)(-\text{cosec}^2 x)$
$= -7\cot^6 x\,\text{cosec}^2 x$

e) $\frac{dy}{dx} = u\frac{dv}{dx} + v\frac{du}{dx} = 4x^3\cot x + x^4(-\text{cosec}^2 x)$
$= 4x^3\cot x - x^4\text{cosec}^2 x$
$= x^3(4\cot x - x\text{cosec}^2 x)$

f) $\frac{dy}{dx} = \frac{dy}{du} \times \frac{du}{dx} = 2(x + \sec x)(1 + \sec x\tan x)$

g) $\frac{dy}{dx} = \frac{dy}{du} \times \frac{du}{dx} = 2x(-\text{cosec}\,(x^2 + 5)\cot\,(x^2 + 5))$
$= -2x\text{cosec}\,(x^2 + 5)\cot\,(x^2 + 5)$

h) $\frac{dy}{dx} - u\frac{dv}{dx} + v\frac{du}{dx} = e^{3x}\sec x\tan x + 3e^{3x}\sec x$
$= e^{3x}\sec x(\tan x + 3)$

i) $\frac{dy}{dx} = \frac{dy}{du} \times \frac{du}{dx} = 3(2x + \cot x)^2(2 - \text{cosec}^2 x)$

Q2 $f'(x) = \frac{v\frac{du}{dx} - u\frac{dv}{dx}}{v^2} = \frac{(x + 3)\sec x\tan x - \sec x}{(x + 3)^2}$

Q3 $f'(x) = \frac{dy}{du} \times \frac{du}{dx} = (\sec \tfrac{1}{x} \tan \tfrac{1}{x})(-\tfrac{1}{x^2})$
$= -\frac{\sec \tfrac{1}{x}\tan \tfrac{1}{x}}{x^2}$

Q4 $f'(x) = \frac{dy}{du} \times \frac{du}{dx} = (\sec \sqrt{x} \tan \sqrt{x})(\tfrac{1}{2} \times \tfrac{1}{\sqrt{x}})$
$= \frac{\sec \sqrt{x}\tan \sqrt{x}}{2\sqrt{x}} = \frac{\tan \sqrt{x}}{2\sqrt{x}\cos \sqrt{x}}$

Q5 $f'(x) = \frac{dy}{du} \times \frac{du}{dx}$
$= 2(\sec x + \text{cosec}\,x)(\sec x\tan x - \text{cosec}\,x\cot x)$

Q6 $f(x) = \frac{1}{x\cot x} = \frac{\tan x}{x}$

$f'(x) = \frac{v\frac{du}{dx} - u\frac{dv}{dx}}{v^2} = \frac{x\sec^2 x - \tan x}{x^2}$

Q7 $f'(x) = u\frac{dv}{dx} + v\frac{du}{dx} = e^x(-\text{cosec}\,x\cot x) + e^x\text{cosec}\,x$
$= e^x\text{cosec}\,x(1 - \cot x)$

Q8 $f'(x) = u\frac{dv}{dx} + v\frac{du}{dx} = 3e^{3x}\sec x + e^{3x}\sec x\tan x$

Q9 $f'(x) = u\frac{dv}{dx} + v\frac{du}{dx} = 3e^{3x}\cot\,(4x) - 4e^{3x}\text{cosec}^2\,(4x)$

The chain rule was used here to find dv/dx — write it out in stages if you're struggling.

Q10 $f'(x) = u\frac{dv}{dx} + v\frac{du}{dx}$
$= 2e^{-2x}\text{cosec}\,(4x) - 4e^{-2x}\text{cosec}\,(4x)\cot\,(4x)$
$= -2e^{-2x}\text{cosec}\,(4x)(1 + 2\cot\,(4x))$

Q11 $f'(x) = u\frac{dv}{dx} + v\frac{du}{dx} = \frac{\text{cosec}\,x}{x} - \ln x\,\text{cosec}\,x\cot x$

Q12 $f'(x) = \frac{dy}{du} \times \frac{du}{dx} - (\tfrac{1}{2}\tfrac{1}{\sqrt{\sec x}}) \times \sec x\tan x$
$= \frac{\sec x\tan x}{2\sqrt{\sec x}} = \frac{1}{2}\tan x\sqrt{\sec x}$

Q13 $f'(x) = g'(x)e^{g(x)} = e^{\sec x}\sec x\tan x$

Q14 a) $f'(x) = \frac{g'(x)}{g(x)} = \frac{-\text{cosec}\,x\cot x}{\text{cosec}\,x} = -\cot x$

b) $\ln(\text{cosec}\,x) = \ln(\frac{1}{\sin x}) = \ln 1 - \ln(\sin x)$
$= -\ln(\sin x)$ (as $\ln 1 = 0$)

Here you could also rearrange by saying
$\ln(1/\sin x) = \ln(\sin x)^{-1} = -\ln(\sin x)$

$f'(x) = -\frac{\cos x}{\sin x} = -\frac{1}{\tan x} = -\cot x$

Q15 $f'(x) = \frac{g'(x)}{g(x)} = \frac{1 + \sec x\tan x}{x + \sec x}$

Q16 $\frac{dy}{dx} = \frac{dy}{du} \times \frac{du}{dx}$

$= \frac{2x}{2\sqrt{x^2 + 5}} \times \sec \sqrt{x^2 + 5}\,\tan \sqrt{x^2 + 5}$

$= \frac{x\sec \sqrt{x^2 + 5}\,\tan \sqrt{x^2 + 5}}{\sqrt{x^2 + 5}}$

Review Exercise — Chapter 4

Q1 a) Chain rule.
b) Product rule.
c) Chain and product rules.
d) Chain and quotient rules.
e) Chain, product and quotient rules.
f) Chain, product and quotient rules.

Q2 a) $y = u^{\frac{1}{2}}$, $u = x^3 + 2x^2$

$$\Rightarrow \frac{dy}{du} = \frac{1}{2}u^{-\frac{1}{2}} = \frac{1}{2}(x^3 + 2x^2)^{-\frac{1}{2}}, \frac{du}{dx} = 3x^2 + 4x$$

$$\frac{dy}{dx} = \frac{dy}{du} \times \frac{du}{dx} = (3x^2 + 4x)(\frac{1}{2}(x^3 + 2x^2)^{-\frac{1}{2}})$$

$$= \frac{3x^2 + 4x}{2\sqrt{x^3 + 2x^2}}$$

b) $y = u^{-\frac{1}{2}}$, $u = x^3 + 2x^2$

$$\frac{dy}{dx} = \frac{dy}{du} \times \frac{du}{dx} = ((-\frac{1}{2}) \times \frac{1}{(\sqrt{x^3 + 2x^2})^3})(3x^2 + 4x)$$

$$= -\frac{3x^2 + 4x}{2(\sqrt{x^3 + 2x^2})^3}$$

c) $\frac{dy}{dx} = f'(x)e^{f(x)} = 10xe^{5x^2}$

d) $\frac{dy}{dx} = \frac{f'(x)}{f(x)} = -\frac{2x}{6 - x^2}$

Q3 a) $\frac{dx}{dy} = 2f'(y)e^{f(y)} = 4e^{2y} \Rightarrow \frac{dy}{dx} = \frac{1}{(\frac{dx}{dy})} = \frac{1}{4e^{2y}} = \frac{1}{2x}$

b) $\frac{dx}{dy} = \frac{f'(y)}{f(y)} = \frac{2}{2y + 3} \Rightarrow \frac{dy}{dx} = \frac{2y + 3}{2} = \frac{e^x}{2}$

Q4 a) $f(x) = \sin^2(x + 2) \Rightarrow y = u^2$, $u = \sin(x + 2)$

$$\Rightarrow \frac{dy}{du} = 2u = 2\sin(x + 2), \frac{du}{dx} = \cos(x + 2)$$

$$f'(x) = \frac{dy}{du} \times \frac{du}{dx} = 2\sin(x + 2)\cos(x + 2)$$

b) $y = 2\cos u$, $u = 3x$

$$f'(x) = \frac{dy}{du} \times \frac{du}{dx} = -6\sin(3x)$$

c) $f(x) = \sqrt{\tan x} \Rightarrow y = u^{\frac{1}{2}}$, $u = \tan x$

$$\Rightarrow \frac{dy}{du} = \frac{1}{2}u^{-\frac{1}{2}} = \frac{1}{2\sqrt{\tan x}}, \frac{du}{dx} = \sec^2 x$$

$$f'(x) = \frac{dy}{du} \times \frac{du}{dx} = (\frac{1}{2\sqrt{\tan x}})(\sec^2 x) = \frac{\sec^2 x}{2\sqrt{\tan x}}$$

Q5 a) $u = e^{2x}$, $v = x^2 - 3 \Rightarrow \frac{du}{dx} = 2e^{2x}, \frac{dv}{dx} = 2x$

$$\frac{dy}{dx} = u\frac{dv}{dx} + v\frac{du}{dx} = 2xe^{2x} + 2e^{2x}(x^2 - 3)$$

$$= 2e^{2x}(x + x^2 - 3)$$

When $x = 0$, $\frac{dy}{dx} = 2 \times (-3) = -6$

b) $u = \ln x$, $v = \sin x \Rightarrow \frac{du}{dx} = \frac{1}{x}, \frac{dv}{dx} = \cos x$

$$\frac{dy}{dx} = u\frac{dv}{dx} + v\frac{du}{dx} = \ln x \cos x + \frac{1}{x}\sin x$$

When $x = 1$, $\frac{dy}{dx} = (0 \times \cos 1) + (1 \times \sin 1)$
$$= 0.841 \text{ to 3 s.f.}$$

Q6 $u = 6x^2 + 3$, $v = 4x^2 - 1 \Rightarrow \frac{du}{dx} = 12x, \frac{dv}{dx} = 8x$

$$\frac{dy}{dx} = \frac{v\frac{du}{dx} - u\frac{dv}{dx}}{v^2} = \frac{(4x^2 - 1)12x - (6x^2 + 3)8x}{(4x^2 - 1)^2}$$

$$= \frac{48x^3 - 12x - 48x^3 - 24x}{(4x^2 - 1)^2} = -\frac{36x}{(4x^2 - 1)^2}$$

When $x = 1$, $\frac{dy}{dx} = \frac{-36 \times 1}{3^2} = -4$

$y = mx + c \Rightarrow 3 = ((-4) \times 1) + c \Rightarrow c = 7$
So the equation of the tangent is $y = 7 - 4x$

Q7 a) $y = \sqrt{\text{cosec } x}$, so let $y = u^{\frac{1}{2}}$ where $u = \text{cosec } x$

$$\Rightarrow \frac{dy}{du} = \frac{1}{2}u^{-\frac{1}{2}} = \frac{1}{2\sqrt{\text{cosec } x}}, \frac{du}{dx} = -\text{cosec } x \cot x$$

$$\frac{dy}{dx} = \frac{dy}{du} \times \frac{du}{dx}$$

$$= (\frac{1}{2\sqrt{\text{cosec } x}}) \times (-\text{cosec } x \cot x)$$

$$= -\frac{\text{cosec } x \cot x}{2\sqrt{\text{cosec } x}} = -\frac{1}{2}\cot x \sqrt{\text{cosec } x}$$

b) $y = \cot(x^2 + 5)$, so let $y = \cot u$ where $u = x^2 + 5$

$$\Rightarrow \frac{dy}{du} = -\text{cosec}^2 u = -\text{cosec}^2(x^2 + 5), \frac{du}{dx} = 2x$$

$$\frac{dy}{dx} = \frac{dy}{du} \times \frac{du}{dx} = -2x\,\text{cosec}^2(x^2 + 5)$$

c) $u = \sec x$, $v = x^2 \Rightarrow \frac{du}{dx} = \sec x \tan x, \frac{dv}{dx} = 2x$

$$\frac{dy}{dx} = \frac{v\frac{du}{dx} - u\frac{dv}{dx}}{v^2} = \frac{x \sec x \tan x - 2\sec x}{x^3}$$

$$= \frac{\sec x(x \tan x - 2)}{x^3}$$

d) $u = e^{2x}$, $v = \text{cosec}(5x)$

$$\Rightarrow \frac{du}{dx} = 2e^{2x}, \frac{dv}{dx} = -5\text{cosec}(5x)\cot(5x)$$

$$\frac{dy}{dx} = u\frac{dv}{dx} + v\frac{du}{dx}$$

$$= (e^{2x} \times -5\text{cosec}(5x)\cot(5x)) + 2e^{2x}\text{cosec}(5x)$$

$$= e^{2x}\text{cosec}(5x)(-5\cot(5x) + 2)$$

Q8 $y = \text{cosec}(3x - 2)$, so let $y = \text{cosec } u$ where $u = 3x - 2$

$$\Rightarrow \frac{dy}{du} = -\text{cosec } u \cot u = -\text{cosec}(3x - 2)\cot(3x - 2)$$

$$\frac{du}{dx} = 3$$

$$\frac{dy}{dx} = \frac{dy}{du} \times \frac{du}{dx} = -3\text{cosec}(3x - 2)\cot(3x - 2)$$

When $x = 0$, $\frac{dy}{dx} = -3\text{cosec}(-2)\cot(-2) = 1.51$ to 2 d.p.

Q9 Turning points occur when the gradient is 0.

$u = e^x$, $v = \sqrt{x} \Rightarrow \frac{du}{dx} = e^x, \frac{dv}{dx} = \frac{1}{2\sqrt{x}}$

$$\frac{dy}{dx} = \frac{v\frac{du}{dx} - u\frac{dv}{dx}}{v^2} = \frac{\sqrt{x}e^x - e^x\frac{1}{2\sqrt{x}}}{x}$$

When $\frac{dy}{dx} = 0$, $\sqrt{x}e^x - e^x\frac{1}{2\sqrt{x}} = 0$

$$\Rightarrow \sqrt{x} = \frac{1}{2\sqrt{x}} \Rightarrow x = \frac{1}{2}$$

When $x = \frac{1}{2}$, $y = \frac{e^{\frac{1}{2}}}{\sqrt{\frac{1}{2}}} = \sqrt{2}\,e^{\frac{1}{2}}$

So the coordinates of the turning point are $(\frac{1}{2}, \sqrt{2}\,e^{\frac{1}{2}})$

Q10 $y = 3\operatorname{cosec} \frac{x}{4}$, so let $y = 3\operatorname{cosec} u$ where $u = \frac{x}{4}$

$\Rightarrow \frac{dy}{du} = -3\operatorname{cosec} u \cot u = -3 \operatorname{cosec} \frac{x}{4} \cot \frac{x}{4}, \frac{du}{dx} = \frac{1}{4}$

$\frac{dy}{dx} = \frac{dy}{du} \times \frac{du}{dx} = -\frac{3}{4} \operatorname{cosec} \frac{x}{4} \cot \frac{x}{4}$

When $x = \pi$, $y = 3\sqrt{2}$

and $\frac{dy}{dx} = -\frac{3}{4} \times \sqrt{2} \times 1 = -\frac{3\sqrt{2}}{4}$.

So the gradient of the normal is $\frac{4}{3\sqrt{2}} = \frac{2\sqrt{2}}{3}$.

$y = mx + c \Rightarrow 3\sqrt{2} = \frac{2\sqrt{2}\,\pi}{3} + c$

$\Rightarrow c = 3\sqrt{2} - \frac{2\sqrt{2}\,\pi}{3}$

So the equation of the normal is

$y = \frac{2\sqrt{2}}{3}x + 3\sqrt{2} - \frac{2\sqrt{2}\,\pi}{3}$

Q11 $f'(x) = g'(x)e^{g(x)}$

$g(x) = \cos(3x)$, so let $y = \cos u$ where $u = 3x$

$g'(x) = \frac{dy}{du} \times \frac{du}{dx} = -3\sin(3x)$

$f'(x) = g'(x)e^{g(x)} = -3e^{\cos(3x)} \sin(3x)$

Q12 $u = \cos x^2$, $v = \ln(2x) \Rightarrow \frac{du}{dx} = -2x\sin x^2, \frac{dv}{dx} = \frac{1}{x}$

The chain rule was used here to find du/dx and dv/dx — write out each step if you need to.

$f'(x) = \dfrac{v\dfrac{du}{dx} - u\dfrac{dv}{dx}}{v^2}$

$= \dfrac{\ln(2x)(-2x\sin x^2) - \cos x^2(\frac{1}{x})}{(\ln(2x))^2}$

$= -\dfrac{2x\sin x^2}{\ln(2x)} - \dfrac{\cos x^2}{x(\ln(2x))^2}$

Q13 $u = \sin(4x)$, $v = \tan x^3$

$\Rightarrow \frac{du}{dx} = 4\cos(4x), \frac{dv}{dx} = 3x^2 \sec^2 x^3$

$f'(x) = u\frac{dv}{dx} + v\frac{du}{dx}$

$= 3x^2(\sec^2 x^3)(\sin(4x)) + 4\cos(4x)\tan x^3$

Q14 $u = e^{x^2}$, $v = \sqrt{x+1}$

Using the chain rule to differentiate u and v:

$\frac{du}{dx} = 2xe^{x^2}$

$\frac{dv}{dx} = \frac{1}{2} \times (x+1)^{-\frac{1}{2}} = \frac{1}{2\sqrt{x+1}}$

$\frac{dy}{dx} = u\frac{dv}{dx} + v\frac{du}{dx} - \frac{e^{x^2}}{2\sqrt{x+1}} + 2xe^{x^2}\sqrt{x+1}$

When $x = 1$, $\frac{dy}{dx} = \frac{e^1}{2\sqrt{1+1}} + (2 \times 1 \times e^1\sqrt{1+1})$

$= \frac{e + (2\sqrt{2})2\sqrt{2}\,e}{2\sqrt{2}} = \frac{e + 8e}{2\sqrt{2}} = \frac{9\sqrt{2}\,e}{4}$

Q15 a) $y = \sqrt{(e^x + e^{2x})} \Rightarrow y = u^{\frac{1}{2}}, u = e^x + e^{2x}$

$\frac{dy}{du} = \frac{1}{2}u^{-\frac{1}{2}} = \frac{1}{2\sqrt{u}} = \frac{1}{2\sqrt{e^x + e^{2x}}}$

$\frac{du}{dx} = e^x + 2e^{2x}$

So $\frac{dy}{dx} = \frac{dy}{du} \times \frac{du}{dx} = \frac{e^x + 2e^{2x}}{2\sqrt{e^x + e^{2x}}}$.

b) For $y = 3e^{2x+1} - \ln(1 - x^2) + 2x^3$, use the chain rule for the first 2 parts separately:

For $y = 3e^{2x+1} = 3e^{f(x)}$, $\frac{dy}{dx} = 3f'(x)e^{f(x)} = 6e^{2x+1}$

For $y = \ln(1 - x^2) = \ln(f(x))$, $\frac{dy}{dx} = \frac{f'(x)}{f(x)} = -\frac{2x}{1 - x^2}$

So putting it all together:

$\frac{dy}{dx} = 6e^{2x+1} + \frac{2x}{1 - x^2} + 6x^2$.

Q16 a) $y = (x^2 - 1)^3$, so let $y = u^3$ where $u = x^2 - 1$

$\Rightarrow \frac{du}{dx} = 2x, \frac{dy}{du} = 3u^2 = 3(x^2 - 1)^2$

So $\frac{dy}{dx} = \frac{dy}{du} \times \frac{du}{dx} = 6x(x^2 - 1)^2$

b) When $x = 2$, $y = (2^2 - 1)^3 = 27$

And from part **a)**,

$\frac{dy}{dx} = 6 \times 2 \times (2^2 - 1)^2 = 12 \times 9 = 108$

The gradient of the normal is $-1 \div \frac{dy}{dx} = -\frac{1}{108}$.

The equation of the straight line is:

$y = mx + c \Rightarrow 27 = (-\frac{1}{108} \times 2) + c$

$\Rightarrow c = 27\frac{1}{54}$

So the equation of the normal is

$y = -\frac{1}{108}x + 27\frac{1}{54} \Rightarrow y + \frac{1}{108}x - 27\frac{1}{54} = 0$

To make a, b, and c integers, multiply by 108:

$x + 108y - 2918 = 0$

Q17 a) $u = \cos x$, $v = \ln x^2 = 2\ln x$

$\Rightarrow \frac{du}{dx} = -\sin x, \frac{dv}{dx} = \frac{2}{x}$

$\frac{dy}{dx} = u\frac{dv}{dx} + v\frac{du}{dx} = \frac{2}{x}\cos x - \ln x^2 \sin x$

b) $u = e^{x^2 - x}$, $v = (x+2)^4$

$\Rightarrow \frac{du}{dx} = (2x - 1)e^{x^2 - x}, \frac{dv}{dx} = 4(x+2)^3$

$\frac{dy}{dx} = \dfrac{v\dfrac{du}{dx} - u\dfrac{dv}{dx}}{v^2}$

$= \dfrac{(x+2)^4(2x - 1)e^{x^2 - x} - 4e^{x^2 - x}(x+2)^3}{(x+2)^8}$

$= \dfrac{(x+2)(2x - 1)e^{x^2 - x} - 4e^{x^2 - x}}{(x+2)^5}$

Q18 For $y = \dfrac{\sqrt{x^2 + 3}}{\cos(3x)}$, use the quotient rule and the chain rule:

Quotient rule: $u = \sqrt{x^2 + 3}$ and $v = (\cos 3x)$.

Using the chain rule for $\dfrac{du}{dx} = \dfrac{2x}{2\sqrt{x^2 + 3}}$

$\qquad\qquad\qquad = \dfrac{x}{\sqrt{x^2 + 3}}$

Using the chain rule for $\dfrac{dv}{dx} = -3\sin(3x)$.

So $\dfrac{dy}{dx} = \dfrac{v\dfrac{du}{dx} - u\dfrac{dv}{dx}}{v^2}$

$= \dfrac{[\cos(3x) \times \dfrac{x}{\sqrt{x^2 + 3}}] - [\sqrt{x^2 + 3} \times (-3\sin(3x))]}{\cos^2(3x)}$

Then multiply top and bottom by $\sqrt{x^2 + 3}$ to get:

$\dfrac{dy}{dx} = \dfrac{x\cos(3x) + 3(x^2 + 3)\sin(3x)}{(\sqrt{x^2 + 3})\cos^2(3x)}$

$\qquad = \dfrac{x + 3(x^2 + 3)\tan(3x)}{(\sqrt{x^2 + 3})\cos(3x)}$

Exam-Style Questions — Chapter 4

1 **a)** For $y = \ln(3x + 1)\sin(3x + 1)$,

use the product rule and the chain rule:

Product rule: $u = \ln(3x + 1)$ and $v = \sin(3x + 1)$

Using the chain rule for $\dfrac{du}{dx} = \dfrac{3}{3x + 1}$ *[1 mark]*.

Using the chain rule for $\dfrac{dv}{dx} = 3\cos(3x + 1)$ *[1 mark]*.

So $\dfrac{dy}{dx} = u\dfrac{dv}{dx} + v\dfrac{du}{dx}$

$= [\ln(3x + 1) \times 3\cos(3x + 1)] + [\sin(3x + 1) \times \dfrac{3}{3x + 1}]$ *[1 mark]*

$= 3\ln(3x + 1)\cos(3x + 1) + \dfrac{3\sin(3x + 1)}{3x + 1}$ *[1 mark]*.

b) For $y = \sin^3(2x^2)$, use the chain rule twice:

$y = u^3$ where $u = \sin(2x^2)$.

$\dfrac{dy}{du} = 3u^2 = 3\sin^2(2x^2)$ *[1 mark]*.

$\dfrac{du}{dx} = 4x\cos(2x^2)$ (using chain rule) *[1 mark]*.

So $\dfrac{dy}{dx} = 12x\sin^2(2x^2)\cos(2x^2)$ *[1 mark]*.

c) For $y = 2\csc(3x)$, use the chain rule:

$y = 2\csc u$ where $u = (3x)$.

$\dfrac{dy}{du} = -2\csc u \cot u = -2\csc(3x)\cot(3x)$.

$\dfrac{du}{dx} = 3$ *[1 mark for both]*,

so $\dfrac{dy}{dx} = -6\csc(3x)\cot(3x)$ *[1 mark]*.

2 $f(x) = \sec x = \dfrac{1}{\cos x}$, so using the quotient rule:

$u = 1 \Rightarrow \dfrac{du}{dx} = 0$ and $v = \cos x \Rightarrow \dfrac{dv}{dx} = -\sin x$

$\dfrac{dy}{dx} = \dfrac{v\dfrac{du}{dx} - u\dfrac{dv}{dx}}{v^2} = \dfrac{(\cos x \times 0) - (1 \times (-\sin x))}{\cos^2 x}$

$\qquad = \dfrac{\sin x}{\cos^2 x}$

Since $\tan x = \dfrac{\sin x}{\cos x}$, and $\sec x = \dfrac{1}{\cos x}$

$f'(x) = \dfrac{dy}{dx} = \dfrac{\sin x}{\cos x} \times \dfrac{1}{\cos x} = \sec x \tan x$

[4 marks available – 1 mark for correct identity for sec x, 1 mark for correct entry into quotient rule, 1 mark for correct answer from quotient rule, and 1 mark for correct rearrangement to sec x tan x.]

3 **a)** For $f(x) = 4\ln(3x)$, use the chain rule:

$y = 4\ln u$ where $u = 3x$, so

$\dfrac{dy}{du} = \dfrac{4}{u} = \dfrac{4}{3x}$ and $\dfrac{du}{dx} = 3$ *[1 mark for both]*,

so $f'(x) = \dfrac{dy}{dx} = \dfrac{12}{3x} = \dfrac{4}{x}$ *[1 mark]*.

So for $x = 1$, $f'(1) = 4$ *[1 mark]*.

b) When $x = 1$, $y = 4\ln(3 \times 1) = 4\ln 3$

Equation of a straight line (where m is the gradient):

$y = mx + c \Rightarrow 4\ln 3 = (4 \times 1) + c \Rightarrow c = 4\ln 3 - 4$

So the equation of the tangent is:

$y = 4x + 4\ln 3 - 4$

[3 marks available – 1 mark for finding y = 4ln 3, 1 mark for correct substitution of (1, 4ln 3) and gradient from (a), and 1 mark for correct final answer.]

4 **a)** For $y = e^x\sin x$, use the product rule:

$u = e^x \Rightarrow \dfrac{du}{dx} = e^x$

$v = \sin x \Rightarrow \dfrac{dv}{dx} = \cos x$

So $\dfrac{dy}{dx} = u\dfrac{dv}{dx} + v\dfrac{du}{dx} = (e^x\cos x) + (\sin x\, e^x)$

$\qquad\qquad = e^x(\cos x + \sin x)$ *[1 mark]*

At the turning points, $\dfrac{dy}{dx} = 0$, so:

$e^x(\cos x + \sin x) = 0$ *[1 mark]*.

$\Rightarrow$ turning points are when $e^x = 0$ or $\cos x + \sin x = 0$. e^x can't be 0, so the turning points are when $\cos x + \sin x = 0$ *[1 mark]*.

$\Rightarrow \sin x = -\cos x \Rightarrow \dfrac{\sin x}{\cos x} = -1 \Rightarrow \tan x = -1$
[1 mark]

Use the graph of tan x or the CAST diagram to help you find all the solutions.

There are two solutions for $\tan x = -1$ in the interval $-\pi \leq x \leq \pi$: $x = -\dfrac{\pi}{4}$ and $x = \pi - \dfrac{\pi}{4} = \dfrac{3\pi}{4}$, so the values of x at each turning point are $-\dfrac{\pi}{4}$ *[1 mark]* and $\dfrac{3\pi}{4}$ *[1 mark]*.

b) To determine the nature of the turning points, find $\frac{d^2y}{dx^2}$ at the points:

For $\frac{dy}{dx} = e^x(\cos x + \sin x)$, use the product rule:

$u = e^x \Rightarrow \frac{du}{dx} = e^x$

$v = \cos x + \sin x \Rightarrow \frac{dv}{dx} = \cos x - \sin x$, so:

$\frac{d^2y}{dx^2} = u\frac{dv}{dx} + v\frac{du}{dx} = [e^x(\cos x - \sin x)]$
$\qquad\qquad + [(\cos x + \sin x)e^x]$
$\qquad\qquad = 2e^x\cos x$ **[1 mark]**

When $x = -\frac{\pi}{4}$, $\frac{d^2y}{dx^2} > 0$ **[1 mark]**, so this is a minimum point **[1 mark]**.

When $x = \frac{3\pi}{4}$, $\frac{d^2y}{dx^2} < 0$ **[1 mark]**, so this is a maximum point **[1 mark]**.

5 a) For $x = \sqrt{y^2 + 3y}$, find $\frac{dx}{dy}$ first

(using the chain rule): $x = u^{\frac{1}{2}}$ where $u = y^2 + 3y$

$\frac{dx}{du} = \frac{1}{2}u^{-\frac{1}{2}} = \frac{1}{2\sqrt{u}} = \frac{1}{2\sqrt{y^2 + 3y}}$ **[1 mark]**.

$\frac{du}{dy} = 2y + 3$ **[1 mark]**.

So $\frac{dx}{dy} = \frac{2y + 3}{2\sqrt{y^2 + 3y}}$ **[1 mark]**.

(Now, flip the fraction upside down for dy/dx)

$\frac{dy}{dx} = \frac{2\sqrt{y^2 + 3y}}{2y + 3}$ **[1 mark]**.

At the point $(2, 1)$, $y = 1$, so:

$\frac{dy}{dx} = \frac{2\sqrt{1^2 + 3}}{2 + 3} = \frac{4}{5}$ $(= 0.8)$ **[1 mark]**.

b) Equation of a straight line is:

$y = mx + c \Rightarrow 1 = (0.8 \times 2) + c \Rightarrow c = -0.6$

So the equation of the tangent is:

$y = mx + c \Rightarrow y = 0.8x - 0.6$

[2 marks available – 1 mark for correct substitution of (2, 1) and gradient from a) and 1 mark for final answer.]

6 a) For $y = \sqrt{e^x + e^{2x}}$, use the chain rule:

$y = u^{\frac{1}{2}}$ where $u = e^x + e^{2x}$.

$\frac{dy}{du} = \frac{1}{2}u^{-\frac{1}{2}} = \frac{1}{2\sqrt{u}} = \frac{1}{2\sqrt{e^x + e^{2x}}}$ **[1 mark]**.

$\frac{du}{dx} = e^x + 2e^{2x}$ **[1 mark]**.

So $\frac{dy}{dx} = \frac{e^x + 2e^{2x}}{2\sqrt{e^x + e^{2x}}}$ **[1 mark]**.

b) For $y = 3e^{2x+1} - \ln(1 - x^2) + 2x^3$, use the chain rule for the first 2 parts separately:

For $y = 3e^{2x+1}$, $y = 3e^u$ where $u = 2x + 1$,

so $\frac{dy}{du} = 3e^u = 3e^{2x+1}$ and $\frac{du}{dx} = 2$,

so $\frac{dy}{dx} = 6e^{2x+1}$ **[1 mark]**.

For $y = \ln(1 - x^2)$, $y = \ln u$ where $u = 1 - x^2$,

so $\frac{dy}{du} = \frac{1}{u} = \frac{1}{1 - x^2}$ and $\frac{du}{dx} = -2x$,

so $\frac{dy}{dx} = -\frac{2x}{1 - x^2}$ **[1 mark]**.

So overall: $\frac{dy}{dx} = 6e^{2x+1} + \frac{2x}{1 - x^2} + 6x^2$ **[1 mark]**.

7 For $y = \sin^2 x - 2\cos(2x)$, use the chain rule on each part:

For $y = \sin^2 x$, $y = u^2$ where $u = \sin x$,

so $\frac{dy}{du} = 2u = 2\sin x$ and $\frac{du}{dx} = \cos x$,

so $\frac{dy}{dx} = 2\sin x \cos x$ **[1 mark]**.

For $y = 2\cos(2x)$, $y = 2\cos u$ where $u = 2x$,

so $\frac{dy}{du} = -2\sin u = -2\sin(2x)$ and $\frac{du}{dx} = 2$,

so $\frac{dy}{dx} = -4\sin(2x)$ **[1 mark]**.

Overall $\frac{dy}{dx} = 2\sin x \cos x + 4\sin(2x)$.

(Think 'double angle formula' for the sin x cos x...)

$\sin(2x) \equiv 2\sin x \cos x$, so:

$\frac{dy}{dx} = \sin(2x) + 4\sin(2x) = 5\sin(2x)$ **[1 mark]**.

(For gradient of the tangent, put the x value into dy/dx...)

Gradient of the tangent when $x = \frac{\pi}{12}$ is:

$5 \times \sin\frac{\pi}{6} = \frac{5}{2}$ **[1 mark]**.

8 For $y = \frac{e^x + x}{e^x - x}$, use the quotient rule:

$u = e^x + x \Rightarrow \frac{du}{dx} = e^x + 1$.

$v = e^x - x \Rightarrow \frac{dv}{dx} = e^x - 1$.

$\frac{dy}{dx} = \frac{v\frac{du}{dx} - u\frac{dv}{dx}}{v^2} = \frac{(e^x - x)(e^x + 1) - (e^x + x)(e^x - 1)}{(e^x - x)^2}$

When $x = 0$, $e^0 = 1$, and

$\frac{dy}{dx} = \frac{(1 - 0)(1 + 1) - (1 + 0)(1 - 1)}{(1 - 0)^2} = \frac{2 - 0}{1^2} = 2$.

[3 marks available — 1 mark for finding u, v and their derivatives, 1 mark for dy/dx (however rearranged), and 1 mark for dy/dx = 2 when x = 0.]

9 For $x = \sin(4y)$, $\frac{dx}{dy} = 4\cos(4y)$ (chain rule) **[1 mark]**

and so $\frac{dy}{dx} = \frac{1}{4\cos(4y)}$ **[1 mark]**.

At $(0, \frac{\pi}{4})$, $y = \frac{\pi}{4}$ and so $\frac{dy}{dx} = \frac{1}{4\cos\pi} = -\frac{1}{4}$ **[1 mark]**.

(This is the gradient of the tangent at that point, so to find the gradient of the normal do −1 ÷ gradient of tangent...)

Gradient of normal at $(0, \frac{\pi}{4}) = -1 \div -\frac{1}{4} = 4$ **[1 mark]**.

Equation of a straight line is:

$y = mx + c$, so $\frac{\pi}{4} = (4 \times 0) + c \Rightarrow c = \frac{\pi}{4}$ **[1 mark]**

So the equation of the normal is $y = 4x + \frac{\pi}{4}$ **[1 mark]**.

Chapter 5: Numerical Methods

1. Location of Roots

Exercise 1.1 — Locating roots by changes of sign

Q1 $f(2) = 2^3 - 5 \times 2 + 1 = -1$
$f(3) = 3^3 - 5 \times 3 + 1 = 13$
There is a sign change (and the function is continuous in this interval) so there is a root in this interval.
They wouldn't ask you if there's a root if the function wasn't continuous in this interval, but it's worth saying anyway just to keep your answer 'strictly true'.

Q2 $f(0.9) = \sin(1.8) - 0.9 = 0.0738...$
$f(1.0) = \sin(2.0) - 1.0 = -0.0907...$
There is a sign change (and the function is continuous in this interval) so there is a root in this interval.

Q3 $f(1.2) = 1.2^3 + \ln 1.2 - 2 = -0.089...$
$f(1.3) = 1.3^3 + \ln 1.3 - 2 = 0.459...$
There is a sign change (and the function is continuous in this interval) so there is a root in this interval.

Q4 $f(2.5) = 2.5^2 + \dfrac{1}{2.5} - 7 = -0.35$
$f(2.6) = 2.6^2 + \dfrac{1}{2.6} - 7 = 0.14...$
There is a sign change (and the function is continuous in this interval) so there is a root in this interval.

Q5 $f(-0.8) = \cos(-0.8) - 0.8 = -0.10...$
$f(-0.7) = \cos(-0.7) - 0.7 = 0.06...$
There is a sign change (and the function is continuous in this interval) so there is a root in this interval.

Q6 $f(1) = e^1 + 1 - 8 = -4.28...$
$f(2) = e^2 + 2 - 8 = 1.38...$
There is a sign change (and the function is continuous in this interval) so there is a root in this interval.

Q7 $f(1.6) = (3 \times 1.6) - 1.6^4 + 3 = 1.24...$
$f(1.7) = (3 \times 1.7) - 1.7^4 + 3 = -0.25...$
There is a sign change (and the function is continuous in this interval) so there is a root in this interval.
$f(-1) = (3 \times (-1)) - (-1)^4 + 3 = -1$
$f(0) = (3 \times 0) - 0^4 + 3 = 3$
There is a sign change (and the function is continuous in this interval) so there is a root in this interval.

Q8 $f(0.01) = e^{0.01 - 2} - \sqrt{0.01} = 0.0366...$
$f(0.02) = e^{0.02 - 2} - \sqrt{0.02} = -0.0033...$
There is a sign change (and the function is continuous in this interval) so there is a root in this interval.
$f(2.4) = e^{2.4 - 2} - \sqrt{2.4} = -0.057...$
$f(2.5) = e^{2.5 - 2} - \sqrt{2.5} = 0.067...$
There is a sign change (and the function is continuous in this interval) so there is a root in this interval.

Q9 The upper and lower bounds are 2.75 and 2.85.
$f(2.75) = 2.75^3 - (7 \times 2.75) - 2 = -0.45...$
$f(2.85) = 2.85^3 - (7 \times 2.85) - 2 = 1.19...$
There is a sign change between the upper and lower bounds (and the function is continuous in this interval), so a solution to 1 d.p. is $x = 2.8$.

Q10 Upper and lower bounds are 0.65 and 0.75
$f(0.65) = (2 \times 0.65) - \dfrac{1}{0.65} = -0.23...$
$f(0.75) = (2 \times 0.75) - \dfrac{1}{0.75} = 0.16...$
There is a sign change between the upper and lower bounds (and the function is continuous in this interval), so a solution to 1 d.p. is $x = 0.7$.

Q11 $f(0.245) = e^{0.245} - 0.245^3 - (5 \times 0.245) = 0.037...$
$f(0.255) = e^{0.255} - 0.255^3 - (5 \times 0.255) = -0.001...$
There is a sign change between the upper and lower bounds (and the function is continuous in this interval), so a solution to 2 d.p. is $x = 0.25$.

Q12 $f(2.4855) = 2.4855^3 - (2 \times 2.4855^2) - 3 = -0.00072...$
$f(2.4865) = 2.4865^3 - (2 \times 2.4865^2) - 3 = 0.0078...$
There is a sign change between the upper and lower bounds (and the function is continuous in this interval), so a solution to 3 d.p. is $x = 2.486$.

Q13 $f(-2.3) = (4 \times -2.3) - (2 \times (-2.3)^3) - 15 = 0.134$
$f(-2.2) = (4 \times -2.2) - (2 \times (-2.2)^3) - 15 = -2.504$
There is a sign change (and the function is continuous in this interval) so there is a root in this interval.

Q14 $f(0.23) = \ln(0.23 + 3) - (5 \times 0.23) = 0.022...$
$f(0.24) = \ln(0.24 + 3) - (5 \times 0.24) = -0.024...$
There is a sign change (and the function is continuous in this interval) so there is a root in this interval.

Q15 $f(0) = e^{3 \times 0} \sin 0 - 5 = -5$
$f(1) = e^{3 \times 1} \sin 1 - 5 = 11.9...$
There is a sign change (and the function is continuous in this interval) so there is a root in this interval.

Exercise 1.2 — Sketching graphs to find approximate roots

Q1 a)
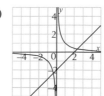

b) The graphs cross twice, so the equation has 2 roots.

c) $f(2.4) = 2.4 - \dfrac{1}{2.4} - 2 = -0.016...$
$f(2.5) = 2.5 - \dfrac{1}{2.5} - 2 = 0.1$
There is a sign change (and the function is continuous in this interval) so there is a root in this interval.

Q2 a)
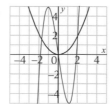

b) The graphs cross 3 times, so the equation has 3 roots.

c) $f(-2) = (2 \times (-2)^3) - (-2)^2 - (7 \times -2) = -6$
$f(-1) = (2 \times (-1)^3) - (-1)^2 - (7 \times -1) = 4$
There is a sign change (and the function is continuous in this interval) so there is a root in this interval.

Q3 a)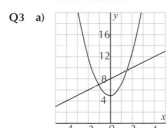

b) The graphs cross twice so the equation has 2 roots.

c) $f(1) = (2 \times 1^2) - 1 - 3 = -2$
$f(2) = (2 \times 2^2) - 2 - 3 = 3$
There is a sign change (and the function is continuous in this interval) so there is a root in this interval.

Q4 a)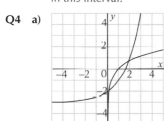

b) The graphs cross twice so the equation has 2 roots

c) $f(1.8) = \ln(1.8) - 2^{1.8} + 3 = 0.105...$
$f(2.2) = \ln(2.2) - 2^{2.2} + 3 = -0.806...$
There is a sign change (and the function is continuous in this interval), so there is a root in this interval.

$f(2.0) = \ln(2.0) - 2^{2.0} + 3 = -0.306...$
So the root is between 1.8 and 2.0

$f(1.9) = \ln(1.9) - 2^{1.9} + 3 = -0.090...$
So the root is between 1.8 and 1.9

$f(1.85) = \ln(1.85) - 2^{1.85} + 3 = 0.010...$

There is a sign change (and the function is continuous) between 1.85 and 1.9, so the root is at $x = 1.9$ (to 1 d.p.).

Q5 a)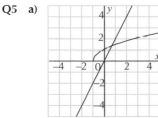

b) The graphs cross once so the equation has 1 root.

c) $f(0.6) = \sqrt{0.6 + 1} - (2 \times 0.6) = 0.064...$
$f(0.7) = \sqrt{0.7 + 1} - (2 \times 0.7) = -0.096...$

There is a sign change, so there is a root in the interval.

d) $\sqrt{x+1} = 2x \Rightarrow x + 1 = 4x^2 \Rightarrow 4x^2 - x - 1 = 0$
From quadratic formula root is $x = 0.640$ to 3 s.f.
You can ignore the other solution to this quadratic equation — you know the root is between 0.6 and 0.7.

Q6 a)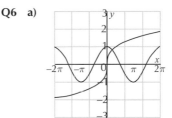

b) The graphs cross once so the equation has 1 root.

c) $f(0.5) = \cos 0.5 - \sqrt[3]{0.5} = 0.083...$
$f(0.6) = \cos 0.6 - \sqrt[3]{0.6} = -0.018...$
There is a sign change (and the function is continuous in this interval) so there is a root in this interval.

d) $f(0.55) = \cos 0.55 - \sqrt[3]{0.55} = 0.033...$
So the root is between 0.55 and 0.6.

$f(0.58) = \cos 0.58 - \sqrt[3]{0.58} = 0.002...$
So the root is between 0.58 and 0.6.

$f(0.59) = \cos 0.59 - \sqrt[3]{0.59} = -0.007...$
So the root is between 0.58 and 0.59

$f(0.585) = \cos 0.585 - \sqrt[3]{0.585} = -0.002...$

So the root is between 0.58 and 0.585, so the value to 2 significant figures is $x = 0.58$.

Q7 a)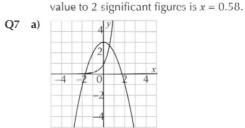

b) If the two functions are set equal to each other they can be rearranged to make $e^{2x} + x^2 = 3$. The graphs cross twice, so the equation has 2 roots.

c) Rearrange to $f(x) = 0$ so $e^{2x} + x^2 - 3 = 0$
$f(-2) = e^{(2 \times -2)} + (-2)^2 - 3 = 1.01...$
$f(-1) = e^{(2 \times -1)} + (-1)^2 - 3 = -1.86...$

There is a sign change (and the function is continuous in this interval) so there is a root in this interval.

$f(-1.5) = e^{(2 \times -1.5)} + (-1.5)^2 - 3 = -0.70...$
So the root is between -1.5 and -2

$f(-1.7) = e^{(2 \times -1.7)} + (-1.7)^2 - 3 = -0.07...$
So the root is between -1.7 and -2

$f(-1.8) = e^{(2 \times -1.8)} + (-1.8)^2 - 3 = 0.26...$
So the root is between -1.7 and -1.8

$f(-1.75) = e^{(2 \times -1.75)} + (-1.75)^2 - 3 = 0.09...$

So the root is between -1.7 and -1.75, so the value to 1 decimal place is $x = -1.7$.

2. Iterative Methods

Exercise 2.1 — Using iteration formulas

Q1 a) $f(1) = 1^3 + 3 \times 1^2 - 7 = -3$
$f(2) = 2^3 + 3 \times 2^2 - 7 = 13$
There is a sign change (and the function is continuous in this interval) so there is a root in this interval.

b) $x_1 = \sqrt{\dfrac{7 - x_0^3}{3}} = \sqrt{\dfrac{7 - 1^3}{3}} = 1.414,$
$x_2 = 1.179, \ x_3 = 1.337, \ x_4 = 1.240$

Q2 a) $x_1 = 2 + \ln x_0 = 2 + \ln 3.1 = 3.1314,$
$x_2 = 3.1415, \ x_3 = 3.1447, \ x_4 = 3.1457,$
$x_5 = 3.1460$

b) $\alpha = 3.146$

Q3 a) $f(1.4) = 1.4^4 - (5 \times 1.4) + 3 = -0.1584$
$f(1.5) = 1.5^4 - (5 \times 1.5) + 3 = 0.5625$
There is a sign change (and the function is continuous in this interval) so there is a root in this interval.

b) $x_1 = \sqrt[3]{5 - \dfrac{3}{x_0}} = \sqrt[3]{5 - \dfrac{3}{1.4}} = 1.419,$
$x_2 = 1.424, \ x_3 = 1.425, \ x_4 = 1.425,$
$x_5 = 1.425, \ x_6 = 1.425$

c) The last 4 iterations round to the same answer, so to 2 d.p. $x = 1.43$

Q4 a) $f(5) = 5^2 - (5 \times 5) - 2 = -2$
$f(6) = 6^2 - (5 \times 6) - 2 = 4$
There is a sign change (and the function is continuous in this interval) so there is a root in this interval.

b) $x_1 = \dfrac{2}{x_0} + 5 = \dfrac{2}{5} + 5 = 5.4,$
$x_2 = 5.370, \ x_3 = 5.372, \ x_4 = 5.372$

Q5 $x_1 = 2 - \ln x_0 = 2 - \ln 1.5 = 1.595,$
$x_2 = 1.533, \ x_3 = 1.573, \ x_4 = 1.547, \ x_5 = 1.563,$
$x_6 = 1.553, \ x_7 = 1.560, \ x_8 = 1.555, \ x_9 = 1.558$

The iterative sequence is bouncing up and down but closing in on the correct answer.

The last three iterations round to the same answer to 2 d.p., so to 2 d.p. $x = 1.56$

Q6 a) $f(3) = e^3 - (10 \times 3) = -9.914...$
$f(4) = e^4 - (10 \times 4) = 14.598...$
There is a sign change (and the function is continuous in this interval) so there is a root in this interval.

b) Using starting value $x_0 = 3$:
$x_1 = \ln(10x_0) = \ln(10 \times 3) = 3.401$
$x_2 = 3.527, \ x_3 = 3.563, \ x_4 = 3.573$

You could have started with x_0 as anything between 3 and 4, in which case you'd get different values for $x_1 - x_4$.

c) The upper and lower bounds are 3.5765 and 3.5775.
$f(3.5765) = e^{3.5765} - (10 \times 3.5765) = -0.016...$

$f(3.5775) = e^{3.5775} - (10 \times 3.5775) = 0.0089...$
There is a sign change between the upper and lower bounds (and the function is continuous in this interval), so the root to 3 d.p. is $x = 3.577$.

d) Using new iterative formula with $x_0 = 3$
$x_1 = 2.00855..., \ x_2 = 0.74525.., \ x_3 = 0.21069...,$
$x_4 = 0.12345..., \ x_5 = 0.11313..., \ x_6 = 0.11197...,$
$x_7 = 0.11184..., \ x_8 = 0.11183...$

The formula appears to converge to another root at $x = 0.112$ (to 3 d.p.).

Q7 a) $x_1 = \dfrac{x_0^2 - 3x_0}{2} - 5 = \dfrac{(-1)^2 - (3 \times (-1))}{2} - 5 = -3$
$x_2 = 4, \ x_3 = -3, \ x_4 = 4$
The sequence is alternating between −3 and 4.

b) Using the iterative formula given:
$x_1 = 6.32455..., \ x_2 = 6.45157..., \ x_3 = 6.50060...,$
$x_4 = 6.51943..., \ x_5 = 6.52665..., \ x_6 = 6.52941...,$
$x_7 = 6.53047..., \ x_8 = 6.53087...$

The last 4 iterations all round to 6.53, so the value of the root is $x = 6.53$ to 3 s.f. To verify this, check it's between the upper and lower bounds of 6.53:
$f(6.525) = 6.525^2 - (5 \times 6.525) - 10 = -0.049...$
$f(6.535) = 6.535^2 - (5 \times 6.535) - 10 = 0.031...$

There is a sign change between the upper and lower bounds (and the function is continuous in this interval) so this value is correct to 3 s.f.

Exercise 2.2 — Finding iteration formulas

Q1 a) $x^2 - 5x + 1 = 0 \Rightarrow x^2 = 5x - 1 \Rightarrow x = \sqrt{5x - 1}$

b) $x^2 - 5x + 1 = 0 \Rightarrow x^2 = 5x - 1 \Rightarrow x = 5 - \dfrac{1}{x}$

c) $x^2 - 5x + 1 = 0 \Rightarrow 5x = x^2 + 1 \Rightarrow x = \dfrac{x^2 + 1}{5}$

Q2 a) $x^4 + 7x - 3 = 0 \Rightarrow x^4 = 3 - 7x \Rightarrow x = \sqrt[4]{3 - 7x}$

b) $x^4 + 7x - 3 = 0 \Rightarrow x^4 = 3 - 7x \Rightarrow x = \dfrac{3}{x^3} - \dfrac{7}{x^2}$

c) $x^4 + 7x - 3 = 0 \Rightarrow x^4 + 5x + 2x - 3 = 0$
$\Rightarrow 2x = 3 - 5x - x^4 \Rightarrow x = \dfrac{3 - 5x - x^4}{2}$

d) $x^4 + 7x - 3 = 0 \Rightarrow x^4 = 3 - 7x$
$\Rightarrow x^2 = \sqrt{3 - 7x} \Rightarrow x = \dfrac{\sqrt{3 - 7x}}{x}$

Q3 a) $x^3 - 2x^2 - 5 = 0 \Rightarrow x^3 = 2x^2 + 5 \Rightarrow x = 2 + \dfrac{5}{x^2}$

b) $x_1 = 2 + \dfrac{5}{2^2} = 3.25$
$x_2 = 2.473..., \ x_3 = 2.817...,$
$x_4 = 2.629..., \ x_5 = 2.722...,$
So $x_5 = 2.7$ to 1 d.p.

c) $f(2.65) = 2.65^3 - (2 \times 2.65^2) - 5 = -0.43...$
$f(2.75) = 2.75^3 - (2 \times 2.75^2) - 5 = 0.67...$
There is a sign change between the upper and lower bounds (and the function is continuous in this interval) so this value is correct to 1 d.p.

Q4 a) $x^2 + 3x - 8 = 0 \Rightarrow x^2 = 8 - 3x \Rightarrow x = \dfrac{8}{x} - 3$

b) $f(-5) = (-5)^2 + (3 \times -5) - 8 = 2$
$f(-4) = (-4)^2 + (3 \times -4) - 8 = -4$
There is a sign change (and the function is continuous in this interval) so there is a root in this interval.

c) $x_1 = \dfrac{a}{x_0} + b = \dfrac{8}{-5} - 3 = -4.6$
$x_2 = -4.739$, $x_3 = -4.688$, $x_4 = -4.706$,
$x_5 = -4.700$, $x_6 = -4.702$
So $x = -4.70$ to 2 d.p.

Q5 a) $2^{x-1} = 4\sqrt{x} \Rightarrow 2^{x-1} = 2^2 x^{\frac{1}{2}}$
$\Rightarrow 2^{x-1} \times 2^{-2} = x^{\frac{1}{2}} \Rightarrow 2^{x-3} = x^{\frac{1}{2}}$
$\Rightarrow (2^{x-3})^2 = x \Rightarrow x = 2^{2x-6}$

b) Using the iterative formula given:
$x_1 = 0.0625$, $x_2 = 0.0170$, $x_3 = 0.0160$,
$x_4 = 0.0160$

c) $f(0.01595) = 2^{0.01595-1} - 4\sqrt{0.01595} = 0.00038...$
$f(0.01605) = 2^{0.01605-1} - 4\sqrt{0.01605} = -0.0016...$
There is a sign change between the upper and lower bounds (and the function is continuous in this interval) so this value is correct to 4 d.p.

Q6 a) $f(0.4) = \ln(2 \times 0.4) + 0.4^3 = -0.159...$
$f(0.5) = \ln(2 \times 0.5) + 0.5^3 = 0.125$

There is a sign change (and the function is continuous in this interval) so there is a root in this interval.

b) $\ln 2x + x^3 = 0 \Rightarrow \ln 2x = -x^3$
$\Rightarrow 2x = e^{-x^3} \Rightarrow x = \dfrac{e^{-x^3}}{2}$

c) Using iterative formula $x_{n+1} = \dfrac{e^{-x_n^3}}{2}$ with starting value $x_0 = 0.4$:
You know the root is between 0.4 and 0.5, so it's a good idea to use one of these as your starting value
$x_1 = \dfrac{e^{-x_0^3}}{2} = \dfrac{e^{-0.4^3}}{2} = 0.4690...,$
$x_2 = 0.4509...$, $x_3 = 0.4561...$, $x_4 = 0.4547...,$
$x_5 = 0.4551...$, $x_6 = 0.4550...$
So the value of the root is $x = 0.455$ to 3 d.p.

Q7 a) $x^2 - 9x - 20 = 0 \Rightarrow x^2 = 9x + 20 \Rightarrow x = \sqrt{9x + 20}$
So an iterative formula is $x_{n+1} = \sqrt{9x_n + 20}$

b) $x_1 = \sqrt{9x_0 + 20} = \sqrt{(9 \times 10) + 20} = 10.488...,$
$x_2 = 10.695...$, $x_3 = 10.782...$, $x_4 = 10.818...,$
$x_5 = 10.833...$, $x_6 = 10.839...$
The last 4 iterations round to 10.8, so the value of the root is $x = 10.8$ to 3 s.f.

c) $x^2 - 9x - 20 = 0 \Rightarrow x^2 - 5x - 4x - 20 = 0$
$\Rightarrow 5x = x^2 - 4x - 20 \Rightarrow x = \dfrac{x^2 - 4x}{5} - 4$
So an iterative formula is $x_{n+1} = \dfrac{x_n^2 - 4x_n}{5} - 4$

d) $x_1 = \dfrac{x_0^2 - 4x_0}{5} - 4 = \dfrac{1^2 - (4 \times 1)}{5} - 4 = -4.6,$
$x_2 = 3.912$, $x_3 = -4.0688...$, $x_4 = 2.5661...,$
$x_5 = -4.7358...$, $x_6 = 4.2744...$, $x_7 = -3.7653...,$
$x_8 = 1.8479...$

e) The iterations seem to be bouncing up and down without converging to any particular root.

Review Exercise — Chapter 5

Q1 There are 2 roots (the graph crosses the x-axis twice in this interval).

Q2 a) $f(3) = \sin(2 \times 3) = -0.2794...$
$f(4) = \sin(2 \times 4) = 0.9893...$
There is a sign change (and the function is continuous in this interval) so there is a root in this interval.

b) $f(2.1) = \ln(2.1 - 2) + 2 = -0.3025...$
$f(2.2) = \ln(2.2 - 2) + 2 = 0.3905...$

There is a sign change (and the function is continuous in this interval) so there is a root in this interval.

c) First rearrange so that $f(x) = 0$:
$x^3 - 4x^2 = 7 \Rightarrow x^3 - 4x^2 - 7 = 0$

$f(4.3) = 4.3^3 - 4 \times 4.3^2 - 7 = -1.453$
$f(4.5) = 4.5^3 - 4 \times 4.5^2 - 7 = 3.125$

There is a sign change (and the function is continuous in this interval) so there is a root in this interval.

Q3 If 1.2 is a root to 1 d.p. then there should be a sign change for $f(x)$ between upper and lower bounds:
$f(1.15) = 1.15^3 + 1.15 - 3 = 0.3291...$
$f(1.25) = 1.25^3 + 1.25 - 3 = 0.2031...$

There is a sign change (and the function is continuous) between the upper and lower bounds, so the answer must be between them and so be rounded to 1.2 to 1 d.p.

Q4 $x_1 = -\dfrac{1}{2}\cos(-1) = -0.2701...$

$x_2 = -\dfrac{1}{2}\cos(-0.2701...) = -0.4818...$

$x_3 = -\dfrac{1}{2}\cos(-0.4818...) = -0.4430...$

$x_4 = -\dfrac{1}{2}\cos(-0.4430...) = -0.4517...$

$x_5 = -\dfrac{1}{2}\cos(-0.4517...) = -0.4498...$

$x_6 = -\dfrac{1}{2}\cos(-0.4498...) = -0.4502...$

x_4, x_5 and x_6 all round to -0.45, so to 2 d.p.
$x = -0.45$.

Q5 $x_1 = \sqrt{\ln 2 + 4} = 2.1663...$
$x_2 = \sqrt{\ln 2.1663... + 4} = 2.1847...$
$x_3 = \sqrt{\ln 2.1847... + 4} = 2.1866...$
$x_4 = \sqrt{\ln 2.1866... + 4} = 2.1868...$
$x_5 = \sqrt{\ln 2.1868... + 4} = 2.1868...$
x_3, x_4 and x_5 all round to 2.187, so to 3 d.p.
$x = 2.187$.

Q6 a) (i) $2x^2 - x^3 + 1 = 0 \Rightarrow 2x^2 - x^3 = -1$
$\Rightarrow x^2(2 - x) = -1 \Rightarrow x^2 = \dfrac{-1}{2 - x}$
$\Rightarrow x = \sqrt{\dfrac{-1}{2 - x}}$

(ii) $\Rightarrow 2x^2 - x^3 + 1 = 0 \Rightarrow x^3 = 2x^2 + 1$
$\Rightarrow x = \sqrt[3]{2x^2 + 1}.$

(iii) $2x^2 - x^3 + 1 = 0 \Rightarrow 2x^2 = x^3 - 1$

$\Rightarrow x^2 = \dfrac{x^3 - 1}{2} \Rightarrow x = \sqrt{\dfrac{x^3 - 1}{2}}$

b) Using $x_{n+1} = \sqrt{\dfrac{-1}{2 - x_n}}$ with $x_0 = 2.3$ gives:

$x_1 = \sqrt{\dfrac{-1}{2 - 2.3}} = 1.8257...$

$x_2 = \sqrt{\dfrac{-1}{2 - 1.8257...}}$ has no real solution
so this formula does not converge to a root.

Using $x_{n+1} = \sqrt[3]{2x_n^2 + 1}$ with $x_0 = 2.3$ gives:

$x_1 = \sqrt[3]{2 \times (2.3)^2 + 1} = 2.2624...$
$x_2 = \sqrt[3]{2 \times (2.2624...)^2 + 1} = 2.2398...$
$x_3 = \sqrt[3]{2 \times (2.2398...)^2 + 1} = 2.2262...$
$x_4 = \sqrt[3]{2 \times (2.2262...)^2 + 1} = 2.2180...$
$x_5 = \sqrt[3]{2 \times (2.2180...)^2 + 1} = 2.2131...$
$x_6 = \sqrt[3]{2 \times (2.2131...)^2 + 1} = 2.2101...$
$x_7 = \sqrt[3]{2 \times (2.2101...)^2 + 1} = 2.2083...$

x_5, x_6 and x_7 all round to 2.21,
so to 2 d.p. $x = 2.21$ is a root.

Using $x_{n+1} = \sqrt{\dfrac{x_n^3 - 1}{2}}$ with $x_0 = 2.3$ gives:

$x_1 = \sqrt{\dfrac{2.3^3 - 1}{2}} = 2.3629...$

$x_2 = \sqrt{\dfrac{2.3629...^3 - 1}{2}} = 2.4691...$

$x_3 = \sqrt{\dfrac{2.4691...^3 - 1}{2}} = 2.6508...$

$x_4 = \sqrt{\dfrac{2.6508...^3 - 1}{2}} = 2.9687...$

This sequence is diverging so does not converge
to a root. The only formula that converges to a root
is $x_{n+1} = \sqrt[3]{2x_n^2 + 1}$.

Q7 a)

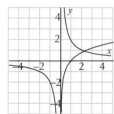

1 crossing point and therefore 1 root.

b) $f(2) = \ln 2 - \dfrac{2}{2} = -0.306...$

$f(3) = \ln 3 - \dfrac{2}{3} = 0.431...$

There is a sign change (and the function is
continuous in this interval) so there is a root
in this interval.

Q8 a)

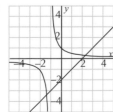

b) $f(-1.4) = \dfrac{1}{-1.4 + 1} - (-1.4) + 2 = 0.9$

$f(-1.3) = \dfrac{1}{-1.3 + 1} - (-1.3) + 2 = -0.033..$

There is a sign change (and the function is
continuous in this interval) so there is a root
in this interval.

c) $\dfrac{1}{x + 1} - x + 2 = 0 \Rightarrow 1 - x(x + 1) + 2(x + 1) = 0$
$\Rightarrow 1 - x^2 - x + 2x + 2 = 0 \Rightarrow -x^2 + x + 3 = 0$
$\Rightarrow x^2 - x - 3 = 0$

Q9 a) $f(1.5) = 1.5^{1.5} - 3 = -1.16...$, $f(2) = 2^2 - 3 = 1$

There is a sign change (and the function is
continuous in this interval) so there is a root in
this interval.

b) Using $x_0 = 1.5$ (though anything between 1.5 and
2 is fine):

$x_1 = 3^{\frac{1}{x_0}} = 3^{\frac{1}{1.5}} = 2.08008...$,
$x_2 = 1.69580...$, $x_3 = 1.91140...$, $x_4 = 1.77671...$,
$x_5 = 1.85584...$, $x_6 = 1.80755...$, $x_7 = 1.83636...$,
$x_8 = 1.81893...$,

x_6 to x_8 round to give $x = 1.8$ to 1 d.p.

c) Using the iterative formula given:
$x_1 = 2.44948...$, $x_2 = 0.81876...$, $x_3 = 2.89323...$,
$x_4 = 0.40143...$, $x_5 = 1.73724...$

The formula appears to be bouncing up and
down without converging to a root.

Q10 a) $f(1.1) = 2 \times 1.1 - 5 \times \cos 1.1 = -0.06...$
$f(1.2) = 2 \times 1.2 - 5 \times \cos 1.2 = 0.58...$

There is a sign change (and the function is
continuous in this interval) so there is a solution
in this interval.

b) $2x - 5\cos x = 0 \Rightarrow 2x = 5\cos x$

$\Rightarrow x = \dfrac{5}{2}\cos x$ so $p = \dfrac{5}{2}$

c) Using the iterative formula $x_{n+1} = \dfrac{5}{2}\cos x_n$:

$x_1 = \dfrac{5}{2}\cos x_0 = \dfrac{5}{2}\cos 1.1 = 1.1340$

$x_2 = 1.0576$, $x_3 = 1.2274$, $x_4 = 0.8418$,
$x_5 = 1.6653$, $x_6 = -0.2360$, $x_7 = 2.4307$,
$x_8 = -1.8945$

The sequence at first looks like it might converge
to the root in part a) but then it continues to jump
up and down.

d) $2x - 5\cos x = 0$
$5\cos x = 2x$
$\cos x = 0.4x$
$x = \cos^{-1} 0.4x$

So the iterative formula is $x_{n+1} = \cos^{-1} 0.4x_n$

$x_0 = 1.1$, $x_1 = 1.1151...$, $x_2 = 1.1084...$,
$x_3 = 1.1114...$, $x_4 = 1.1100...$

So $x = 1.11$ to 3 s.f.

$f(1.105) = (2 \times 1.105) - 5\cos 1.105 = -0.035...$
$f(1.115) = (2 \times 1.115) - 5\cos 1.115 = 0.029...$

There is a sign change (and the function is
continuous in this interval) so there is a root in
this interval. The root is $x = 1.11$ correct to 3
significant figures.

Exam-Style Questions — Chapter 5

1

a) There will be a change of sign between $f(0.7)$ and $f(0.8)$ if p lies between 0.7 and 0.8.

$f(0.7) = (2 \times 0.7 \times e^{0.7}) - 3 = -0.1807...$ *[1 mark]*

$f(0.8) = (2 \times 0.8 \times e^{0.8}) - 3 = 0.5608...$ *[1 mark]*

$f(x)$ is continuous, and there is a change of sign, so $0.7 < p < 0.8$ *[1 mark]*.

b) If $2xe^x - 3 = 0$, then $2xe^x = 3 \Rightarrow xe^x = \frac{3}{2}$

$\Rightarrow x = \frac{3}{2e^x} \Rightarrow x = \frac{3}{2}e^{-x}$.

[2 marks available — 1 mark for partial rearrangement, 1 mark for correct final answer.]

c) $x_{n+1} = \frac{3}{2}e^{-x_n}$ and $x_0 = 0.7$, so:

$x_1 = \frac{3}{2}e^{-0.7} = 0.74487... = 0.7449$ to 4 d.p.

$x_2 = \frac{3}{2}e^{-0.74487...} = 0.71218... = 0.7122$ to 4 d.p.

$x_3 = \frac{3}{2}e^{-0.71218...} = 0.73585... = 0.7359$ to 4 d.p.

$x_4 = \frac{3}{2}e^{-0.73585...} = 0.71864... = 0.7186$ to 4 d.p.

[3 marks available — 1 mark if x_1 is correct, 1 mark if x_2 is correct, 1 mark if all 4 are correct.]

d) If the root of $f(x) = 0$, p, is 0.726 to 3 d.p. then there must be a change of sign in $f(x)$ between the upper and lower bounds of p.

Lower bound = 0.7255.
$f(0.7255) = (2 \times 0.7255 \times e^{0.7255}) - 3 = -0.0025...$

Upper bound = 0.7265.
$f(0.7265) = (2 \times 0.7265 \times e^{0.7265}) - 3 = 0.0045...$

$f(x)$ is continuous, and there's a change of sign, so $p = 0.726$ to 3 d.p.

[3 marks available — 1 mark for identifying upper and lower bounds, 1 mark for finding value of the function at both bounds, 1 mark for indicating that the change in sign and the fact that it's a continuous function shows the root is correct to the given accuracy.]

2

a) Where $y = \sin 3x + 3x$ and $y = 1$ meet,
$\sin 3x + 3x = 1 \Rightarrow \sin 3x + 3x - 1 = 0$ *[1 mark]*

$x = a$ is a root of this equation, so if $x = 0.1$ and $x = 0.2$ produce different signs, then a lies between them. So for the continuous function $f(x) = \sin 3x + 3x - 1$:

$f(0.1) = \sin (3 \times 0.1) + (3 \times 0.1) - 1 = -0.4044...$ *[1 mark]*

$f(0.2) = \sin (3 \times 0.2) + (3 \times 0.2) - 1 = 0.1646...$ *[1 mark]*

There is a change of sign, so $0.1 < a < 0.2$ *[1 mark]*

b) $\sin 3x + 3x = 1 \Rightarrow 3x = 1 - \sin 3x$

$\Rightarrow x = \frac{1}{3}(1 - \sin 3x)$.

[2 marks available — 1 mark for partial rearrangement, 1 mark for correct final answer.]

c) $x_{n+1} = \frac{1}{3}(1 - \sin 3x_n)$ and $x_0 = 0.2$:

$x_1 = \frac{1}{3}(1 - \sin (3 \times 0.2)) = 0.1451...$ *[1 mark]*

$x_2 = \frac{1}{3}(1 - \sin (3 \times 0.1451...)) = 0.1927...$

$x_3 = \frac{1}{3}(1 - \sin (3 \times 0.1927...)) = 0.1511...$

$x_4 = \frac{1}{3}(1 - \sin (3 \times 0.1511...)) = 0.1873...$

So $x_4 = 0.187$ to 3 d.p. *[1 mark]*.

3

a) $x_{n+1} = \sqrt[3]{x_n^2 - 4}$, $x_0 = -1$:

$x_1 = \sqrt[3]{(-1)^2 - 4} = -1.44224...$
$= -1.4422$ to 4 d.p.

$x_2 = \sqrt[3]{(-1.4422...)^2 - 4} = -1.24287...$
$= -1.2429$ to 4 d.p.

$x_3 = \sqrt[3]{(-1.2428...)^2 - 4} = -1.34906...$
$= -1.3491$ to 4 d.p.

$x_4 = \sqrt[3]{(-1.3490...)^2 - 4} = -1.29664...$
$= -1.2966$ to 4 d.p.

[3 marks available — 1 mark if x_1 is correct, 1 mark if x_2 is correct, 1 mark if all 4 are correct.]

b) If b is a root of $x^3 - x^2 + 4 = 0$, then $x^3 - x^2 + 4 = 0$ will rearrange to form $x = \sqrt[3]{x^2 - 4}$, the iteration formula used in (a).
(This is like finding the iteration formula in reverse...)

$x^3 - x^2 + 4 = 0 \Rightarrow x^3 = x^2 - 4 \Rightarrow x = \sqrt[3]{x^2 - 4}$,

and so b must be a root of $x^3 - x^2 + 4 = 0$.

[2 marks available — 1 mark for stating that b is a root if one equation can be rearranged into the other, 1 mark for correct demonstration of rearrangement.]

c) If the root of $f(x) = x^3 - x^2 + 4 = 0$, b, is -1.315 to 3 d.p. then there must be a change of sign in $f(x)$ between the upper and lower bounds of b, which are -1.3145 and -1.3155.

$f(-1.3145) = (-1.3145)^3 - (-1.3145)^2 + 4$
$= 0.00075...$

$f(-1.3155) = (-1.3155)^3 - (-1.3155)^2 + 4$
$= -0.00706...$

$f(x)$ is continuous, and there's a change of sign, so $b = -1.315$ to 3 d.p.

[3 marks available — 1 mark for identifying upper and lower bounds, 1 mark for finding value of the function at both bounds, 1 mark for indicating that the change in sign and the fact that it's a continuous function shows the root is correct to the given accuracy.]

4

a) For $f(x) = \ln(x + 3) - x + 2$, there will be a change in sign between $f(3)$ and $f(4)$ if the root lies between those values.

$f(3) = \ln (3 + 3) - 3 + 2 = 0.7917...$ *[1 mark]*

$f(4) = \ln (4 + 3) - 4 + 2 = -0.0540...$ *[1 mark]*

There is a change of sign, and the function is continuous for $x > -3$, so the root, m, must lie between 3 and 4 *[1 mark]*.

b) $x_{n+1} = \ln(x_n + 3) + 2$, and $x_0 = 3$, so:

$x_1 = \ln(3 + 3) + 2 = 3.7917...$
$x_2 = \ln(3.7917... + 3) + 2 = 3.9157...$
$x_3 = \ln(3.9157... + 3) + 2 = 3.9337...$
$x_4 = \ln(3.9337... + 3) + 2 = 3.9364...$
$x_5 = \ln(3.9364... + 3) + 2 = 3.9367...$

So $m = 3.94$ to 2 d.p.

[3 marks available — 1 mark for correct substitution of x_0 to find x_1, 1 mark for evidence of correct iterations up to x_5, 1 mark for correct final answer to correct accuracy.]

c) From b), $m = 3.94$ to 2 d.p. If this is correct then there will be a change of sign in f(x) between the upper and lower bounds of m, which are 3.935 and 3.945.

$f(3.935) = \ln(3.935 + 3) - 3.935 + 2 = 0.00158...$
$f(3.945) = \ln(3.945 + 3) - 3.945 + 2$
$\quad = -0.00697...$

f(x) is continuous for $x > -3$, and there's a change of sign, so $m = 3.94$ is correct to 2 d.p.

[3 marks available — 1 mark for identifying upper and lower bounds, 1 mark for finding value of the function at both bounds, 1 mark for indicating that the change in sign and the fact that it's a continuous function shows the root is correct to the given accuracy.]

5 a) For f(x) = cot x + 3cos x − 1 there will be a change in sign between f(1.3) and f(1.4) if the root lies between those x values.

$f(1.3) = \cot 1.3 + 3 \cos 1.3 - 1 = 0.080...$
[1 mark]

$f(1.4) = \cot 1.4 + 3 \cos 1.4 - 1 = -0.317...$
[1 mark]

There is a change of sign, and the function is continuous for $1.3 \le x \le 1.4$, so the root must lie between 1.3 and 1.4. *[1 mark]*

Remember cot x is just 1/tan x

b) Rearrange first into form "x = f(x)":

$\cot x + 3\cos x - 1 = 0 \Rightarrow 3\cos x = 1 - \cot x$

$\Rightarrow \cos x = \dfrac{1 - \cot x}{3}$ *[1 mark]*

$\Rightarrow x = \arccos\left(\dfrac{1 - \cot x}{3}\right)$ *[1 mark]*

And hence the iterative formula can be made:

$x_{n+1} = \arccos\left(\dfrac{1 - \cot x_n}{3}\right)$ *[1 mark]*

c) $x_{n+1} = \arccos\left(\dfrac{1 - \cot x_n}{3}\right)$, $x_0 = 1.4$

$x_1 = \arccos\left(\dfrac{1 - \cot 1.4}{3}\right) = 1.2913$

$x_2 = \arccos\left(\dfrac{1 - \cot 1.2913...}{3}\right) = 1.3308$

$x_3 = \arccos\left(\dfrac{1 - \cot 1.3308...}{3}\right) = 1.3163$

$x_4 = \arccos\left(\dfrac{1 - \cot 1.3163...}{3}\right) = 1.3216$

$x_5 = \arccos\left(\dfrac{1 - \cot 1.3216...}{3}\right) = 1.3197$

$x_6 = \arccos\left(\dfrac{1 - \cot 1.3197...}{3}\right) = 1.3204$

[3 marks available — 1 mark if x_1 is correct, 1 mark if x_2 is correct, 1 mark if all are correct.]

d) x_3 to x_6 all round to 1.32, so the value of the root is $x = 1.32$ to 2 decimal places *[1 mark]*.

Chapter 6: Proof

1. Proof

Exercise 1.1 — Different types of proof

Q1 **a)** Take two even numbers, $2j$ and $2k$ (where j and k are integers), then their product is $2j \times 2k = 4jk = 2(2jk) = $ even.

b) Take one even number, $2l$ and one odd number $2m + 1$ (where l and m are integers), then their product is $2l \times (2m + 1) = 4lm + 2l = 2(2lm + l)$ – even.

Q2 Proof by exhaustion:
Take three consecutive integers $(n − 1)$, n and $(n + 1)$. Their product is $(n − 1)n(n + 1) = n(n^2 − 1) = n^3 − n$. Consider the two cases — n even and n odd. For n even, n^3 is even (as even × even = even) so $n^3 − n$ is also even (as even − even = even). For n odd, n^3 is odd (as odd × odd = odd) so $n^3 − n$ is even (as odd − odd = even). So $n^3 − n$ is even when n is even and when n is odd, and n must be either odd or even, so the product of three consecutive integers is always even.

Another approach to this proof is to take the product of three consecutive integers $n(n + 1)(n + 2)$ and consider n odd and n even. If n is odd:
$n(n + 1)(n + 2) = (odd \times even) \times odd = even \times odd = even.$
If n is even:
$n(n + 1)(n + 2) = (even \times odd) \times even = even \times even = even.$

Q3 The simplest way to disprove the statement is to find a counter-example. Try some values of n and see if the statement is true for them:
$n = 3 \implies n^2 − n − 1 = 3^2 − 3 − 1 = 5$ — prime
$n = 4 \implies n^2 − n − 1 = 4^2 − 4 − 1 = 11$ — prime
$n = 5 \implies n^2 − n − 1 = 5^2 − 5 − 1 = 19$ — prime
$n = 6 \implies n^2 − n − 1 = 6^2 − 6 − 1 = 29$ — prime
$n = 7 \implies n^2 − n − 1 = 7^2 − 7 − 1 = 41$ — prime
$n = 8 \implies n^2 − n − 1 = 8^2 − 8 − 1 = 55$ — not prime
$n^2 − n − 1$ is not prime when $n = 8$.
So the statement is false.

Sometimes good old trial and error is the easiest way to find a counter-example. Don't forget, if you've been told to disprove a statement like this, then a counter-example must exist.

Q4 Proof by contradiction:
Suppose that the statement is not true, that is, the graph has a turning point. That means that there is at least one value of x for which $\frac{dy}{dx} = 0$. $\frac{d}{dx}(\ln x) = \frac{1}{x}$ but there is no value of x for which $\frac{1}{x} = 0$, so we've contradicted the statement that the graph has a turning point, hence the original statement is true.

Q5 Find a counter-example for which the statement isn't true. Take $x = −1$ and $y = 2$. Then
$\sqrt{x^2 + y^2} = \sqrt{(− 1)^2 + 2^2} = \sqrt{1 + 4} = \sqrt{5} = 2.236...$
and $x + y = −1 + 2 = 1$. $2.236... > 1$, so the statement is not true.

Q6 Direct proof:
$$\cos^2\theta(1 − \tan^2\theta) \equiv \cos^2\theta\left(1 − \frac{\sin^2\theta}{\cos^2\theta}\right)$$
$$\equiv \cos^2\theta − \frac{\sin^2\theta\cos^2\theta}{\cos^2\theta}$$
$$\equiv \cos^2\theta − \sin^2\theta \equiv \cos 2\theta$$
This proof used the fact that $\tan \theta = \sin \theta / \cos \theta$ and the double angle formula for cos.

Q7 **a)** Proof by exhaustion:
Consider the two cases — n even and n odd.
Let n be even.
$n^2 − n = n(n − 1)$.
If n is even, $n − 1$ is odd so $n(n − 1)$ is even (as even × odd = even). This means that $n(n − 1) − 1$ is odd.
Let n be odd. If n is odd, $n − 1$ is even, so $n(n − 1)$ is even (as odd × even = even). This means that $n(n − 1) − 1$ is odd.
As any integer n has to be either odd or even, $n^2 − n − 1$ is odd for any value of n.

b) As $n^2 − n − 1$ is odd, $n^2 − n − 2$ is even. The product of even numbers is also even, so as $(n^2 − n − 2)^3$ is the product of 3 even numbers, it will always be even.

Index

M

many-to-one functions 18
mapping diagrams 12, 13
mappings 12, 13, 16
  restricting domains 16
modelling growth and decay
    94-96
modulus 27-33
  graphs 27-29
  solving equations 31-33

N

natural logarithms 89-93,
    110, 111

O

one-to-one functions 18

P

population growth and decay
    94-96
product rule 117-119, 127
  proof 117
proof 62, 65, 66, 80, 83,
    117, 121, 149-152
proof by contradiction 151
proof by direct argument 150
proof by exhaustion 151
Pythagoras' Theorem 47, 60

Q

quotient rule 121-123, 125
  proof 121

R

R addition formulas 75-78
ranges 12-16, 18, 20-24,
    45, 46, 88, 89
rational numbers 150
real numbers 12
remainders 10
roots 133-145

S

sec 49-62
  graph 50
simplifying expressions 1-5

T

table of common angles 47
tangent to a curve 122
transformations (of graphs) 35-38,
    51, 77, 89, 90
  cosec, sec and cot 51
trial and improvement 138
trigonometry 45-83
  functions 113-116
  identities 58-64, 68-83,
    113-116, 123, 150

U

upper bounds 133-136

Z

zombie apocalypse 100

C3 Formula Sheet

These are the formulas you'll be given in the exam, but make sure you know exactly **when you need them** and **how to use them**. You might also need any formulas from the C1 and C2 formula sheets in C3.

Logs and Exponentials

$$e^{x \ln a} = a^x$$

Differentiation

$f(x)$	$f'(x)$
$\tan kx$	$k \sec^2 kx$
$\sec x$	$\sec x \tan x$
$\cot x$	$-\csc^2 x$
$\csc x$	$-\csc x \cot x$
$\dfrac{f(x)}{g(x)}$	$\dfrac{f'(x)g(x) - f(x)g'(x)}{(g(x))^2}$

Trigonometric Identities

$$\sin(A \pm B) \equiv \sin A \cos B \pm \cos A \sin B$$

$$\cos(A \pm B) \equiv \cos A \cos B \mp \sin A \sin B$$

$$\tan(A \pm B) \equiv \frac{\tan A \pm \tan B}{1 \mp \tan A \tan B} \quad \left(A \pm B \neq \left(k + \tfrac{1}{2}\right)\pi\right)$$

$$\sin A + \sin B \equiv 2 \sin\frac{A+B}{2} \cos\frac{A-B}{2}$$

$$\sin A - \sin B \equiv 2 \cos\frac{A+B}{2} \sin\frac{A-B}{2}$$

$$\cos A + \cos B \equiv 2 \cos\frac{A+B}{2} \cos\frac{A-B}{2}$$

$$\cos A - \cos B \equiv -2 \sin\frac{A+B}{2} \sin\frac{A-B}{2}$$

MEC3T61